D1274095

BIRDS AND THEIR ATTRIBUTES

BY

GLOVER MORRILL ALLEN, Ph.D.

DOVER PUBLICATIONS, INC.
NEW YORK

This new Dover edition, first published in 1962, is an unabridged and unaltered republication of the work first published by Marshall Jones Company in 1925.

Library of Congress Catalog Card Number: 62-2593

Manufactured in the United States of America

Dover Publications, Inc.
180 Varick Street
New York 14, N. Y.

TO MY WIFE

PREFACE

The following chapters were originally prepared as a series of lectures under the auspices of the New England (now Northeastern) Bird Banding Association to serve as an introduction to a general survey of Birds, their structure, their habits and their relations to ourselves. In view of the present widespread delight found by out-of-door people in the companionship of birds it was believed that such a course would help to foster a more intelligent interest in this group of creatures, and it is with this hope that the lectures are now brought out in book form.

Acknowledgments are due many who have helped to make the book attractive. Especially are my grateful thanks due to Mr. Frank W. Benson for permission to use as a frontispiece his splendid painting of Wild Geese rising. My sincere appreciation I would also express to the following for the use of illustrative material:

Dr. Arthur A. Allen, Albert F. Bigelow, L. W. Brownell, Dr. Jonathan Dwight, Charles Macnamara, Professor Loye H. Miller, George Nelson, Dr. R. W. Shufeldt, Dr. Wm. Lord Smith, and through its late Superintendent Ned Hollister, the National Zoölogical Park.

G. M. A.

CONTENTS

ILLUSTRATIONS

FULL PAGE ILLUSTRATIONS

ILLUSTRATIONS

ILLUSTRATIONS IN THE TEXT

BIRDS AND THEIR ATTRIBUTES

CHAPTER I

SOME HUMAN RELATIONS WITH BIRDS

THE very great general interest in birds seen at the present day is perhaps not surprising when we consider briefly how closely concerned is the natural life of men with that of birds. From earliest times the appearance of birds was looked upon as of a certain significance, whether for good or evil. The lectures on which these chapters are based were appropriately announced as given under the *auspices* of one of our bird clubs; for the word *auspices* comes from the Latin *avis*,—a bird,—and *spicere*,—to look at,—and relates to the ancient custom of divination from flights of birds, or the notes of tame birds, or from an examination of the entrails of birds kept by the *augures* for the purpose of foretelling the probable outcome of any undertaking. Among the ancient Latins this was an important matter, and no enterprise was begun without first making the proper application to the sacred birds to learn of its probable success. Moreover, the credit for the final success, as of a victory or a safe journey, was given not to the commanding general or the resourceful traveler, but to the one who had made the propitious augury. It is clear, therefore, that any helpfulness these brief essays may bring, will be due to the favorable *auspices* of the bird club that instituted them.

But if the days of divination by the aid of birds are now remote, it remains true that both in the past and at the present time, many crises in human life and many important events of everyday existence are intimately associated with birds. Are we not ushered into earth-life by the Stork, thus continuing in the New World an ancient tradition of the Old? It is a remarkable fact that so large a bird as the Common Stork of Europe, belonging to a group of uncommonly wary species, should have established what is in effect a relation of *symbiosis* with man; that is, the two species live together with mutual advantage. For in central Europe, where this bird chiefly nests, it is considered a bringer of good luck, and is encouraged to build its platform of sticks on roof or chimney-top, while in return for this protection the bird acts as a useful scavenger as well as an inspiration. It is said that its numbers in Europe are at the present day noticeably decreasing, partly perhaps because of the cleaner conditions imposed by modern sanitation and the consequent reduction of the birds' food supply. I can think of no other wild bird that is so obviously in mutual and helpful association with man.

Some other instances of the usefulness of birds at critical times in human experience are worth recalling. The cackling of the sacred Geese of Juno's temple in time to waken the sleeping guard and thus save Rome from the attack of the Gauls, is familiar history. Not only Geese, but Tree Ducks and the Old-World Sheldrakes were often kept even by savage tribes in the capacity of watch-dogs, for they feed much at night and are quick to give vent to their alarm at any unusual or untoward circumstance.

The timely arrival of great flocks of Migratory Quail, it may be recalled, saved the Israelites from starvation in their wanderings in Arabia. But though it seemed a miracle to them, we now know that it was but the usual yearly migration of the birds, after all perhaps a miracle in a wider sense of the word.

Dr. Frank M. Chapman was the first to point out (1896) the important part played by birds in Columbus's discovery of America. The great navigator sailed from Cadiz in southern Spain in the late summer of 1492, and on reaching the Canary Islands in latitude 36° 30′ north, bade farewell to these westerly outposts of the Old World and bore away westward on this same parallel, with the favoring northeast trades, into unknown seas. On September 18, Pinzon, who commanded one of the three caravels, hailed the Admiral and informed him that "from the flight of a great number of birds, and from the appearance of the northern horizon, he thought there was land in that direction." Two days later Columbus records the visit of several small birds to his ships: "Three of a small kind which keep about orchards and groves, came in the morning and flew away again in the evening," cheering the hearts of the dismayed mariners. The next two weeks of the voyage were without special event, and daily the crews became more and more discontented and mutiny threatened as the disheartened sailors grew more and more certain that they had sailed too far beyond the bounds of ocean ever to reach land again. On October 3, we find them uttering "murmurs and menaces," but the next day they were visited "by such flights of birds, and the various indications of land became so numerous, that from a state of despondency they passed to one of confident expectation." They were now some 650 miles from the Bahamas. Finally, on October 7, birds became so numerous and the direction of their flight so uniformly southwest, that Columbus actually changed his course to correspond with their line of flight. Fiske, the historian, remarks that this was a fortunate circumstance, for had he persisted on the parallel, he might have reached northern Florida after 720 miles, but the change brought him to the Bahama Islands with a saving of over 200 miles ere making land. It was therefore due to birds alone that Columbus materially shortened his venturesome voyage and landed in these islands instead of on the continent. What the birds that he saw in such numbers were it is impossible to say. No doubt, however, he was in the line of flight of many species that visit the Bermudas in fall migration (then at its height) and thence strike overseas for the West Indies and South America. Such species as the Eskimo Curlew and Golden Plover were probably among those seen. As Chapman remarks, it is an open question whether, in the absence of these migratory birds, Columbus would have been able to influence his timid and superstitious sailors to press on to the Great Discovery.

A bird to which many hardy navigators owe their lives is the Penguin—of which many species abound in the southern hemisphere. The Dutch navigator, De Weert, in the latter part of 1599, found himself almost without provision for his men in the two vessels under his command after making the Straits of Magellan in an attempt to reach the East Indies by way of the Pacific. By good fortune he was able to provision his ships with Penguins and so, with half of his crew, finally returned to Holland. In our own day, two men of one of the recent Antarctic expeditions were cast away and kept alive throughout the long winter until help came, living on Penguins.

We may never know just how much English literature owes to Penguins. Ruskin relates, however, that whenever he felt distressed in mind or disheartened, he sought out the gallery in the British Museum where the Penguins stood, and looked at them till he was forced to laugh, they appeared so "sympathetically ridiculous." So were his spirits revived; and this one can easily appreciate from a reproduction of the Penguin figured in De Weert's account of his voyage, and perhaps one of the earliest pictures of this remarkable bird,—about 1600.

The attempt made a few years ago to kill Penguins by the wholesale, to boil them down for soap-grease, has, I believe, been stopped by the intervention of the British Government.

So far as I know the only monument to birds in the world is that in our own country erected in grateful testimony to the flocks of Franklin's Gulls which appeared at a critical time and devoured the hordes of locusts that threatened destruction to the first crop of the pioneers at Salt Lake, Utah. For if this crop failed they were without provision for the winter or seed for another sowing.

The value of insect-eating birds to the agriculturalist is a matter that is often made much of, and rightly too, for they are important allies in keeping down these all-devouring pests. But fairness makes it necessary that we should not overestimate the part they play, which is after all a secondary one, for the two factors that chiefly hold insects in check are (1) fungous diseases and (2) other insects. Were it not so, we ourselves should long since have been overwhelmed. But insects form a world of their own. Most species have enemies in the shape of parasitic insects, which are so specialized that each kind of parasite attacks some particular kind of insect, and more than that, one set of parasites attacks only the egg, a second species only the young grub, a third attacks a succeeding stage, and so on. Should the insect preyed upon increase through some favorable combination of circumstances, its parasites will do likewise, until they have reduced its numbers to normal or even small proportions, and presently themselves become rare. When this condition is reached, the host species, suddenly relieved of attack, may again break forth in enormous numbers, and gain a great lead before the parasites can increase fast enough to check it. So the see-saw process goes on between the insect on the one hand and its parasites, ably seconded by insect-eating birds, on the other.

It is not necessary to dwell upon the relation of birds to art, but a few points may be noted. The oldest-known figures of birds are probably those discovered a few years since graven in the walls of some of the limestone caverns of southern Spain, the work of men of the Stone Age who lived in these shelters perhaps 25,000 years ago. Some of them were no mean artists, and their crude figures scratched in the cave walls picture with much freedom and skill the outlines of horses, reindeer, even the mammoth and the rhinoceros now long since extinct in Europe. Though most of the figures are of quadrupeds, a few are of birds, including some obvious Flamingos, and others that may be geese or ducks. In the New World, the ancient Mayas of Central America had a highly developed civilization when the white men arrived, and had reached a remarkable degree of skill in drawing and in carving on wood or stone

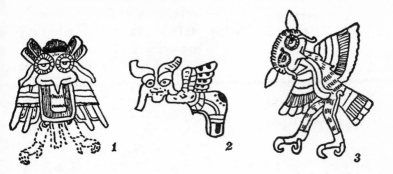

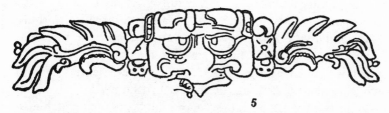

The Great Horned Owl as a motif in pre-Columbian designs by Central American Indians. 1 and 3, Mexican; 2, Maya of Yucatan; 4, stone carving, Yucatan; 5, owl in flight, carved in wood, Yucatan

the native creatures familiar to their everyday life. Some
of the figures of the Great Horned Owl are wonderfully
expressive and were used in a most decorative manner to
fill a panel or an irregularly shaped space. In their picture-
writing they used the conventionalized representations of
various birds as well as of other creatures. A very interesting series of figures can be brought together from one

FIG. I

Conventionalized heads of the King Vulture showing the stages in reduction from a natural head to the characteristic, a bill with square
wattle (Mexican)

of the manuscripts still preserved of these ancient people,
showing the stages in conventionalization of the head of a
King Vulture from that of the full naturalistic figure with
the squarish wattle on the beak to a glyph in which nothing
remains but the beak and the wattle to stand for the bird.
These two represent the irreducible residue, and constitute
what is known as the "characteristic" or essential symbol
whereby the identity of the bird is proclaimed.

The Egyptians of course had a highly developed hiero-
glyphic writing in which many of the characters are birds
familiar to them. The outline figures of these are made in

a conventionalized, and indeed a prescribed style, yet are readily identified. Among them are seen the vulture, swallow, sparrow, sparrowhawk, pintail duck, ibis—all familiar and common species in the Nile delta to this day. The Ibis was a sacred bird, and the Sparrowhawk was the sign for the sun god, Horus (identified with the Greek Apollo). The *soul* was signified by the figure of a long-legged bird,

FIG. II

Pre-Columbian design combining Ocellated Turkey and King Vulture (Yucatan Maya Indians)

possibly the Stone Plover or Thick-knee, a common species of north African streams, active largely by night, and much given to plaintive cries at that time, like a wandering spirit. In the Egyptian alphabet, the Horned Owl was the equivalent of the letter M, which though believed to be derived from the conventional zigzag sign denoting water, seems nevertheless suspiciously like the outline of an owl's ears.

Few of us realize the really enormous numbers of birds annually killed for food even in the United States. Some recent statistics on the subject in Grinnell, Bryant, and Storer's "Game Birds of California" (1918) are illuminating. In that State a decrease in numbers of ducks and geese was noticeable fifty years ago, though the degree of reduction rested mainly on the general impressions of careful observers; but statements of this sort are of relatively small value, for they amount to little more than a comparison of several unknown quantities. The writers mentioned, however, give the actual numbers of ducks received by game-transfer companies in San Francisco, from which it appears that a single company in 1909–10 handled over 20,000 geese; another in 1910–11 nearly 72,000 ducks; a third, in the five seasons 1906–11, a total of over 357,000 ducks of various species! Dr. J. C. Phillips records that, according to information furnished him by the Game Commissioner of California, between 800,000 and 1,000,000 ducks are annually killed in that State, and even greater figures are given for the yearly toll in Minnesota. Dr. Phillips concludes from a careful survey of the statistics available, that in the United States alone, between six and ten million ducks are killed every year, and this is probably about half of what it was before the more recent enactment of better laws for the protection of these birds. We do not realize how very greatly the face of our country is changing. In many parts of the West, where once were vast areas of open land suitable for the breeding of these birds, there are now irrigated farms, square miles in extent. Lakes and sloughs have been drained, forests have been ruthlessly cut down or as carelessly burned, and the entire aspect of the country changed. At the present time the clearing and draining process is rapidly progressing in Florida and will eventually greatly affect the existence of many of the larger

A WHITE STORK AND BROOD ON A GERMAN HOUSE-TOP
Auerbach, phot.

TRAINED CORMORANTS FISHING
From an old engraving by De Bry

birds there. In my own college days, before the sale of game had been stopped, it was a common sight to see Prairie Chickens hanging by dozens in our markets at Christmas time. At the present day they have been so reduced in the middle West, partly through intensive cultivation, that I have not been able to obtain a specimen needed for some investigations.

Among peculiar and interesting uses to which birds are put, it may be recalled that the Chinese and Japanese have long employed tame Cormorants to catch fish for their masters. The birds are prevented from swallowing the results of their fishing by having a strap placed about the throat, and at intervals dive from the rowboat in pursuit and bring back the fish in their gullet to the waiting Chinaman. An old engraving by De Bry in 1590 depicts this, and I have seen a moving picture of the same thing made within a few years.

In former times the use of hawks in falconry was a common sport in the Old World. The Duck Hawk or Peregrine was a favorite, though several species were used, and trained to pursue and kill game for their masters or mistresses, for even the gentler sex found diversion in this art. The literature of hawking is very extensive and there grew up a code and nomenclature all its own of words and phrases descriptive of its many aspects. An interesting point brought out is the difference in method used by various sorts of hawks; the falcons for example—open-country birds—strike their prey to the ground by the force of a terrific blow of the foot, while the wood-inhabiting species as Goshawk or Sharp-shin, grasp or "truss" the quarry and bear it to earth, an adaptation perhaps to the different habitat of the two groups, for a wood-haunting species, if it struck its prey down, might easily lose it in the undergrowth.

The use of homing or carrier pigeons seems to have been known even in the days of Noah. These are merely specially bred birds of the same wild stock as our common street pigeon, and are trained to return to their home-loft across long distances. But to this subject we will return later (under Migration). The practical value of carrier pigeons was demonstrated in the Great War, where they proved of effective service in the sending of messages and were much used by the French armies.

It is but a step from the taming of young birds captured wild to the domestication of a useful species. Yet it must be borne in mind that the number of species that can be successfully domesticated is very limited, and even at the present day we have really domesticated perhaps fewer than ten. For though many birds will bear captivity well, even breed under careful management, nevertheless the conditions of life under domestication are so very upsetting to all the normal functions of body and mind, that very few creatures are able to thrive under them. Their natural food is no longer obtainable, causing changes in their growth; their natural exercise is reduced, weakening the general tone of their systems; they are fattened, protected from enemies, and kept in unnatural surroundings without need for watchfulness against danger or keenness in searching for food. Small wonder therefore that a bird so naturally alert and sagacious as the goose should so lose its brain-power that its very name becomes synonymous with idiot or numskull! The most serious result under conditions of captivity is the disturbance to the reproductive system, for there are very few birds that can or will breed at all readily if confined, and it is only such birds as can mate and nest freely under restraint that may really be called domesticated.

At the risk of seeming trivial, it is worth mentioning the few species that men have thus turned to their own use in this way and succeeded in making part of their household. Foremost in importance is our Barnyard Fowl. Domesticated since very ancient times in eastern Asia, perhaps Burma, it was a favorite with the Chinese in antiquity, and according to tradition they received it from the west about 1400 B. C. The hen is mentioned in the older Sanskrit Veddas (poems). An ancient law forbade it as an article of food in India on account of its usefulness in laying eggs, which perhaps was what first gave it a domestic value. Soon after the time of Alexander the Great, a figure of a hen appears on the coin (drachm) of King Sophytes. It plays an important part in the rites of Zoroastrians, the crow of the cock scaring away evil spirits of the night. Its earliest representation in Europe is found in Crete, and it was pictured by the Greeks in works of art after the 6th century B. C. It was probably brought into Europe as a result mainly of the Persian invasions. Aristophanes mentions it as the "Persian bird." A dwarf race was known to the Venetians, which was said by Aristotle to lay an egg daily. The Romans had a "hen oracle" at least as early as 322 B. C., and Lucilius mentions cockfights. Roman henhouses had ladders, roosts or sleeping porches, and nesting boxes, and the Romans were particular that for breeding purposes hen and cock should be of the same color, with poorly developed breast, but powerful build and carriage, majestic tail, erect red comb, and above all, a very pugnacious temperament. Cockfighting was much in vogue with the ancient Greeks, who even used iron spurs for the fighting birds. This form of sport is still common with Latin peoples. In those days, white hens were in disfavor in breeding, on account of their more easily falling prey to hawks; but for certain purposes they were especially kept and used, as in Egypt as an offering to Anubis (a white-and-yellow hen). Pythagoras forbade his children to eat a white hen, as it was sacred to Zeus. Elsewhere a white hen was the appropriate sacrifice to the nymphs and to Aphrodite. In early times, hens were used to hatch eggs of peacocks and ducks, apparently first by the Egyptians. Black hens were used as offerings to the Goddess of Night, according to Ovid.

Apparently the Jungle-fowl, *Gallus sonnerati,* of southern India, is closely like the old representations and accounts of domestic fowls. It is said to be sterile with the Domestic Hen. Perhaps, too, *Gallus bankiva* (or better, *G. gallus,* the older name), of northern India to Cochin China is a wild prototype. This Jungle-fowl lays eight to twelve eggs. It is strange that the Egyptian monuments do not depict the Common Fowl, although a chick seemingly of this species is used for the equivalent of our letter U in the Egyptian alphabet, and often appears in their hieroglyphics.

The Common Duck was probably first domesticated in southern Europe. Bones in the Swiss lake-dwellings and in the caverns of Europe are those of wild birds. They were apparently but rarely kept as domestic creatures by the Greeks and the Italians, and probably at first those in captivity were merely wild-caught birds being fattened. The Romans made elaborate pens for the fattening of wild ducks for the table, consisting of an enclosure with a 15-foot wall, the top screened with wide-mesh netting to keep the birds in and hawks or eagles out; there was in the center a dry place where plants were set, and the whole must be near a swamp or lake, with a canal for introduction of running water. Such a *nessotrophium,* as it was called, is described in the villa of Seius. The Germans are supposed to have received domestic ducks from the Romans, and they were apparently kept by the dwellers on Cyprus and Rhodes associated, too, with the worship of Venus. In Egypt ducks were used as offerings to the Sun God, Ra, to whom the God of the Nile brings among other water-products a bundle of ducks. The Egyptians hatched ducks' eggs by setting them under hens. The common Domestic Duck is undoubtedly but a tame Mallard, and according to Dr. J. C. Phillips (1923) it takes but a couple of generations to domesticate the bird almost completely, so readily does it thrive under these artificial conditions.

But one other species of duck has been really domesticated. This is the so-called Muscovy Duck, a native of Central and South America. It is a large, dark-brown bird with a white area at the bend of the wing, and with curious pinkish excrescences or caruncles about the bill and eye. It was apparently already domesticated by the native Americans at the time of the discovery, for Columbus and his men found on their arrival in the West Indies that the islanders had "ducks as large as geese" about their dwellings. Oviedo, the early Spanish historian of the New World, describes them. They were found in 1514 domesticated among the Indians of Colombia and were exported by the Spaniards from Peru to the Central American settlements and to Europe. The early ornithologists, Belonius, Gesner, and Caius, describe them as coming from the New World in the middle of the 16th century. The name

Muscovy Duck is said to be derived from the name of the Muysca Indians of Nicaragua and later corrupted into Muscovy.

Our tame Geese are apparently in all their various breeds descended from the common wild Gray-lag Goose of Europe, a species which until very recent years at least still bred sparingly in the British Isles, and is the most southerly breeding goose of Europe. It is not known when it was first domesticated, but no doubt this dates from very early times, perhaps the latter part of the Stone Age or in the early Bronze Age when men began to dwell in settled communities. At all events the Germans had geese when Cæsar's armies invaded central Europe, and in later days the German geese were especially sought by the Romans. Their chief value lay in their feathers, which were plucked *five* times yearly (for feather beds came before furnaces) and in their livers which formed one of the chief delicacies of those days and one that now survives in the "foie gras" of the epicure. The German geese were pure white, much as are the Embden Geese, a breed of the present day.

We, in these times of fountain pens, seldom recollect that our immediate ancestors used instead the long wing-quills of geese. With occasional repointing by a sharp knife, these did very well and it is said that Dickens wrote an entire book with a single quill-pen. We still use the word "penknife" for a small sharp blade, though no longer is it employed for cutting quill points.

In the East, the Chinese Goose, a distinct species, is domesticated.

The Turkey is the only bird of the New World (except the Muscovy Duck) that has been successfully added to the category of domesticated animals. It first appears in print in the account of the West Indies and Mexico published in 1527 by Oviedo, a Spaniard, who spent several years in these newly discovered countries. The Mexican Turkey had already been domesticated by the natives of that part of America, and it was from them that the Spaniards obtained it and brought it to Europe, where it was established as early at least as 1530. It seems not to have been known in England much before 1541. The name was also applied mistakenly sometimes to the Guinea Fowl. The earliest published figures of the Turkey were those by Belonius and by Gesner, both, through a coincidence, in the same year, 1555. From Europe the bird was reintroduced into America by our Pilgrim forefathers, who likewise found a related race wild here in New England in the earlier days. Morton, in his "New English Canaan," written in 1637, tells of Turkeys "which divers times in great flocks have sallied by our doores; and then a gunne being commonly in a redinesse, salutes them with such a courtesie, as makes them take a turne in the cooke roome." There is some reason to suppose that the New England Turkeys were sometimes kept tame here, but they were not truly domesticated. The Mexican bird differs from ours in having whitish-tipped feathers, and this distinguishing character the domestic race persistently retains. The Wild Turkey in New England was not wholly exterminated until about the middle of the last century when a few still remained on Mt. Tom in western Massachusetts and ranged the wild country of that region. Gradually the flocks became broken up and the birds ceased to breed. A few old gobblers remained here and there and were either finally hunted down and killed or, if by reason of their great wariness they escaped being shot, they eventually disappeared from other causes.

The late William Brewster relates how a single old and wary Turkey cock lived in the Concord region about 125 years ago, the last of its race in these parts. Though many hunters sought its life, it was never shot, but finally succumbed to other enemies or died of old age. In England Turkeys were early dedicated to the Christmas feast. It was natural therefore that our forefathers having the wild Turkey here at their doors, regarded it as a proper bird for their Thanksgiving feasts. To this day the Vermont- or Rhode Island-bred Turkey is famed for its excellent flesh. It will not occur to many, however, that the English Sparrow has any connection with the present scarcity and high cost of our Thanksgiving dinner. This is nevertheless the case, and is a point of great interest in its bearing on the interrelations of diverse species. For it seems that young Turkeys are highly susceptible to a disease of the intestine called "blackhead," which is due to the activity of a microscopic amœba-like creature belonging to the same group of one-celled beings as many other disease-organisms —the Protozoa,—and to that group of Protozoa provided with a whip-like appendage, by the lashing of which it is able to move about. This minute organism passes one of its stages in damp ground, and is carried and spread by the sparrow, which, however, is immune from its attack. The sparrows in visiting the barnyards for grain infect the Turkeys' surroundings, so that in some localities the raising of these birds for the table has had to be almost completely abandoned. In this boomerang fashion do we reap our reward for upsetting Nature's balance by bringing in new and untried elements among creatures whose systems have not become accustomed to cope with them.

To this brief list of domesticated birds may be added the

Peacock, originally a native of peninsular India and Ceylon, and always used as a symbol of pride. King Solomon imported it first into Palestine, and it was known to the Greeks, more especially after the eastern conquests of Alexander. In early times its flesh was esteemed as a delicacy, and in the days of chivalry one of the most solemn oaths was taken "on the peacock," served up garnished with its own plumage.

The Ostrich of South and East Africa has been partly domesticated in more recent years, not only in its native country but in California as well, where it is now successfully farmed for its decorative plumes. It makes a somewhat unattractive pet, however, for at times the cock birds become rather belligerent, kicking out powerfully with a downward sweep in front that might easily disembowel a man. When the time comes to pluck their plumes, the birds are driven into a narrow alley of boards, a long-legged stocking is slipped over the head of each bird to quiet it, and the plumes are clipped near the base. The stumps of the quills are later pulled out when they have become more mature. There is of course no truth in the popular tradition that they thrust their heads in the sand if frightened, in the belief that they are thus concealed from their enemies.

The Guinea-hen, a native of Africa, was early brought to Europe and seems to have been known to the Greeks and Latins. It was carried to our own West Indies in the days of the slave trade, and even now is found wild in some of these islands, as in Haiti. A breed with partly white wings has been developed, but otherwise it seems to have changed little or none under the short period of domestication.

The Pigeon is perhaps to be added to the list of domesticated birds, though in common with the European House Sparrow it is perhaps to be classed with the so-called "foveal" or fireside species that thrive in human association, like flies, dogs, mice, certain weeds, grass. It is interesting that the number of such adaptable species is so small, yet fortunate perhaps that it is no larger.

HISTORICAL

It would be interesting to trace the earlier history of ornithology and to examine in detail some of the older works by European authors. Some of these are reviewed by Gurney (1922) in his recently published "Early Annals of Ornithology." In the Middle Ages a mass of fabulous tales and interesting legends or bits of folklore were widely current among the credulous; indeed, no small amount of such beliefs survives among us to this day, and it should be our care to make a note of these things for the interest of future students, for with our rapidly changing customs much of this legendary and traditional lore will presently vanish. There are many such classical references that are familiar to all, like that of the Swan's dying song, which Socrates declared all good men should imitate, who, perceiving what gain there was in death, should die singing with joy. The ancient belief that the Ostrich had the power of digesting iron is referred to by Shakespeare in Henry VI, where he makes Jack Cade declare, "I'll make thee eat iron like an Ostrich, and swallow my sword like a great pin." The Ostrich in heraldry is often represented with a horseshoe in its beak. I recall the surprise of an English officer visiting an ostrich farm in East Africa, when one of the birds reached over the fence and in a flash had plucked a rifle-cartridge from the clip on the breast of his uniform and swallowed it.

The Raven as a bird of ill-omen is most familiar, but on what ground this undeserved reputation may rest is not altogether clear. There is an ancient belief that the Raven was originally white but was turned black for its disobedience. The Greek legend is that Apollo sent the bird to the fountain for water, but on arrival it found a fig tree with fruit so nearly ripe that it decided to wait until it was quite so; and since an excuse for the delay was necessary, it brought back to the god a water snake in its pitcher with the explanation that the creature had drunk the fountain dry. In the Middle Ages, the disobedience was traced, however, to the failure of Noah's Raven to return when sent forth to test the state of the waters. Raven broth was once supposed to be good for the gout.

Owls, partly from their mysterious night habits, perhaps too from their look of wisdom, are almost universally regarded as of uncanny meaning. The elder Pliny in his "Natural History" says that "the scritch-owle betokeneth alwaies some heavie newes, and is most execrable and accursed . . . if he be seene within citties or otherwise abroad in any place it is not for good, but prognosticateth some fearful misfortune." No doubt the uncordial reception that owls receive from other birds helped to strengthen these beliefs. But the younger Pliny had too much of the critical spirit to accept this supposition blindly, for in his work he says, "I myself know that it hath perched upon many houses of private men and yet hath no evil followed." It is said that in many rural districts of England owl broth has been regarded as invaluable in whooping-cough.

Among the ancient Mexicans and the Mayas of Yucatan, owls played an important part in ceremonial usages. Some remarkable designs involving the Great Horned Owl as the subject are found in their carvings still preserved in wood and stone. Some of these are highly conventionalized owls, but may be recognized by the ear-tufts and the sharp hooked beak, which always appear as the characteristic.

Classical writings have many allusions to the Kingfisher or Halcyon, and it was believed that so favored was the bird by the heavenly powers that during the two weeks preceding the winter solstice, when the Kingfisher was hatching her young, there prevailed a great calm lest the nest (which was supposed to be floating serenely on the sea) should be disturbed. These were the halcyon days. There was also a charming superstition that a dead King- fisher suspended by the bill will always turn its breast in the direction whence the wind blows, and a weather vane of this sort was often hung in the chimney corner. It is interesting to find that the versatile Sir Thomas Browne in his book, "Enquiry into Vulgar Errors" (1662), him- self a Doubting Thomas, actually made a number of experi- ments to test this belief, even hanging two separate birds in the same room together, and finally suspending them in "large and spacious glasses closely stopped," until he proved to his complete satisfaction that the long-current supersti- tion was unworthy of belief. Sir Thomas was therefore one of the first to apply the experimental method in the exact study of ornithology.

To this day there are those here in New England who will foretell the severity of the coming winter by the thick- ness of a goose's feathers or from an examination of the pin feathers of a hen.

BELONIUS, AN EARLY FRENCH ORNITHOLOGIST

But it was by such observant and thinking men as the younger Pliny and Sir Thomas Browne that truth was gradually demonstrated and natural history gradually became shorn of its legends and finally reached the more secure basis which we find in the works of the eighteenth-century naturalists.

The first book on birds that treats them from anything like the modern point of view is that of William Turner, an English clergyman and one-time Dean of Wells Cathedral, who, in 1544, published his History of Birds, particularly of those mentioned in the works of Pliny and Aristotle. This was of course in Latin, but a modern reprint and translation is available (Turner, 1903). In it he gives brief descriptions of many of the European species with short accounts of their habits partly quoted from these classical authors and partly from his own observations. He seems to have had no knowledge of American species at this date. Eleven years later, in 1555, appeared two very important works on birds: the Ornithology of Belonius, a Frenchman, and that of Conrad Gesner, a huge Latin tome, largely a compilation from classical sources of all available references to birds. Belonius's book was more of an original piece of work, and included an account of the anatomy of birds as well as pictures and descriptions with something on the habits of the species known to him. Several later authors, as Aldrovandus, Johnstonus, were largely compilers, though the former brought together many bits of apparently original matter.

Collections.—At first there were no specimens for study, only pictures and collections of portraits and descriptions, sought by scholars from their correspondents.

So William Turner, 1544, in the postscript to his "Avium

Historia," begs his readers to send him drawings of any birds they find that are unknown to them.

Gesner (1555) and Aldrovandus (1645) had large natural-history collections, but apparently *no birds* among them. The latter had a great collection of drawings and pictures, still preserved in the Bologna Academy and unpublished.

Willughby (1635–1672) and Ray (1628–1705), the two greatest ornithologists of the 17th century, were Englishmen. Both were rarely able to have a "dried" bird for study and had apparently no ornithological collections of their own. Their joint work was issued in 1676, "Ornithologiæ libri III, in quibus aves omnes hactenus cognitæ . . . accurate describuntur . . . iconibus elegantissimis et vivarum avium simillimis aere incisis illustrantur" —folio, London, 77 plates. Even up to the end of the 18th century many birds were described from unpublished drawings.

The voyages of exploration in the 1500's–1600's familiarized people with many foreign species. Prepared skins of birds must have been already brought from America early in the 1500's, for Belonius in 1555 wrote that "those who carry on traffic for merchandise in the new lands, lose no chance to bring back curiosities which they claim to have bought there; indeed, since they can not bring back the birds alive in their vessels, they dry them, in order to have their skins, chiefly those of the most beautiful colors, among which is the one here described, by which the mariners have great profit, called the Merle de brésil." This was a bright-colored Brazilian Tanager (*Rhamphocœlus brasilius*) and is one of the first American birds to be described and figured by a European naturalist. Belonius gives directions to his readers for preserving birds by removing the entrails, stuffing with salt and hanging the bird up by the legs to dry. He adds that so preserved the specimen will keep indefinitely unless destroyed by worms—a fate unfortunately that overtook most of the birds in the early collections.

About 1590, one Ferrante Imperato, a rich apothecary of Naples, had a large natural-history cabinet (as it was then called) which contained among other things some birds described in Latin as, "Trochilus pusilla Volucris, fulgida violaceis pennis"—perhaps a hummingbird; "avis Diomedeæ" (supposed to have been a Shearwater); "Halcyones" (or Kingfishers, once used suspended as weather vanes); "*Apodes,*" meaning either Swifts (the common European species) or Birds of Paradise—trade skins no doubt, obtained from the East Indies and called Apodes, or without feet, because in preparing them, the feet were cut off by the natives, which gave rise to the belief that the birds never came to earth but floated always in the air. Finally this remarkable collection contained a bird described as *picus marinus,* a bird of shining red feathers brought from America—perhaps a Scarlet Ibis.

A most important early collection was Tradescant's Museum in England. His son John was sent to Virginia in 1637–40 by King Charles I to "gather all rarities of flowers, plants, and shells," and he brought back also a number of birds. This museum collection was left by the younger Tradescant to Sir Elias Ashmole, who in 1669 gave it to Oxford University on condition a building be erected for it. The remnant of this collection is still at

Oxford. It contained among other things a Dodo from Mauritius now long extinct; and a feather of the fabulous Phœnix.

In the 18th century a good many collections were made in Europe, but the birds, although somewhat better prepared, almost universally fell prey to insects and have not survived, with the exception of some half dozen birds in the museum at Upsala, Sweden, and a few specimens in the collection of Jean Fourcault (died 1775), who conceived the idea of hermetically sealing the birds in glass bottles. About a dozen of these specimens are still in existence at the Museum of the University of Parma and after 150 years are, with the exception of those at Upsala given in 1747, the oldest birds' skins now extant.

The use of arsenic came in about 1740, and aided against the ravages of insect pests.

Many other important collections were made in Europe in the latter part of the eighteenth century and served as the basis for some of the great natural-history works of the time—such as Seba's Cabinet so often quoted by Linnæus.

England led in natural-history collections. The bird collection of Sir Hans Sloane consisted at his death in 1753 of over 1100 specimens. It was then bought by the British Government and formed the nucleus of the great British Museum of Natural History, the most important in the world at the present time, for it contains, besides specimens of a large part of the known species of birds, a great many others of priceless value historically. To the British Museum were sent many collections of birds made by the earlier naturalists, among them specimens from John Bartram of Pennsylvania, the collections of Mrs. Anna Blackburn (chiefly North American birds), for whom our Blackburnian Warbler was named; Sir Joseph Banks and Sir Ashton Lever made important donations, but of these nearly all were entirely destroyed. In this century, too, the "Cabinet of the King" at Paris was a growing collection, and contained many birds. It became in 1793 the Musée d'Histoire Naturelle, the great Paris Museum, where Cuvier, Milne-Edwards, the Geoffroys, and other eminent naturalists did splendid work in making known the fauna of the earth.

In later days the national museums of England, France, Germany, Sweden, and Russia have magnificent study collections of birds, while the newer institutions of our own country at Cambridge, Washington, New York, Philadelphia, Chicago, and in California, have set excellent standards in methods of preparation and storage of study material. For the modern museum no longer places all its specimens on exhibition, but instead a selection is made for public show, and the real bulk of the collection is stored in cases that protect the specimens from light, dust and insects. Of large American bird collections that at the Academy of Natural Sciences, in Philadelphia, is the oldest and contains many specimens of historical interest, such as the collection of Australian birds made by Gould and illustrated by his folio work; other birds are among the first brought back from our own West by the earlier expeditions overland. The National Museum at Washington had its inception through the Smithsonian Institution, founded by the generosity of James Smithson, an Englishman, son of the Duke of Northumberland, who in 1826, for lack of heirs, bequeathed to the United States the whole of his property, amounting to about half a million dollars, to found "at Washington, under the name of the Smithsonian Institution, an establishment for the increase and diffusion of knowledge among men." This amount did not become available till 1838, but it was not until 1850, when Spencer F. Baird was appointed Assistant Secretary of the Institution, that the natural-history museum was well established and under his guidance became, as it now stands, one of the foremost in the world (see S. F. Baird's biography by W. H. Dall, 1915).

Among early American collections, Audubon himself had several hundred skins, indifferently prepared and largely unlabeled. Part of this collection is now preserved at Amherst College, and a few of the more important original specimens were given by Audubon to Baird for the National Museum. Mention should be made of the Old Boston Museum, which among its various curios had a number of mounted birds, originally a part of Peale's Museum at Philadelphia. Many of these birds were unquestionably the very ones that served Alexander Wilson for his colored figures, and may be matched detail for detail with his plates. Some of these are now preserved in the Agassiz Museum at Cambridge.

I have dwelt thus briefly on museums and collections, for just as the record of observations in notebooks and literature forms the basis of historical ornithology, so the collections of birds in the museums of the world form the only proper basis for the exact study of the different species, their plumages, variations, distribution, and many kindred problems. In no other way is it possible to "take stock," so to speak, of the species of birds making up the bird population of the world, for it is only by the actual comparison of specimens side by side that we can properly discriminate the different kinds and the amount of their variation in color or structure.

The latest estimate of the number of known different kinds of birds in the world is very nearly 19,000, belonging to about 2810 genera. If the reader will count up the number of species he knows and subtract it from 19,000, he will have some conception of the possibilities that lie yet before him.

One of the first notable works on North American birds is that of Mark Catesby, whose "Natural History of Carolina, Florida and the Bahama Islands" included many birds illustrated with well-executed folio plates, some in colors, accompanied by brief descriptions. The first published picture of the Heath-hen is found here. Catesby was an Englishman who traveled in America in 1710–19 and again in 1722–26. His two large volumes appeared in 1731 to 1743, and were the first really pretentious works on North American zoölogy, for the eighteenth century shows a dearth of ornithological literature concerning this continent.

In 1794, however, there arrived at Newcastle, Delaware, a Scotchman who was destined to become one of the foremost ornithologists of his time, Alexander Wilson. Born at Paisley in 1766, he learned the weaver's trade, but at twenty-one adopted the life of a pedlar. He had the Scotch gift for song, and his first volume of poems was published in 1790, though it met with a cool reception. Two years later he published "Watty and Meg" anonymously, which, becoming attributed to Robert Burns, quickly sold 100,000 copies! For having written a scathing satire upon a Paisley person, Wilson was thrown into prison and afterward forced to burn the libel with his own hand at Paisley Cross. It was upon his release from jail that he came to this country and, turning schoolmaster, taught in several Pennsylvania schools. It was here, too, that he made the acquaintance of William Bartram, the botanist, who stimulated his already keen interest in birds. In 1806 he was engaged to assist in editing Rees's American Cyclopedia, and shortly prepared the first volume of his American Ornithology which appeared in 1808, followed by seven others illustrated from plates drawn by himself, largely from mounted birds. His frail strength failed him here, for he had much overtaxed himself in the labor of preparing the text and plates for press. He died in 1813 at Philadelphia. His was the first real ornithology to be published in this country; for it was more than a series of plates with explanatory text, it treated largely of the habits of the birds, illustrated and described them carefully, and constituted a large original contribution to science.

North American ornithology may be said to have started an independent career early in the last century. In those days a remarkable group of scientific men was gathered at Philadelphia and before its second decade had founded the Academy of Natural Sciences and started the long series of volumes comprising its Journal and Proceedings. Among these men was a young Englishman, Thomas Nuttall, from whom the Nuttall Ornithological Club of Cambridge takes its name. Born in Yorkshire in 1786 in humble circumstances, he became a journeyman printer, and when only twenty-two years of age came in 1808 to Philadelphia, impelled partly by a love of natural sciences, partly perhaps by a desire to improve his condition of life. Here he made the acquaintance of the botanist Professor B. S. Barton, and was fired with zeal to spend his life in the study of plants. He made several journeys into the far West, then an almost unknown region, passing through various Indian tribes, making large botanical collections, and returning to Philadelphia to write up the results of his researches. He underwent many hardships and accomplished astonishing journeys in his enthusiastic love of science. Such a reputation did this devotion and his writings on botany, geology, and travel bring him, that in 1822 he was called to Cambridge to fill the chair of Natural Science at Harvard. His occasional lectures allowed him time to devote to his favorite studies. He was much of a recluse, yet genial and entertaining when among his friends. He felt the restraint of academic life and as an antidote set eagerly to work at the suggestion of his friend, James Brown, to write a "Manual of the Ornithology of the United States and Canada." This (published in 1832–34) was the first of many handbooks on birds to be issued in this country. His further travels again took him West. He crossed the continent with J. K. Townsend in 1834, thence visited the Hawaiian Islands and returned to Boston by sailing around Cape Horn in 1835, but straightway went back to Philadelphia to continue his studies. In these years an uncle without family of his own bequeathed him an estate called Nutgrove near Liverpool, England, on condition that he reside there at least nine months a year, which with some reluctance he at length decided to do. He only once again visited this country, and since he could not be absent for more than three months in a year, he took the last three months of 1847 and the first three of 1848, busying himself again at Philadelphia for part of the time. His death in 1857 was partly due to overstraining himself in unpacking a heavy case of specimens.   Many amusing tales are told of him.   On one occasion he wandered away from the cara-van which he was accompanying across the western country and his party sent back some friendly Indians to search for him.   These presently found him, busied as usual in his search for plants and minerals, but believing him a great medicine-man, they feared to approach and kept at a re-spectful distance.   Nuttall, who had the greatest horror of Indians, shortly discovered that he was being watched and, exercising his utmost cunning, hiding in ravines and behind every bush and tree, finally succeeded in escaping as he thought and regained his party after three days without food or sleep.

Philadelphia in the early part of the last century con-tinued to be a chief center of scientific activity, numbering among its notable men Prince Lucien Bonaparte, who wrote a four-volume supplement to Wilson's Ornithology; Titian Peale, who accompanied Long's expedition to the Rocky Mountains and later Wilkes's voyage of exploration to the Antarctic Seas; Charles Rafinesque, the eccentric naturalist and friend of Audubon, of whom it is related that during a visit at the latter's house, after the household had retired for the night, Audubon hearing a lively noise issuing from his guest's room, on going to inquire its cause, found Rafi-nesque dashing wildly about the room holding in his hand the battered remains of his host's favorite violin with which he was endeavoring to strike down a bat that had entered, and in which his eager eyes saw a species as yet unknown to science!   John Cassin was another of this remarkable com-pany of men at Philadelphia.   The wonderful collection of birds at the Academy was under his charge.   He was author of the volume on birds in the great series of government reports on the explorations for a railway route to the Pacific coast.

But the most romantic figure in American ornithology is John James Audubon, whose genius still burns in our midst. Numerous biographies may be consulted for details of his life, the most recent, that of Professor F. H. Herrick (1917) in two volumes. His French parentage gave him the fire and enthusiasm that carried him ahead through all fortunes and made his writings at once vivid, intimate, and sympathetic. Born in the West Indian island of Haiti, he was educated in France, and early resolved to master the art of painting in order that he might fulfil his ambition to prepare a series of portraits of American birds. In France he studied drawing under the great artist David, and returned to this country in 1798, taking possession of a farm owned by his father near Philadelphia, where he became one of that galaxy of notable men of science in the early part of the last century. Here in 1808 he married Lucy Bakewell, the daughter of an English neighbor, and shortly moved to Kentucky and later to Louisiana. Business was little to his taste and for a time he found himself obliged to paint portraits, teach dancing and fencing to eke out his slender resources. Always he labored at his task of gathering notes and specimens for his great work, the Ornithological Biography, which appeared in five volumes, beginning in 1833, and is really the text, of which the 400 and more elephant-folio plates of his Birds of America form the atlas. In 1842, after twelve years spent chiefly in travel and exploration, he bought a home on the Hudson River (now within the city limits of New York), where with his two sons and their families he passed the remaining years. He was less of a trained scientific man than a keen and sympathetic observer with a love for outdoors and unbounded delight in the beauty of birds and their lively ways, an appreciation which he was amply able to impart to his readers, for to this day there has not appeared in the compass of a single work so great a store of anecdotes, descriptions of habits, and general observations on our own birds, well told, as are found in the Ornithological Biography.

CHAPTER II

BIRDS are distinguished from all other groups of animals by the possession of feathers, just as mammals are distinguished by having a covering of hair, or at least traces of it. The amphibians, that is frogs and salamanders, have a smooth skin, more or less glandular, while reptiles have their skin thrown into rather definite folds which mark off scales, to be carefully distinguished from the scales of fishes, each of which is a distinct structure, homologous with a tooth, and can be stripped off, as all know who have "scaled" a perch. Most birds have the feet devoid of feathers, but the skin is thrown into folds of a definite form, differing in different kinds of birds. Some birds, as the owls, have the scales of the foot more or less completely replaced by feathers, which indicates a certain community of origin for both. A moment's reflection will recall that the only other animals having the skin fashioned into scales are reptiles, as snakes and lizards. And this likeness is more than an accidental resemblance, for feathers and scales, as we shall presently see, are probably comparable in their nature. A recent writer (Bornstein, 1912) has investigated this matter, studying the origin of feathers in connection with the scales of the foot. In the Ruffed Grouse the toes are provided in winter with a curious fringe of horny points which act as a support like snowshoes. In our domestic pigeon some breeds have feathers growing out at the sides of the toes, and the same is true of certain

35

breeds of fowl.   Such feather-growths appear in connection
with the scales.   A microscopical study of the developing
foot shows that the scale arises as a little projection of the
outer horny layer of skin, while the feather starts from
adjacent layers a little deeper, soon growing up to meet the
scale which itself sinks in slightly.   When the structure is
nearly mature, it is seen that the feather is borne on the
outer part of the scale.   The inference is *not* that feathers
are transformed scales, but that the feather is an outgrowth
of the same tissue and that both are parts of a single structure so that by suppression of the scaly portion, the feather
is left.   This development of feathers from scales was perhaps one of the first ways in which birds diverged from
true reptiles in the very early history of their evolution.
And at once the possession of a feathery covering gave
them an immense advantage and became a potent factor in
their subsequent remarkable development.   For the first
result of a downy covering (for such was the probable
nature of the early feathers) was to prevent the escape of
animal heat from the body.   For fishes and frogs, for
example, take their temperature from the medium in which
they live, so that if the water becomes cold they have no
recourse but to become equally chilled, and their activities
are consequently reduced.   In like manner reptiles, with
their skin exposed to the air, take their body temperature
more or less nearly from it.   The result is that their
geographic range is limited to the warmer regions of the
globe, and as they approach the temperate areas, they are
either wholly absent or the few species that occur are
obliged to suspend activity during the colder months.
Birds, however, with their feathery covering interposed between themselves and the outer air, are protected as by a

sort of double-window, for the air held in by the feathers is so non-conductive of heat that the warmth of the body is not so readily lost. This double-window effect can be somewhat increased by puffing out the feathers by the action of certain skin muscles and thus making a deeper layer for retaining the air, as we see Chickadees or other birds doing in zero weather. The occasionally disastrous result of wetting such fluffy plumage as the Chickadee's was exemplified a few years ago in our region, when a long-day's drizzle in midwinter was ended by a sudden change to intense cold. The busy little birds could hardly have escaped somewhat of a wetting and the suddenness of the freeze must have chilled many of them fatally, for they disappeared henceforth from this neighborhood almost utterly. Flocks that had haunted the street and garden trees at Cambridge all winter, coming daily to food-shelves, were seen no more, nor were their places filled in the two winters following. Apparently the regular wintering Chickadees of the neighborhood had been almost entirely wiped out.

It is easily seen that the development of feathers, giving the ability to maintain and retain bodily warmth greater than the surrounding air, permits birds to range farther north or south toward the colder areas of the earth and thereby greatly enlarges the domain they may occupy. Moreover, instead of hibernating like our northern reptiles, they are able to remain active all winter, even in arctic latitudes, so long as sufficient food is available to maintain the body. This retention of heat increases the body temperature, and implies an increase as well of the creature's activity, so that birds in addition to being the warmest-blooded animals are at the same time the quickest and most active. Their temperature normally is from 100° Fahrenheit to 110°, that of mammals not usually exceeding 98° F. The recent work of Wetmore (1921) has shown that those birds generally considered the less highly organized, as grebes, herons, pelicans, have a distinctly lower temperature than the more highly organized species, such as pigeons, woodpeckers, sparrows.   There is also a marked day-time range of temperature in small birds, which may be 6° or 7° warmer in midday; while in owls, which are most active by night, the reverse is true.

It is assumed that the first form of plumage developed by the ancient types of birds was down, because young birds still go through a downy plumage as a first stage, and down is the simplest form of feather.   What the second plumage to be developed, could have been like it is not easy to guess. In some of the more primitive birds whose descendants are still living, we may perhaps find some indication of this former prevalent type of plumage.   In the Emu the body feathers are found to be *double!*   For near the base of the web there grows a second web with shaft, barbs, and barbules, as long as the other.   This second part is called the aftershaft and is found usually in a reduced or shortened condition in the feathers of many widely different birds. Thus some ducks have it but other ducks do not; it is as long as the main shaft in the Emu but absent in the South American Rhea or Ostrich.   It is well developed in the Cassowary and in Grouse.   In its origin, it appears on the *under* side of the developing feather opposite the main shaft.   It is supposed (1) that this is an ancient type of feather, (2) that many primitive birds may have had these double plumes, and (3) that the simple type of feather is derived from it by a gradual disappearance of the aftershaft.

In a bird such as the Robin or Crow in which there are

SPINE-TIPPED TAIL-FEATHERS OF CHIMNEY SWIFT
Courtesy of Charles Macnamara
BODY-FEATHERS OF (a) CRANE, (b) GROUSE, (c) FOWL SHOWING
AFTERSHAFT (in front of the paper strip)

no obviously peculiar feathers, the visible part of the plumage is seen to consist of the smaller feathers covering the body and limbs and the larger feathers constituting the wings and tail. These are called "contour feathers," as they give the bird its general outline. For convenience, names have been given to various groups of these feathers. Thus the long flight feathers of the terminal joint or hand of the wing are *primaries,* those of the second joint or part corresponding to our forearm are the *secondaries* and are differently shaped, less stiff, and with more rounded ends. The few at the end of the humerus or elbow are the *tertiaries.* Each of these larger feathers is accompanied by a shorter one above and below, called a covert and there are several rows of these, distinguished as greater, middle, and lesser coverts. The long feathers of the tail are called *rectrices* from the Latin meaning steering feathers, in contrast to the long feathers of the wing called *remiges* or rowing feathers. Just as each of the long feathers of the wing has a medium-sized feather or *major covert* growing at its base, so each of the large feathers of the tail has typically a major covert at the base. This no doubt was the primitive arrangement in the older types of birds, but Dr. H. L. Clark (1918) has recently shown that there are some interesting deviations from it. For although in loons, penguins, cormorants, terns, and small gulls, nearly all waders, hawks, pigeons, swifts, and others, the number of major coverts is the same as that of the tail-feathers, there are some birds in which they are more in number, and the added ones are usually at the outer edge of the tail, as if the latter had been reduced in the number of its rectrices, while the coverts corresponding had remained. This is the case in owls, some gulls, ducks, geese, and swans. The opposite condition in which coverts are *fewer* than the tail-feathers is found in some of the grouse and pheasants, and is typical of the Passeres—that is the small land-birds, as finches, flycatchers, orioles, warblers, thrushes. In these the rule is six tail-feathers on each side, but the outermost has no covert, either because it is displaced inward, or wanting altogether.

In the wing of most water-birds and some others, there is a curious discrepancy in the rule that there is one greater covert to each of the secondaries. For in very many birds it is found that on counting the larger coverts, arranged one at the base of each secondary, when the fifth is reached, there stands the covert in its place but no secondary feather corresponding to it. So noticeable is this peculiar gap that its presence has received a technical name, *diastataxis,* or arrangement with a gap, while the condition in which the fifth covert *does* have a corresponding flight feather is called *eutaxis* or typical arrangement. (There are other Latin names for the same thing—but one is enough.) This curious gap is found in loons, petrels, cormorants, herons, most pigeons, hawks, ducks, and others. It is not found in fowls, tinamous, cuckoos, woodpeckers, and other so-called perching birds. Several theories have been advanced to account for this condition. It is noticeable that there is no intermediate stage, the fifth secondary is either present or not, and since it occurs in so many groups of species that are only distantly related, it is taken to be a primitive trait once common to all birds. Of the many theories to account for this space the most ingenious is perhaps that of Mitchell, who suggests that in the primitive bird the rows of feathers on the hand as it was folded back against the forearm, ran lengthwise along the fingers, while those of the forearm ran diagonally across it as we now see them. At the bend of the wrist, therefore, an adjustment between these two sets of directions became necessary and was effected by setting the feathers in such a way that they formed the points of a triangle, a method often seen where, as in the zebra, two sets of stripes running at different angles to the mid-line meet. If the tip of the triangle were the fourth secondary, the two coverts forming the points of its base would afford the extra one. In the later evolution of the hand with the shifting of the quills of the three digits and the wrist back on to the forearm, the place where this triangle comes is still represented in certain birds by the blank space of adjustment. In most of the small land-birds a still further adjustment and condensation of the wing feathers has obliterated the interval, so that the so-called *eutaxic* condition resulting is a derived one, not the original one. The most recent investigator of this matter is Steiner (1916). He finds that the crosswise rows of feathers on the forearm are composed of a certain number of feathers each, the outermost of which is enlarged to form the secondary, while the others form the coverts. In birds having the gap, the first five crosswise rows consist of one more feather than the remaining ones, which he interprets as meaning that the rows from the elbow out to the sixth have shifted outward, so that in these the outermost feather of each row has become pushed around to the under side of the wing and forms the lower major covert, while the *second* feather of each cross-row is enlarged to form the secondary; whereas in the five terminal rows there is no such shoving over of the outermost feather, for in these rows it forms the true secondary. What appears to be the solitary covert standing in the gap is therefore really a small secondary, which is so crowded as not to have completely developed.

There are many curious modifications of the tail feathers that would be interesting to trace. At one extreme are certain thrush- and wren-like birds that spend much of their lives on the ground, in thickets and undergrowth, seldom flying any distance (*Pitta,* etc.). In these the tail has so degenerated as to be a mere tuft of little stumpy feathers. On the other hand it is much developed in some species, as the Scissor-tailed Flycatcher, the Barn Swallow, certain Terns, and the Frigate-bird. In these latter species it is the *outermost* tail-feather that is longest, and it is possible that it is advantageous to the bird in giving greater leverage for making the quick changes of direction necessary in catching their actively moving prey, just as a long steering oar is used by the steersman of a whaleboat to manœuver the craft with the greatest speed and least loss of movement. The tail feathers of woodpeckers have the middle pairs specially stiffened and pointed to act as a brace against the trunk when the bird is at work; while in the Chimney Swift all the tail feathers have stiffened tips devoid of web, for use as a support in the same way. Many other interesting and remarkable forms of the tail feathers and their coverts could be described. In some cases it seems fairly obvious that the long feathers of tail or tail-coverts are developed solely for ornamental purposes in display, as in the Peacock, which opens out its gorgeous fan of enormously lengthened coverts. But in the Turkey, whose fan in this case is the tail itself, there is an interesting contrast to be made. For in this bird the tail has not become so overdeveloped that it cannot serve as a perfectly good steering device in flight, while at the same time it serves also the other function of a banner in display. The balancing of two or more separate functions in a single organ is not always easy, for there is often a tendency for one to become the chief function at the expense of the other. An interesting case is seen ir several of the African Weaver-finches. In one small species (*Steganura*) two of the upper tail-coverts are immensely enlarged and grow out with their webs vertically placed. In these latitudes there is usually more or less breeze during the day and the birds find it convenient to perch facing the wind on the topmost twig of some thorn tree, looking like so many little weathercocks, for the long flattened feathers do not manage well in wind. In a still worse predicament is the so-called Black Wydah, a common bird in East Africa. The females are trig little creatures, reminding one somewhat of a female Bobolink in their brown and black streakings. The males, however, are of about the size and appearance of a Red-winged Blackbird, except that the tail feathers are very long, over a foot, and curl downward at the tips. These seem purely ornamental and are used in a peculiar form of display which was well described by the late Colonel Roosevelt. The birds prepare little dancing floors some two feet across in a grassy place, cutting off the grass blades and laying them on the floor. A single cock bird alights in this ring, and presently with wings spread, head thrown back, and tail drooping, hops up to a height of about two feet and drops back again, showing off the plumage to fine effect. When it comes to flying off, however, troubles arise. I once saw a small flock of females and a single male fly off together, but though the former soon dashed out of sight, the gorgeous male, with his long plumes undulating behind him like a kite-tail, was quickly left in the rear, and was so nearly upset by the strong following breeze that he shortly came about and dropped to the ground.

Perhaps the longest feathers of any bird are the two central pairs of tail-feathers of the Reeves's Pheasant, a species of the wooded and steep mountain valleys of central western China.   This beautiful bird is exceedingly wary, keeping closely in cover of the pine and oak forests and azalea thickets of its mountain home.   In flight it is like a meteor, with nearly double the speed of a Common Pheasant.   Those who have observed it say that its extraordinary tail is brought into use during flight when it wishes to make a sharp change of direction.   At such times the bird throws the tail up nearly vertically, turning its expanded surface and that of the wings sharply against the air, which causes the bird to drop at nearly right angles to its course into some thick tree-top.   This "Westinghouse brake," as it has been termed, is therefore after all of value to the bird in the steep valleys of its home in allowing it to turn suddenly back into the jungle.

Among our familiar species, the simple elongation of the feathers at the back of the head is perhaps the commonest change from normal.   Thus in the Blue Jay or the Pileated Woodpecker there is a simple crest.   In some of the owls the crest is developed as two tufts, one at each side of the head, the so-called *horns* of the Screech Owl, Long-eared Owl, or other species.   It is interesting to find similar horns in one of the Whippoorwill-like birds, a group whose relationship to the owls is undoubtedly close.   On the other hand, these tufts are present in a bird so far removed as the Horned Lark.

While the coverts that cover in shingle-fashion the bases of the long feathers are usually short, there are some very remarkable exceptions.   Thus the wonderful fan of the Peacock is not, as some suppose, the tail of the bird, but the upper tail-coverts, extraordinarily enlarged till they far exceed the tail itself. There may be peculiar developments of the primaries as well. Thus there is a certain African nighthawk (the Pennant-winged Night-jar) in which the ninth primary, after forming a short web, develops a very long slender shaft, so that as the bird flies the two ends, one on each side, flap along behind, giving the impression when first seen in the dusk of a large bird flying past pursued by two big moths. It may be that these are of value in the mating antics of the bird, but it seems, too, that they may be less of a disadvantage than would at first appear, for two fairly good marksmen found these birds exceedingly difficult to hit with a shotgun, and discovered that the flapping tags on the ends of the long shafts gave an apparent expanse to the moving target so that they constantly were aiming too far behind the bird itself. It is possible that these appendages would have a similar disconcerting effect on a pursuing owl.

In addition to the contour feathers, giving the general shape to the bird, there are found in many species, on parting this outer covering, a more or less abundant layer of small fluffy feathers or "down," similar to the down which to a greater or less degree forms the first covering of young birds. There is a very interesting relation between these two sorts of feathers: for not only does the downy plumage precede the more advanced stage of contour plumage but the downy feathers of the young bird develop in the same way as do the downy feathers of the old bird. In other words, down, whether found in young or adult bird, is to be looked upon as a primitive kind of feather, and we may suppose that the adult plumage of the ancient ancestors of our present-day birds was chiefly of down. The broader and stiffer feathers were probably developed later in the history of their race, for in the individual bird they are preceded by down feathers except where these have in certain species become suppressed.

Pterylosis.—From the external appearance of a bird one might easily suppose that the feathers grew equally from all parts of the body.   But except in a very few of the living species, including Ostriches and their relatives, as well as Penguins and the South American Screamers, this is far from being the case.   Instead, it is found on plucking a bird that the feathers occur in certain definite feather-tracts (or *pterylæ*) between which are areas of bare skin (termed *apteria*).   The feathering of a bird (that is the distribution of feathers on its body) is spoken of as *pterylosis*.   It would seem reasonable to suppose that the ancestors of our birds had their plumage evenly distributed over the body just as scales of reptiles are.   This would be more likely the case if feathers are small, e. g., in Penguins.   With the increase in size of the feather and the consequent increase in the space it covers, it becomes possible to reduce the number.   Hence it is that we find them in most birds of the present day confined to these feather-tracts or *pterylæ*. There is much variation in the extent and shape of these tracts in different groups of birds, even among those that in other important characters are undoubtedly closely related.   The fact is that birds as a group have so much of their structural peculiarities in common that it is difficult to pick out any single trait which may not be similarly developed in birds otherwise now distantly related.

But in general. there are four chief feather-tracts usually present, namely:

(1) The *spinal tract* which covers the head, most of the

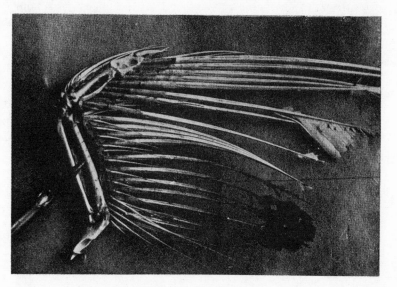

FEATHER TRACTS OF A NESTLING ROBIN

1, Alar or wing tract; 2, humeral tract; 3, head tract; 4, dorsal or spinal tract; 5, ventral tract (in two bands); 6, femoral tract; 7, leg tract; 8, caudal or tail tract.

After Dwight

QUILLS OF A PIGEON'S WING SHOWING (at 5) THE GAP IN THE SECONDARIES *(diastataxis)*

back, and an area along the middle of the back to the base of the tail. Sometimes this tract is interrupted by a featherless space dividing the back into fore and aft areas, or instead there may be an abrupt transition on the back from larger to smaller feathers. Sometimes this tract is divided lengthwise in the middle.

(2) The *ventral* or breast tract, which feathers each side of the breast, and leaves a wider or narrower area bare in the middle. At the sides of the neck this tract is sometimes continuous with the spinal tract and is often forked at the front end.

(3) The *humeral* or upper-arm tract, which is always present as a band of prominent feathers on the upper surface of the upper arm and at nearly right angles to its length.

(4) The *femoral* or thigh tract which is a very similar band crossing the upper side of the thigh.

In addition to these four main tracts the wings and shanks are more or less fully feathered, and various birds show small modifications.

Feather structure.—If we examine a contour feather, we find it to consist of a central tapering axis, the shaft (*rhachis*), the lower part of which is hollow and transparent, with a little hole at the end into which projects the germ whence successive feathers later develop. The upper part of the shaft has a somewhat square cross-section and is filled with pithy substance, while growing out from each side is the main web or *vane* of the feather. The web of the feather is easily pulled apart, and is seen to consist of a long row of barbs (or *rami*), one row on either side of the shaft. Each barb under a microscope looks like a small feather and has a row of barbules (or *radii*) on either side corresponding to the barbs. These barbules therefore spread out on each side of the barb parallel to the main shaft of the feather, and are seen to overlap. The set of barbules on the side toward the tip of the feather overlaps neighboring barbules, and certain small hook-like processes (*hamuli*) on the under side fit into similar hooks on the upper side of the neighboring set, so holding the entire web together. In downy feathers the little hooks are lacking

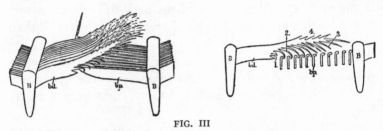

FIG. III

Cross-sections of feather-barbs (*B*) to show interlocking of barbules (*bd.*, *bp.*) by means of the hamuli (*2*)

After Wray

and this is true also of many plume-like feathers as those of the Ostrich or the Egret, so that the barbs are *not* held together and the feather fluffs out. There are many ways in which this structure may be modified to produce peculiar feathers. Thus the hair-like feathers which we singe off from a chicken before cooking are reduced feathers which in their course of development have lost the web and now consist merely of the slender shaft. They are called *filoplumes* or thread-feathers, and in some birds project beyond the contour feathers. The hair-like bristles in some birds are of this nature. In the Birds of Paradise the long wire-like feathers seen in the tail of certain species are merely the elongated middle tail-feathers from which the entire web has disappeared. In our American Motmots (birds of the tropics, distantly related to Kingfishers) the adults have a space devoid of web for an inch or more near the end of the two middle tail-feathers, so that there is a racquet-shaped piece forming the tip of the feather. The curious thing is that in immature birds the feather is entire, and gradually loses the particular part of the web that comes an inch or more below the tip, leaving a stem as it were. It has even been said that the bird actually prunes off the barbs of this portion with its beak, but the real explanation seems to be that in this region they are somewhat brittle and break off during the operation of preening the feathers. Racquet-shaped feathers are found in some other birds, among them a rare kind of Parrot.

Before leaving the subject of down, it will be interesting to mention the peculiar patches of these feathers called "powder-downs," that occur in certain birds, such as herons, bitterns, hawks, and in the Wood Swallows of India. This type of down-feather is somewhat oily and of a peculiarly friable nature, easily breaking up into a sort of powder. Though such feathers may be scattered through the plumage and so easily overlooked, in the herons and other birds just mentioned they form definite matted patches: one in the middle of the breast and one on each side of the lower back. Wetmore (1920) discovered that in young herons these patches are used by the birds in lubricating their plumage. The bill is run through the patches and then the large feathers passed through the mandibles and the entire plumage rubbed over. In the immature stages the oil gland of the tail is too small and undeveloped to be of use for oiling the plumage, so that the function of the powder-down patches is to take its place in the early life of the bird. Wetmore suggests that the oil gland may even have originated from a patch of these peculiar feathers, the many minute oil ducts of which may have combined to form this single large gland.

The developing feather in its earlier stages appears as a minute pimple-like structure, which on microscopic examination is found to consist of a thin horny cylinder (or *follicle*) enclosing the growing tip of the feather. The future feather-barbs are arranged in a circle about the central pulp which sinks into the skin and forms a projection into the base of the feather to supply it with blood during growth. The first barbs of the nestling grow out in a little circular clump and being without hooks to hold their minute barbules together, fluff out as down by the breaking away of the enclosing sheath. They have but a very short tube-like base. When the adult feather starts to grow, the same papilla becomes again active, and the next feather is really a continuation of the down, for this is carried out on the tip of the new feather, and is finally rubbed off. As the growing part of the feather reaches its full size it "sets" or becomes horny and is henceforth cut off from the circulation of the blood, and is really dead, just as the ends of our finger nails may be said to be dead, and no changes in color or form due to growth can henceforth take place in the feather. At certain times of year the living pulp at the base of the feather becomes again active and a new feather is formed following the moult of the old. The more recent investigations seem to favor the view that a new papilla is formed with each moult rather than that the same growing point again becomes active.

The moulting (*ecdysis*) of birds is often a much more complex process than might at first be supposed. For not only do different species differ in the number and time of moults, but there may be individual differences due to various factors, as age, sex, condition, and so on. Very valuable studies of this matter could be made by following the process in birds that have been individualized by "banding," and caught for examination at frequent intervals. Careful notes made at these times should, however, be checked by the examination of preserved specimens, for it will invariably occur that additional points will come out that were not at first noticed. The reference collection is almost indispensable in any serious work of this sort. Studies of caged birds, though interesting, are of relatively less value since captivity tends to reduce the active functions of the bird so that the moulting process is seriously interfered with and is likely to be quite different from that occurring in the natural state. American ornithologists have been foremost in the study of plumage-change in birds. The works of Stone (1899), Chapman, and Dwight (1900) may be especially consulted. While an extensive treatment of the subject cannot be given here, the following general facts are important.

(1) All our smaller land-birds when adult undergo at least an annual moult, at the close of the breeding season, whereby the entire plumage is renewed. In this way the "fall or winter" dress is assumed. Stone considers this moult a "physiological necessity," later moults less so.

(2) In many birds there is a spring moult whereby a fresh breeding dress is donned. But this is commonly only a partial change, for some of the feathers of the previous year are retained. As interesting variations of the process, some species having a well-marked spring moult in their first and second years, may later discontinue it after the full adult plumage is acquired. The male Scarlet Tanager in

its first winter plumage is olive with brown wings and tail. In the following spring it moults to the familiar red and black except that the brown primaries and secondaries of the wing are retained, and do not come in as black feathers till the second summer. Occasionally individual birds of a species may continue to moult *every* spring, while others of the same species do not, after reaching the adult plumage. Such species may perhaps be in a transitional stage of evolution whereby the number of moults is in process of reduction (an apparent advantage), but the habit is not yet firmly established in the race.

(3) As a rule the large feathers of the wing, so important in the life of flying birds, are moulted less often than any other part of the plumage, and the relative order in which these flight feathers are shed, is generally constant among related groups of birds.

It is obvious that the number of different-looking plumages that a bird may have, depends on the number of moults required to reach the final or adult stage. And these different steps may be looked upon as representing in a way some of the stages passed through by the species in its evolutionary history. Thus our common Robin in its first plumage is speckle-breasted, recalling the condition found in the young of many other thrush-like birds, and one still retained in the adult Wood Thrush, for example; whereas the adult Robin may be thought of as having evolved beyond this stage and entered upon another stage in which the breast is wholly red.

The loss of a feather seems to act as a stimulus to the growth of another. Thus it is that in Germany five crops of feathers used to be plucked in old times from the tame geese in the course of a year.

Dwight has suggested special names for the successive plumages of birds: The first of all is called the (1) *natal down,* in which the young bird develops downy feathers only. This plumage is most useful and attains its fullest expression in the young of certain birds that leave the nest very shortly after hatching, such as loons, ducks, sandpipers, the hen and grouse tribe, all of which have a thick covering of down, so familiar in the chicks and ducklings that fill shop-windows at Easter time. In many of these birds the down is a highly specialized dress, simulating very closely the broken background so that the young bird can hide instantly in almost any natural situation. In other birds that spend a longer time in nests, the downy plumage is not so well developed, and is represented often by a mere tuft on the head or back, for in these birds it is important that they develop quickly and attain their flight feathers so as to follow their parents in migration or to shift for themselves. At all events they skip this stage as rapidly as possible. Indeed, it is absent in woodpeckers and hummingbirds, and many others no doubt will altogether suppress it in subsequent ages of progressive evolution. In the Australian Brush Turkey, it is said, the stage is passed through before hatching, so that the downy plumage is not found in the young except in the egg. This process of thrusting stages in development farther and farther back into the earlier course of life is called *acceleration,* and often finally results in the individual skipping the particular stage altogether.

The second covering of feathers is called (2) the first or *juvenal* plumage, and consists of contour feathers, which carry out on their tips the down of the preceding plumage. The wing- and tail-feathers attained by the young bird at this time are of much the same character as those of adult birds but the body feathers are usually more fluffy. This plumage is carried for a varying time, three or four months in some birds, but in others is very soon replaced by

(3) the *first winter* plumage, in which all the feathers are of the same texture as those of adults.   In many birds this plumage is acquired by a *complete* moult, as in the Horned Lark, Red-winged Blackbird, Grackles, Tree Swallow, and the woodpeckers.   In most of our smaller species, however, the tail-feathers, larger wing-feathers and their coverts are not new feathers but are retained from the preceding or juvenal plumage.   It is in this first winter plumage that the birds migrate from our latitudes.   In early spring, probably in correlation with the renewed activity of the sexual organs, there occurs in most birds another moult, more or less nearly complete, whereby the bird in its first spring attains its fourth or *first nuptial* plumage.   Sometimes, as in the Bobolink, the entire plumage is renewed, but in most small birds, the wing- and tail-feathers are held over from the previous plumage.   In some, only a very few of the throat- or head-feathers are renewed at this moult. It appears that those birds that differ markedly in the appearance of the spring and fall dress, undergo the most extensive change at this moult, while those which differ little in plumage the year round have a less-marked moult.   An interesting case is that of the Bobolink and the Snow Buntings whose fresh spring plumage is not that familiar to us. In these birds the tips of the new spring feathers are very brittle and of less intense color than the rest of the feather. They very soon break off and the result is the contrasting black and white livery of the breeding plumage.   The fine black throat of the common House Sparrow likewise results from the breaking off of the feather tips of this part.

The young bird of the previous year has now reached adult life, and it is probable that nearly all the smaller species may breed when a year old, with the attainment of their first nuptial plumage. In some birds, as our Rose-breasted Grosbeak, the most beautiful feathering is not reached until another spring or two, after successive summer and spring moults. It is a question, too, whether some individuals of certain species ever acquire the perfected dress, but remain all their lives in a less brilliant condition. This supposition is strengthened, for example, by the fact of the relatively small proportion of bright crimson male Pine Grosbeaks in the flocks that reach us here in winter. Data on birds of known age might throw much light on matters of this sort, and the problem is one that can best be studied by aid of banded birds.

To sum up this matter of moults and plumages the following table shows their sequence:

Name of Plumage		*Name of Moult*
(1) Natal down	lost by	(1) post-natal moult
(2) Juvenal plumage	" "	(2) post-juvenal moult
(3) First winter plumage	" "	(3) first pre-nuptial moult
(4) First nuptial plumage	" "	(4) first annual or post-nuptial moult

(bird a year old)

(5) Adult or second winter plumage		(5) adult or second pre-nuptial moult
(6) Adult or second nuptial plumage		(6) second post-nuptial moult

(bird two years old)

etc.

It should be understood that while these are the general series of plumages, different species show great variation in the degree of completeness of all but the post-nuptial moult. That is, the entire plumage is always renewed after the breeding season by the annual complete moult, but the pre-nuptial moult is likely to be incomplete, so that the breeding dress may be compounded of parts of two generations of feathers. Of the many interesting variations in time and amount of moults, there is no opportunity to treat in detail. Among the ducks, however, we find that in the annual post-nuptial moult, that is, after the birds have bred, *all* the long wing-feathers are shed at once in some species, so that for a time the birds are incapable of flight and usually retire to dense swamps or extensive marshes until the new feathers are grown. Many male ducks at this time develop a new plumage which very closely resembles the body plumage of the female, so that it is given the name "eclipse" plumage. It is not retained till spring in most species but instead the body feathers are shed in about two months, so that by autumn the bird is once more in its familiar bright plumage which goes through till the next breeding season is over. This is a hastening of the pre-nuptial moult, so that it comes in late summer or autumn instead of in spring, and while it has been called a *tutelar* or protective plumage, because it resembles the duller plumage of the female, it may be that nevertheless there is some other cause for it than protective value. It is perhaps correlated with the early mating of many species of ducks, or perhaps it is a plumage on its way to complete suppression so that in the course of evolution the duration of the original winter plumage will be so shortened that it will disappear altogether and the plumage that once was assumed only in spring, will instead be attained at the annual post-nuptial moult and be worn till the next post-nuptial moult in the following year; that is, we may see here a stage on the evolutionary road toward losing all plumages but the one a year after the nestling stages are by. In fact this is exactly the condition found in some of the most highly organized birds, as even the common House Sparrow, which moults but once a year. This is only one of the many interesting problems connected with the subject of moult.

CHAPTER III

THERE used to be a conundrum: What makes a leopard spotted? The answer is: His spots. But if we inquire what makes the bright or dull colors of birds and why their plumage is thus marked, the answer is not so simple.

We have seen that in the growing feather the developing barbules attain their form and coloring matter, after which they go through a process of hardening, the walls of their minute cells become horny and the living contents of the cells seem to dry up, so that the mature feather is in a way a dead structure, like our finger nails. The coloring of the feather cannot thereafter be changed by the bringing in of new or different coloring matter, for there is no mechanism for this. The only way in which the appearance of the plumage can be changed is through wear, which may break off the minute tips of the barbs or barbules, exposing other coloring that already existed but was hidden by them.

Pigments.—The beautiful colors of birds' feathers are due chiefly to two factors: first, the pigment produced inside the structure of the forming feather, and second, the structure of the feather itself; that is, the light reflected from the surface of a feather may produce an effect of color different from that of the coloring matter in the feather itself. To illustrate this latter case, take the deep-blue feather of an Indigo-bird, place it under the microscope with a drop of oil to submerge the feather surfaces, and on looking at it by light transmitted from below, the layer of pigment granules inside the feather structure is seen to be *brown*.   In the dry feather, of course, the color appears blue because the layer of brown pigment is not directly visible but the peculiar structure of the feather intervenes producing minute reflecting surfaces by means of a layer of cells above those containing the pigment.

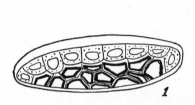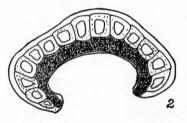

FIG. IV

Cross-section of barb from blue feather of (1) Ant Thrush, *Pitta*, and (2) a Cotinga (greatly magnified), showing a layer of reflecting cells over-lying pigmented cells

After R. M. Strong

A very recent writer (Görnitz, 1923) has given an account of the ordinary pigments of birds that seems fairly simple.   These are of two sorts: (1) *melanins* (meaning blacks) and (2) *lipochromes*, meaning oily or fatty colors. The melanins are present in the feather as minute granules and are soluble in concentrated acids.   They are of two sorts: (a) *eumelanin*, which is black or blackish brown, and soluble with difficulty (in pigeons these grains are unusually large).   This sort of pigment if combined with other coloring has a tendency to appear at the outer end of the feather.   (b) The second sort of melanin is called *phæomelanin*, and varies from reddish brown to dull yellow, or may even be almost colorless.   This sort of pigment when regularly distributed in rows of granules produces some of the delicate reddish colors. These two kinds of melanin granules are chemically similar and the latter may even be the same as the former, only greatly oxidized.

The *lipochromes* are not like the melanin granules, but are like colored oils. They are soluble in ether or in alcohol, and again are of two chief sorts: (a) *zoöxanthin* (or animal yellow) of pure yellow color; and (b) *zoöerythrin* (or animal red) of pure red color.

When the black eumelanin is alone present in the ordinary feather, the bird is black, but if the amount is small the color is less intense and becomes blackish-brown, as in the young Red-shouldered Hawk. The phæomelanin or brown pigment granules give the reddish-brown and yellow-brown colors, which are intense or pale according to the relative amount. Most colors, however, are the result of combinations of one or more of the melanins, lipochromes, and feather structure. Thus:

I. *Pigment combinations may be* (a) of both sorts of melanin, which gives bluish gray like the back of a titmouse if concentrated, or olive brown if dilute; (b) both sorts of lipochromes present together giving orange (like the crest of the Kinglet); (c) the combination of eumelanin and zoöxanthin is frequent and gives yellowish olive-green if concentrated, brownish olive-green if dilute. Thus by the gradual disappearance of the zoöxanthin (lipochrome) in a desert race of the Kinglet (*Regulus*) the bird becomes a paler grayish-green on the back.

II. *Pigment + structural form of the feather* when combined give gray or yellowish-browns and blues with
   the melanin; green is produced by the combination
   of structure, melanin and zoöxanthin. The structural modification often consists of a deep layer
   of unpigmented cells over those carrying the pigment and serves as a sort of reflecting surface.

Iridescent colors as in the neck feathers of pigeons are
found to result from the dark pigment granules near the
feather-tips being *spherical* instead of the usual rod-like
form. Light striking these spherical granules is broken up
and the effect called "Newton's rings" is produced, with
rainbow tints.

There is another remarkable and unique sort of pigment
which is found only in the three genera of Plantain-eaters
or Turacos, a group of African birds, tree-frequenters, related to the cuckoos, the commoner species of which are a
beautiful deep green, with slightly crested heads, and with
the secondaries of the wings a dark-crimson color. The
discovery of this pigment was accidentally made by M.
Jules Verreaux in 1818, in South Africa. At the time of
the torrential rains he noticed that these birds left the
tree-tops and sought refuge in the dense lower branches.
One bird which he had seized by the wing escaped, and
great was his surprise to find that the inside of his hand
was colored a blood red. Some days later he repeated
the experiment with three more birds caught in a soaked
condition, and found that he could rub the red pigment
off from the feathers, reducing them to a pale rose hue.
Verreaux believed that when the feathers were dry the red
pigment was renewed but this is doubted by Sir Arthur

Church (1913), who has lately summed up our knowledge on the subject. It appears that this red coloring matter is easily dissolved in soft (but not hard) water, or water and soap. Tame birds kept by an Englishman "washed themselves nearly white" in the water given them to drink. Sir Arthur Church dissolved out some of this coloring by use of distilled water or weak ammonia and found that by neutralizing with weak hydrochloric acid the crimson pigment, which is called *turacin* (from Turaco the native name), was precipitated out in gelatinous clots which, when collected and dried, form a deep red mass, with a surface luster of purplish. It is insoluble in alcohol, ether, benzol, and other usual solvents of oils. If heated to the boiling temperature of mercury to drive off any oil, and then roasted, there is finally left a black ash, amounting to about $\frac{1}{10}$ of the original weight, which is found to be oxide of copper, about 7% of which is pure metallic copper, and causes a greenish flame when turacin is burned. Traces of copper are found in other animals and in plants, but no other birds are known that owe their color to it, though it was mistakenly reported that turacin was found also in a Philippine cuckoo of a different family.

Görnitz and Rensch (1924) have lately shown that most violet color is structural. In some cases, however, it may be the result of actual violet pigment. They have succeeded in isolating such pigments in the Cotingas and in the Green Pigeons, and have named that of the former cotingin, that of the latter ptilopin after the Latin names of these birds.

A pure white feather is one devoid of the pigment granules in its structure. The many minute cells whose walls, in honeycomb fashion, build up the structure, reflect light from their various surfaces so that the feather appears white since most of the light falling upon it is not absorbed. For it is the absorption of certain of the rays of the light-spectrum by pigment that gives the color to an object. We see only those rays that are reflected back to us. If all the rays are reflected, the object looks white; if the reds, yellows, and greens are absorbed and the blue only is reflected, the object is blue to our eye, and so on; while if all the light is absorbed, the object looks black.

We may now inquire, Of what use are color and pattern to birds? Time was when men believed the purpose was to delight human eyes, for were not all things created for man's use? Yet, even so, it seems unreasonable to have ignored so completely the bird's point of view. The subject is a large one, full of controversial possibilities, yet offering fullest opportunity for careful field observation by discriminating eyes.

In a general way birds may be said to reflect in their plumage certain tones of their surroundings. Thus, many sea birds are black and white, as eiders, guillemots, auks; or bluish and white, as adult gulls and terns, whose color environment is of relatively simple lights and shades, sky and sea. Birds living in sunlit foliage tend to be yellow or yellowish-green with black markings, such as many of the warblers, goldfinches, orioles, and certain weaver-finches; thicket dwellers are dull brown, as Song and White-throated Sparrows, Winter Wrens, certain thrushes. Other birds seem boldly to defy such generalizations, so that it is difficult to interpret the value of their coloring in their life-history. The whole matter is one to be studied carefully.

The subject of concealing colors has been experimentally studied by the late Abbott H. Thayer (G. H. Thayer,

1909), and his work has been somewhat further elaborated by certain English naturalists. In his remarkable book setting forth his experiments and observations, Thayer takes as his main thesis that all coloration in the animal kingdom is for the purpose of concealing its wearer. But we have seen that a single organ may serve more than one purpose, so we may expect to find that some colors are for other purposes than merely concealment.

We distinguish a bird or an object from its background either (1) because it offers a contrast in coloring or (2) because it stands out in relief through the effect of solidity produced by shading. It must be said that a bird standing motionless is likely to be effectually concealed against a considerable variety of backgrounds in contrast to the ease with which the same bird is visible when in motion. The concealment of the motionless bird is the more effective if its coloring reproduces the background against which it is seen. A simple case is that of the Nighthawk squatting motionless among leaves, dead sticks, and lichened stones. The plumage seems almost a continuation of the background. This class of coloration may be called "mimetic"; the bird mimics its surroundings, and so long as it is still, it passes easily as a portion of them. There are many different degrees in the closeness of mimicry. The Nighthawks have developed this method nearly to perfection, and it well suits their ground-nesting habits. In the case of such birds as Quail and Ruffed Grouse the general tone and broken nature of the background are imitated, rather than its minute detail. There is a slightly mimetic effect even in the case of such birds as Starling and Bronzed Grackle which are often difficult to detect if they stand

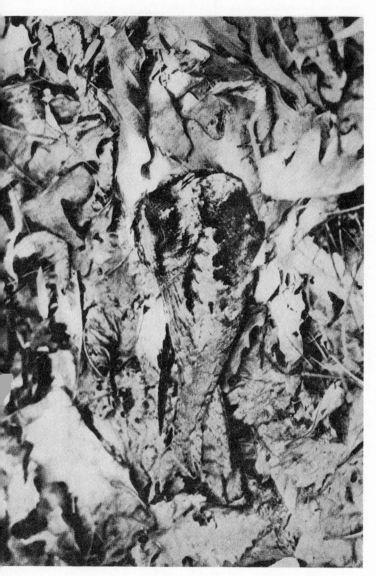

CONCEALING COLORATION IN A BROODING WHIPPOORWILL

Courtesy of Dr. Arthur A. Allen, phot.

quietly among black branches, for they look like something they are not, namely, parts of branches.

But while the Nighthawk is effectually concealed by his mimetic plumage, we must recall that his legs are very short, he squats closely on the ground, and his plumage is in actual continuity with his surroundings. What of the longer-legged bird that does not squat? An additional difficulty comes in here, for however little the bird's body be elevated above the surface, it casts a shadow, and that is equivalent to standing out in relief or being visible to a sharp eye. The principle called by Thayer *obliterative shading,* and first brought to the notice of naturalists by him, now comes into play. I recall the famous artist's demonstration of his discovery at a meeting of the American Ornithologists' Union in Cambridge many years ago. He showed us three potatoes spitted on a wire and supported a few inches above ground. At a distance of about twenty feet the middle potato was nearly invisible, though the two others stood out by reason of the darker shading of the under side. After sufficiently mystifying his audience, he stepped forward and by a turn of the spit inverted the potatoes, when to our surprise we saw that the middle one's lower side had been painted white, thus counterbalancing the effect of its dark shadow. As Dr. Elliott Coues with characteristic ingenuity remarked, it had been "standing in its own light." This in brief is the principle of countershading, the effect of which is to destroy the appearance of relief by counteracting the dark shadow of the lower side so that the object does not stand out from its background in strong relief. It is a widespread method of effective concealment and is taken advantage of by a great variety of species.   Thus it is that birds with white bellies and dark backs are so hard to see when they remain still against an appropriate background.   Sandpipers, grouse, many sparrows and a host of birds that feed much on the ground are commonly colored in this way (if one may speak of white areas as colored).   I think it was Dr. Coues also who remarked, in speaking of this style of coloration, that a pale lower surface is not necessarily for the purpose of giving concealment, for he said, a watermelon is similarly colored!   The truth probably is that very many birds have developed their countershading in response to the principle that absence of light produces a smaller demand for pigment, so that by the elimination of individuals that were more conspicuous because they stood out in greater relief, those that were *less* conspicuous survived to reproduce their kind, and so gradually an exquisite adjustment was reached.

Another interesting color effect is pointed out by Thayer in birds such as Song or Savanna Sparrows, or many shorebirds such as Snipe, Pectoral or Least Sandpipers.   This is the perspective effect of fine streaks or spots which are coarser on the lower part of breast and throat or on the sides than they are on the back, neck, and head.   As one looks at a bird from a little distance against a flat horizon, the coarser markings on the lower areas of the bird chime in with the foreground of the scene, while the finer top-markings correspond to the apparently smaller details of the more distant portion, an effect probably at once more obvious to an artist than to one unused to considering objects in perspective.   In Thayer's own words, this style of top-markings in animals already obliteratively shaded, is a representation of patterns *beyond* the animal, allow-

ing it to appear either as a flat plane (that is, without relief) or as merged into the scenes behind it.

Additional examples of the reproduction of background
patterns in the plumage are readily brought to mind.   The
grass-patterns of alternate dark and light stripes simulating high light and shadows of narrow lengthwise blades are
beautifully illustrated by many swamp-living birds, Snipe,
Woodcock, Swamp Sparrows, Sharp-tailed Finches.   The
striped neck of the Bittern is a familiar example, and many
have probably seen the wary bird stand motionless after
alighting among tall grasses, the pattern of its outstretched
neck closely simulating the light and shade of the stems.

With an artist's authority Thayer describes the *variegated* type of plumage with its abundance of contrasting
markings as a sort of background picturing, comparing the
details of a swimming Wood Duck to a picture made up of
the various elements of its surroundings—thus the alterna-
ting light and dark wavy lines on the flanks simulate wave-
lets like those at the side of the swimming bird; the orange
patch about the eye tones with a bit of a waterlily flower
beyond; white streaks in the plumage pass as glints of
light, and other finer markings tone with other elements
of the background.   So with a variegated bird such as
the Chestnut-sided Warbler, the yellow crown simulates a
sun fleck on a leaf, the black eye-line a dark twig, other
dark marks are shadows, the chestnut side is reddish bark.
Amidst its natural settings the bird is concealed by having
a detail of coloration like that of its average haunts.   All
this is doubtless true,—indeed, is demonstrable,—but is
only one aspect of the matter.   Among tree-living warblers a very great variety of color patterns seems to be
found, made up of these same color elements in different

combinations. The Cape May, Prairie, Pine-creeping, Blackburnian, Black-throated Green, and Parula Warblers all have yellow and green, light and dark markings, some with chestnut tints added, and, for aught we can see, appear to get on equally well. At distances of ordinary vision they all would tone equally with their surroundings among leafy twigs. In other words, there are many combinations of these prevailing tints that would produce the same obliterative effect at a distance of, say, fifty feet or so. There must therefore be an additional significance in the fact that these same color elements are differently arranged in different species. This, I think, indicates a two-fold aspect of such color patterns, namely, that they have (1) an obliterating effect at middle distances, and (2) an individualizing value at close range. A familiar example is the zebra, which at one hundred yards looks as gray-bodied as a donkey, but at a few feet distant shows a handsome pattern of stripes in a contrasting arrangement that pleases at least human eyes. May it not be with many groups of birds having similar color elements in their plumage, that at distances of ordinary danger they are alike concealed more or less effectually by being part of their background, while at other times the differing elements of their mosaic pattern are useful to the different species for display at close range or for help in identifying mates, or for other purposes?

Still another type of coloration is that producing so-called "ruptive" patterns, which, while the bird is still, serve to cut the body into unidentifiable pieces so that it passes unnoticed though in full view. These markings are therefore bold and contrasting. A Semipalmated Plover with its black band across a snowy breast disappears from view wonderfully when standing among pebbles with their rounded contours and alternate light and shade. It is this principle that was widely used during the Great War to reduce the visibility of warships by breaking up their familiar outline into contrasting and irregular pieces of unfamiliar shape. An interesting detail is that of concealing the eye in birds. This bright shiny-black circle might often be conspicuous and serve as a tell-tale mark were it not concealed or masked by a black patch covering more or less of the side of the head. It does not follow, however, that all birds so marked have need for this protection or indeed that they are very much more concealed with or without a dark eye-patch. It is here that observation of the living animal in its natural haunts is absolutely essential to a correct estimate of the part played by coloring as a useful adjunct to the bird's equipment. It is perfectly possible that in many cases the coloring is quite unessential for protection. Thus one does not readily perceive that a bird like the Turkey Vulture has necessity for concealment from enemies. In a great majority of cases we know very little of the actual enemies of birds, how they escape from them or how often their protective devices are unsuccessful. It must be borne in mind, too, that man, and especially the white man, is a comparatively recent factor for wholesale destruction, so that none of the devices named are primarily meant for combating his pursuit.

Thayer frequently emphasizes the point that certain colorings may be of use only occasionally or at particular crises, and at such times serve their purpose, just as a cat carries its claws sheathed except when in the act of seizing.

There are many other ways in which color may be use-

ful. While a bird in more or less rapid motion cannot
escape being seen by watchful enemies, it is possible that
even at such times a pursuer may be balked by color devices.
Take a tennis ball, says Thayer, and mark it so that it is
checkered black and white, and you will be surprised to see
how much more difficult it is to hit. So a male Bobolink with his variegated livery of black, white, and buff may
be harder to catch than if he were all black. And who-
ever saw one caught by a hawk? Possibly the white marks
on wings and tail so commonly seen produce a similar effect in a moving bird. The same author believes that the
dark-and-light barring of a Sharp-shinned Hawk's wing
makes the final dash of this bird less conspicuous, for the
color pattern fits in well with the alternate light and shade
of twigs in the forest. In this case, therefore, the aggres-
sor would be partly concealed by its pattern, just as its
prey, so that the rule works both ways. These may seem
minute matters that would make after all very little difference in an actual chase in full view, and I personally
believe that this is often true. Yet the more we see the
actual pursuit and capture or escape, the more it does
seem that at the critical moment the least thing may turn
the scale in favor of the quarry. As a single instance, I
chanced once to see a Sharp-shinned Hawk in close pursuit
of a Hairy Woodpecker, both birds dashing across a
Cambridge street. As they passed a few yards from me,
with the hawk hardly a wing-beat behind, the woodpecker,
as if realizing its peril, uttered a single loud and peculiar
cry of seeming despair, gamely dashing on for the nearest
tree all the time. At the instant, the hawk, as if surprised by the sudden outburst, perhaps even associating it
with my presence as it went by, slackened speed for the frac-

tion of a second.   That was enough, however.   The wood-pecker gained a good yard and was safe behind the tree trunk in a twinkling.   For at such moments the fraction of a second is a relatively long time; and once the first dash fails, a hawk seldom pursues farther.   A shrike *does*, however, but that is another matter.   This little incident goes to show the difference between life and death that some momentary diversion may make, such as a sudden noise, or some unexpected action that puts an adversary at a psychological disadvantage for even an instant.

Among lizards a type of defense is found which I im-agine may have a counterpart in birds.   If you have ever tried to catch a lizard in your hand, you will know that the usual result is that he is too quick, and you are lucky if you manage to seize his tail.   No doubt other enemies often do the same.   But the resourceful creature has one or more weak places near the root of the tail where, by a quick turn, he can snap the bone and the tail becomes detached in-stantly.   While this member remains wriggling in your fingers to create a diversion, the rest of the lizard runs off, and in time grows a new, though usually less handsome tail. I recall a ground lizard in Haiti that when approached would walk slowly away curling its bright orange tail con-spicuously, as if offering a bait in case of sudden pursuit. Now in the case of a bird pursued by an enemy, the tail is apt to be the nearest part, and if conspicuous might be seized by the pursuer, and pulled out, allowing the bird to escape. This perhaps accounts for some of the prematurely tail-less individuals one sometimes sees.   Again, a sudden opening and shutting of a black-and-white tail might have a mo-mentary startling effect, and make the minute difference between life and death.   Such may be the case with so many birds that have conspicuous white feathers in the tail, as Juncos, Vesper Sparrows, and others. It is equally probable that such a use is likely to be altogether incidental and that such markings are really present from some very different cause. Yet one can imagine how they might prove of advantage. The sudden contrast made by the flashing of white markings may often be helpful in dazzling or confusing a pursuer. We have often had the experience of startling a Nighthawk or a Whippoorwill by day in the woods, and being astonished at its instantaneous disappearance when the conspicuous white patches on wings or tail were hidden as the bird alighted.

Withal we must still bear in mind that such devices, while perhaps in slight degree helpful, are not in their nature concealing. For in most cases a moving object really is conspicuous. Thayer has suggested, however, that motion may be masked by color pattern so as to be deceptive. The most familiar instance I can think of is that of our common striped snakes. If you have ever tried to catch one by stepping on it as it slipped off through the grass, you will realize that the matter is less simple than appears. The lengthwise stripes, so conspicuous on its back, run in the same direction as the snake's motion, so that when only part of the snake is seen it seems to be going much more slowly than is actually the case; for to the eye the same view of the snake is presented until the tip of the tail comes in sight, though meanwhile the head end may be already a foot away. It is possible that lengthwise striping among grass-living birds has a similar effect and that their motions on the ground amid proper surroundings are less conspicuous for this reason. An opposite effect would be produced by cross-striping, such as is so commonly seen in the tails of many species of pheasants. These birds are thicket-haunters. A rapidly moving tail of this pattern would give to the eye the impression of a *faster* motion than reality, on account of the rapid succession of light and dark bars or if fast enough, a blurr would result. Imagine the seven-foot tail-feathers of Reeves's Pheasant running through the jungle before a watching wild-cat. The motion of the tail would be so conspicuous that the cat might easily be confused as to the rate of speed, if not as to the actual whereabouts of the bird's body. Moreover, it is interesting to see that in pheasants both these types of coloring are combined, the body often longitudinally streaked, the tail cross-barred. Some day we may know more about the true meaning of these things, but they afford suggestions to be kept in mind as we observe birds in their natural haunts. A single device may be put to several distinct uses, and perhaps only rarely or accidentally chance to be of value in helping an escape. Yet this one chance may mean the difference between life and death, for after all the most minute things count.

Yet the real or, better, chief function of many conspicuous markings as well as of bright coloration in general may perhaps be in display. For in a great many birds the male is colored differently from the female and more brilliantly, and goes through display antics before his intended mate at the beginning of the breeding period and after mating. At these times ornamental feathers or tufts are erected or handsome plumage spread to best advantage before the female, and it is but natural to suppose that she is in some way affected by this, and that her choice of a mate may in part be governed by the effectiveness of the show. The tufts of white feathers of the Bittern, which usually are concealed under the wing, are at the breeding season flashed in view during the bird's display. The amorous street pigeon, strutting before his mate, turns around and around with lowered head, allowing the play of light to bring out the iridescence of his neck-feathers. In many species the male is not notably different from the female at any season, as in the Savanna Sparrow, Vesper Sparrow, Chickadees, and thrushes, though even in these there may be slight minor differences of tone or local color. In the first autumnal or *juvenal* plumage there is commonly very little difference between the two sexes; but in some species the next moult brings a different dress to male and female. Thus the Chestnut-sided Warbler in its juvenal plumage of the first summer is greenish above, with whitish wing-bars, and usually white below in both sexes. The following moult brings the beautiful chestnut sides, yellow crown, and minor markings, in which the male is brighter than the female. In the Black-throated Blue Warbler the process is hastened, and carried farther. For the male with his black throat and blue-gray back does not pass through a stage in which he resembles the female in her olive-green livery with buffy breast. This stage seems to have been skipped entirely. Why this difference? If the more brilliant plumage is for display before the female, and is thus not useful until the breeding stage of the first spring, why should the Black-throated Blue Warbler attain it while still in the *childhood* stage of the first summer? Why has the stage resembling the female's been dropped out? It does not answer the question to call this a case of accelerated evolution; but it may be an illustration of what Loomis has called "momentum" in evolution; that is, once a start is made along a certain line of development it may continue in response to unknown forces, quite regardless of its need.   The classic case of this is found in an extinct line of nautiluses, which in earlier periods were curled, snail-like; then later the terminal coil grew straight away, and finally in a still later period curled around so that it grew against the erect portion.   This seemed to be unfavorable —a kind of species-suicide—and the race died out.   The Black-throated Blue's case may remind us to be wary in supposing that the difference of color between the two sexes is a result of the male's propensity for display of his plumage before the female, and her choice of the more brilliant males.   But this is no doubt one of the factors, and is called by Darwin (its first exponent) the principle of sexual selection.   It seems more or less evident at first glance that this has been a prime cause for these sexual differences of color, but it may prove to be only a guiding influence on certain growth tendencies which find a sort of inevitable expression in the chemical and physical processes of the body and of whose causes we are still very ignorant.

A remarkable reversal of the principle that the male is the brighter-colored, is seen in the familiar case of the phalaropes, and in less familiar ones of certain of the snipes, in which the *male* is the duller plumaged.   In these birds it is the *male* that is courted by the female, and he it is who undertakes the duties of incubation, showing that birds have anticipated by many thousands of years a condition supposed to be found among certain of the more progressive of our own kind—an illustration perhaps of "parallel evolution"!   This reversed relation of the sexes in courtship, wherein the female seems to do the active love-making, is taken to indicate that her bright plumage has been developed in response to sexual selection; that is, the brightest and most beautiful females would be selected as mates by the males.   This certainly appears to be a reasonable inference, but may not be the entire explanation.

Nor does it seem that the duller color of the female is altogether a device to render her less conspicuous while incubating; for, although this result often does obtain, it is frequently the case that the brighter-colored male assists in this duty.   Thus it is not rare to see the brilliantly marked male Rose-breasted Grosbeak sharing the incubation of the eggs, and Colonel Roosevelt has described the like habit of the male Ostrich.   Yet it does not appear that the male bird is at a disadvantage.   Indeed, the latter author remarks on the difficulty of seeing the male Ostrich as it sat close on the eggs, despite its usually conspicuous black and white plumes.   From these and many other like cases, it is not difficult to infer that among certain species this habit of the male in sharing the incubation might become more and more developed, and result in his performing the entire hatching, quite apart from the process of mate selection through display.   It would be interesting to watch individual birds, of species in which this habit is partially developed, to determine exactly what share the male does take in the process, and to see whether or not different individuals or different species do not show variable degrees of paternal assistance.   This can be done accurately by the study of birds individualized by banding.

Finally, we must not lose sight of the possibility that the brighter or more conspicuous coloring of the male may spell protection and survival for his duller-colored mate and her brood, simply because his very conspicuousness makes him more often the object of pursuit by bird enemies.   This is exemplified in almost any collection of bird skins in which it will usually be found that the bright-plumaged males are far in excess of the duller females and young, showing perhaps the greater conspicuousness of the males. One can easily imagine that a Sharp-shinned Hawk passing over a nesting colony of Bobolinks or Red-winged Blackbirds would find his attention much more readily drawn to the brighter males than to the females, so that a more conspicuous plumage of the male would really serve as a protection to the other members of the colony. Such an altruistic relation may seem unusual, but it is really not, for we know how readily parent birds risk life in defence of their nests or in solicitude for their young.

This very brief discussion will serve to give a slight indication of the really complex nature of the causes and uses of birds' colors, and may serve to suggest a few of the many possibilities that may underlie them. There is a very great opportunity here for close and careful observation of the habits of birds in a free state, with a view to shedding light on these problems. But the observer, in interpreting what he sees, must ever be on his guard lest he lose sight of alternative explanations, and especially lest he be too ready to interpret the motives of birds' actions in terms of human feelings and emotions. Pythagoras held that "Man is the measure of all things," but a well-known biologist has warned us that Man is likely to mislead himself when he puts his own meaning into Nature.

CHAPTER IV

BILLS, FEET, WINGS, AND BONES

A BIRD'S beak serves it for knife, fork, and spoon, as well as for hammer and chisel in many species. Its chief use is in connection with procuring food, so that we find, among birds as a whole, an extreme variety of shapes of bills, adapted for gathering various kinds of food. The simplest form is perhaps the ordinary short, tapering bill found in sparrows, orioles, warblers and thrushes, suited for picking up small objects. But even among these birds there is great variety. The beaks of thrushes for instance are somewhat elongated and pincer-like compared to those of finches, which are heavier and sharper-edged, adapted for picking up, cutting open, or crushing seeds. The bills of flycatchers are broadened sidewise and provided with bristle-like feathers at the base, the more readily to catch their moving prey. A familiar modification of the finch style of beak is that of the crossbill in which the tips of the jaws do not meet when closed but are a trifle out of line, so that they cross. The tip of the lower jaw may cross to the right or to the left of the upper. This device serves as a wedge to pry off scales of pinecones. The seeds thus exposed are deftly picked out by the tips of the beaks which can be brought closely together when the bill is opened slightly.

The beaks of woodpeckers are adapted for being driven in and prying apart the wood of decayed trunks and are

CROWNED HAWK-EAGLE *(Spizaëtus coronatus)* OF AFRICA
Courtesy of National Zoölogical Park

powerfully constructed.   The skull is large in proportion to the neck and heavy-boned to resist the strain of sharp blows.   Imagine how it would feel if our own mouths were extended a yard before our noses and the jar it might give if we attempted to split even soft logs with them!   It is curious to find that the barbets, a group allied to woodpeckers, dig out similar nest-holes in dead wood, but feed largely on soft food which does not have to be extricated from the trunk.   Their bills are not at all chisel-like but more nearly of the short, broad type, and with curved upper profile.

Birds that seize their prey with the feet and tear it to bits with the bill, usually have a hook at the tip of the beak, as in hawks, eagles, and shrikes.   No doubt this sharp projection gives a better hold on a straight pull, and by piercing the flesh in seizing, starts the piece that is being torn out.   The same form of beak is found in vultures, petrels and albatrosses, which feed by pulling the mass of food in pieces.   Cormorants, too, have hooked bills.   In all these groups the feet are probably but little used in holding the food.

It is interesting to find that herons, which by some naturalists are considered not distantly related to cormorants, have a decidedly hooked beak in the embryo.   This soon straightens out in young stages, however, to form the long straight dagger-like bill of the adult.   Most herons feed by quick jabs to catch living prey, from fish and frogs to lizards and butterflies.   For this method a long neck and a long bill are an advantage, giving additional length of thrust and reach after the escaping prey.   The same thing is seen in other unrelated groups, as in the fish-eating loons, grebes, snake-birds and terns.   The same principle is illustrated, too, by cats and dogs, for the former leap on their prey from ambush, seizing by the claws and then biting, while the dog or wolf gives open pursuit and reaches forward to nip with its teeth; partly for this reason, no doubt, cats are short-snouted, dogs long-snouted. Among the herons there is one, the Boatbill, in tropical America which is essentially like our Black-crowned Night Heron but the bill is remarkably broadened. It does not seem to be known how this is correlated with its feeding habits.

Among the sandpipers and related birds there are a number of curious modifications for special ways of feeding. Many sandpipers have a simple, rather long bill for use as a probe. In some this is very long as in the Godwits and Curlews, where it is perhaps correlated with their long legs and wading habits, permitting them to probe the mud while standing in several inches of water. An opposite case is that of Woodcock and Snipe which have long bills but *short* legs. It is obvious that here, too, the bills are suited to feeding habits, for these birds probe mud in places where they can easily walk on its surface, as in swamps, brook beds and grassy marshes. The tip of the upper jaw in the Woodcock is further peculiar in being a delicate organ of touch and capable of slight movement so that it can open when buried in mud and grasp the hidden worm or insect. Another unusual style of bill is seen in the New Zealand Wrybill Plover (*Anarhynchus*), in which the tip end turns off at an angle to the right. Such a one-sided structure is remarkable among birds, and is said to be associated again with peculiar feeding habits. According to one writer this bird follows around the bases of stones, keeping to the right-hand side, but there seem to be few exact observations on the habits. The bills of Oystercatchers are flattened from side to side at their tips, and are often used, it is said, to pry off limpets clinging to the rocks, for which they must be very well suited.

New Zealand is a place of strange birds. One species— the Huia (*Neomorpha*), (a black bird the size of a pigeon, with a curious oval wattle on each cheek)—shows the unusual trait of having the bill of different shape in the two sexes. These birds, now believed to be nearly extinct following the destruction of the forests, were said to mate for life, and the pair always kept in close comradeship. They fed on a certain species of grub living in dead wood. The tunnels of these grubs were dug open by the male with his straight sharp beak, and often if he laid bare the burrow the female, with her longer, more slender, and downward-curving beak, reached in and extracted the dainty. In this way the two birds were said to work together, feeding on the common spoil in a sort of coöperative housekeeping.

In the Galapagos Islands off South America live several closely related sparrow-like birds all placed in the genus *Geospiza* whose beaks in the different species have apparently all developed from a single prototype; some are longer and narrower, others shorter and heavier. It would be thought that the heavy-beaked birds would feed on larger or harder seeds that required strength for crushing, and that the smaller-beaked species would eat thinner-shelled seeds. A detailed examination of habits and stomach-contents of these birds, however, seemed to show that all fed on much the same food and no obvious connection could be established between hardness of food and strength of beak. So one must be careful in making hasty conclusions. Nevertheless it is probably true that the large-beaked species have a potentially wider range of foods than those of weaker bills.

Another group of related birds among which we find diverse types of bills associated with various feeding habits are the hummingbirds. Our Ruby-throat has a straight needle-like bill for probing the corollas of flowers, but in South America we find those with longer beaks, some slightly, others greatly curved; others still are slightly upturned and rapier-like, for feeding on particular species of flowers, certain of which are actually dependent for fertilization upon these birds, through the pollen transferred to the feathers of the head and carried to the pistils of other blossoms as the bird feeds. In the West Indies I have often seen one of the species with a sickle-shaped bill (*Lampornis*) searching for small insects by moving quickly up and down along the under side of a large drooping leaf. They even come into houses and hunt the windows over in the same way, possibly obtaining small spiders. It seems likely that the downward curve of the bill makes easier the gathering of small objects from a vertical or inclined surface. A very similar shape is seen in the bills of some of the African sunbirds, which are also flower-feeders. One in particular (*Drepanorhynchus*), yellow and black in color with sickle-shaped bill, I often saw feeding among yellow blossoms whose corollas were similarly curved. In all these groups of birds where special forms of beaks are developed for feeding on special foods, it seems reasonable to presuppose that they are more or less dependent for life itself on rather stable conditions the year round. Hence it is not surprising to find that many of them perish quickly with any great change in their surroundings. Many birds in the Hawaiian Islands and in

New Zealand, for example, had become so specialized that nearly their entire lives were spent in particular species of trees on whose flowers or other products they fed.   With the destruction of these by men the birds have gone.

The beak of birds is covered with an outer horny sheath called the *rhamphotheca*.   This usually appears as a single piece on each jaw, but is in the embryo of several pieces which fuse more or less intimately as the bird develops. In petrels and albatrosses these pieces remain usually more or less clearly marked, so that, as some one has said, the beak looks as if it opened in several different places.   On the upper jaw there is a terminal piece forming the hook of the bill, and back of this a longer one forming the ridge, continued into two little tubes by which the nostrils open; finally at the sides is at least one pair of plates which cover the sides and edges of the jaw.   Each half of the under jaw has a sheath composed of an upper and a lower as well as an end piece.   In Ostriches and the partridge-like Tina-mous of South America there are, on each jaw, a plate on each side and one at the tip.   Similar compound sheaths are found in the bills of several other groups of birds as cormorants, some herons (as the Night Heron), and penguins, but in most birds it appears as all one piece. Lönnberg, a Swedish zoölogist, has recently shown (1904) that the different horny plates of such compound sheaths are homologous with the scales found in reptiles in front of the eye.   Thus, the terminal plate of the upper jaw is equivalent to the rostral plate of a lizard, the one forming the ridge is equivalent to the internasal, those on each side correspond to the reptilian labials, and that encircling the nostril represents the nasal plate.   Similarly in the lower jaw, the terminal piece is the same as the mental or chin plate, while the one or two plates at the side of the jaw are comparable to the infra-labials of a lizard.   In the peculiar flightless Kiwi or *Apteryx* of New Zealand, it would seem that it is the part *behind* rather than in front of the nostrils that has become lengthened to form the long bill, for in this bird the nostrils are at the *tip* of the beak and open on its *lower* surface!   The horny sheath of the bill is often provided with membranous expansions and in the ducks and geese has little cross-plates that serve in sifting out the minute seeds and larvæ of insects on which the birds feed.   Curiously too, this outer sheath with its bright colors is shed after the breeding season in the Puffins and some of the auks.   In the White Pelican it develops a large knob-like excrescence toward the tip of the upper mandible like a gun-sight, and this too is shed after the nesting period, so we may infer it is some adornment for display during the mating season.

It is clear from these facts that one cannot rely too closely on the shapes and structures of bills as indications of close relationship among birds, for they often assume unusual and specialized forms that are similar in different groups or species where the same mechanical use is made of them.

Tongues.—Nor is a bird's bill always an index of the size of its tongue.   In the cormorants for example and others which swallow whole the fish they catch, it is exceedingly small, so that one wonders if it is of any use whatever.   In most of our small birds, as sparrows, thrushes, warblers, it is thin and horny, slightly brushy at the tip and with backwardly directed spines along the sides. Such tongues are used in the handling of seeds or insects. In the West Indies the little honey-creepers which famil-

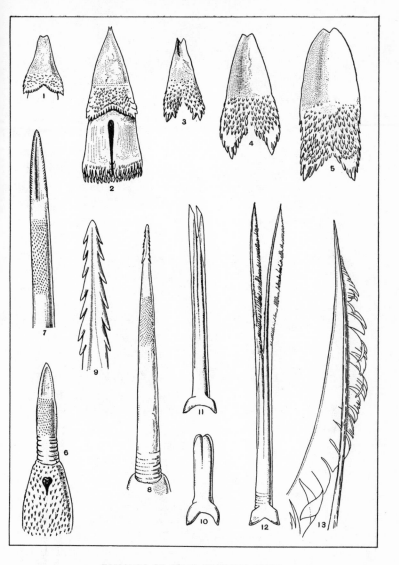

TONGUES OF SOME COMMON BIRDS

1, 2, Chimney Swift, young and adult; 3-5, Screech Owl, young to adult; 6, 8, Downy Woodpecker, young and adult; 7, 9, enlarged tips of same; 10, 11, Ruby-throated Hummingbird, young and adult; 12, a West Indian Hummingbird *(Sericotes holosericus)*, and 13, its tip enlarged.

After F. A. Lucas

iarly come about the houses and gardens have a honey-sucking tongue which is long, with a bushy end. Its sides are partly rolled inward, and by running it into the long tube of a flower it can brush out the nectar. In some of the Old World sun-birds, which are flower-feeders, and in form much resemble the honey-creepers, the rolling is carried still farther so that an actual tube is formed, through which honey can be sucked from deep flowers; the fringing of the tip of these tongues also aids the flow of liquid by capillary attraction. The hummingbirds, also honey-feeders, have long and deeply cleft tongues with a delicate in-rolled membrane on the edge of each half. In feeding, the tongue is protruded and worked quickly back and forth, taking up the honey.

Woodpeckers have extraordinary tongues. In some species they are of great length, slender and pointed, with horny barbs at the tip, but none at the base. The tongue-bones or *hyoids* that support the tongue are so long that instead of being attached at the back of the skull as in most birds, they are in certain woodpeckers forced to curl over the top of the head and actually pass over the fore-head, coming together at the top, and out under one nostril into the tip of the beak. In other species the long ends even curl around the eyeball. This long tongue is obviously useful in reaching up into the tunnels of boring insects and raking out the fat grub. As one might expect, the tongues of Sapsuckers are not so long, but are shorter and very brush-like, for gathering up sap (see Lucas, 1897).

Quite opposite in form are the fleshy tongues of ducks and geese, armed with a series of large barbs along their edges.

A peculiarity of many birds is that, after the food is

swallowed, the gullet is capable of much stretching, so that when picking up food such as seeds, they can rapidly fill the whole *crop,* as this part is called, from the mouth to the stomach, and then let it gradually pass into the first division of the stomach or *gizzard* whose walls are very thick and muscular, and its inner lining hard and rough. Here the food is ground up, partly by aid of small sharp pebbles which are eaten by many birds as a "first aid" to digestion.   The swallowing of stones, however, is a trait occasionally found in birds that would seem to have little need of it.   Penguins commonly swallow pebbles, and these have been found interesting by Antarctic explorers, who would otherwise know little of the nature of the rocks on the sea bottom or land where ice and snow cover so great an area.   Apparently the Great Auk had a similar trait— at all events, small white rounded pebbles of polished quartz were found in numbers among their sub-fossil bones on Funk Island, Newfoundland.   Here may be mentioned the interesting fact that the crop of pigeons produces a whitish fluid on which the baby pigeon is at first fed.   This is the so-called "pigeon's milk," and it is found, on analysis, to be very much like real milk in its nature.

The digestion of birds is very rapid, and this is perhaps due in part to the great length of their small-intestine, to make room for which it is greatly coiled within the body. A minute study of the way in which this coiling takes place has been made by several recent investigators to see if light might be thrown thereby on the relationships of birds. There appear to be two principal ways in which this length-ening is effected: first, by having the intestine arranged in loops that run back and forth lengthwise of the body; and second, by having certain portions of these loops thrown into spiral coils. The first type is the simpler and doubt-less the more primitive; the number of lengthwise loops is usually four. These two sorts may be still further dis-tinguished into at least eight different types of folding.

Birds' feet are as diverse in form as are their bills. In no bird are there normally more than four toes, and these correspond to the four *inner* toes of the five-toed lizard. Probably the outermost or fifth toe was lost in a stage before the bird-like condition was attained, for the ancient lizards called dinosaurs, some of which seem to have sprung from a stock related to the ancestors of birds, were also four-toed, as we know not only from their fossil remains but from their tracks still preserved in stone. In birds, the first or inner toe is the shortest and tends to become very small in walking and running birds as ducks, gulls, plovers. It consists of two joints in addition to the remains of a metatarsal (one of the long bones forming in our-selves the arch of the foot). The three remaining toes have usually three, four, and five joints respectively, so that by counting the number of these one can tell which toe is concerned. Exactly the same formula for the toe joints is found in the four inner toes of lizards. There are, however, a few exceptions among birds, for in swifts all three front toes have three joints each, and in goatsuckers the outer toe has four instead of five. In some birds there are but three toes, as in the Three-toed Woodpeckers, which have lost the innermost toe—though there may sometimes be a minute vestige of it left. In these birds it is the outermost or fourth toe that has turned back; but in most woodpeckers it is usual to find both the first and the fourth toes turned back, the second and third turned forward. This is called a *zygodactyl* or yoke-toed condition, and is of use in climbing. The owls show an intermediate condition, and can turn the fourth toe back at will. In the trogons (bright-plumaged birds of the South American and African tropics) there are similarly two toes front and two toes back, but here it is the first and *second* that turn back, while the third and fourth extend in front. Thus again, as so often among birds, a similar result is obtained in unrelated groups, but in a different way. The greatest reduction of the foot is found in the Ostrich which has but *two* toes, these corresponding to the original third and fourth. This is doubtless a result of the running habit, which tends to bring the weight of the body more or less upon one point—here the fourth toe— and is to be compared to the same thing in the antelope or deer, in which the running habit has caused the reduction of the supporting toes to two from the original five. In the horse, belonging to a group in which the digits are reduced in odd numbers, the final result is that it runs on the tip of a single toe, but no bird has reached this extreme.

The toes are provided each with a claw, which may sometimes be absent as in some albatrosses, and thus affords a case of a part now in process of disappearance. The claws are long, sharp, and powerful in owls, eagles, and hawks that seize their prey, but in some of the carrion-eating species they have lost their sharpness, and are short and blunt. Another curious case of parallel development in unrelated birds, is seen in the middle toe of herons and goatsuckers (Nighthawks, Whippoorwills, etc.) which have the claw long and provided with little comb-like teeth. It is supposed that this comb is useful in dressing their feathers but of this I have seen no careful account.

The nails in many birds are strong and useful in scratch-

Hydralector OF CELEBES, WITH LONG TOES FOR LILY-PAD RUNNING
THE KIWI *(Apteryx)*, A FLIGHTLESS BIRD OF NEW ZEALAND

ing, as in Hens or some of our common finches—Fox Sparrow or Chewink.   In the tropical Jaçanas, however, they
are extremely long and slender, and act like snowshoes for
giving support as the bird runs about over lily-pads and
swamp vegetation.

While most land birds have the toes separate quite to the
base, in others as the barnyard fowl, there is a slight web-
bing between the bases of the three front toes.   This is
greatly developed in swimming birds, as loons, ducks, penguins, flamingos.   Its extreme condition is seen in pelicans
and cormorants in which the web includes not only the three
front toes but the *small hind toe* as well.   Another method
of obtaining a broad surface for swimming is seen in
coots, phalaropes, and grebes in which the skin of the three
front toes grows out in broad lobes that do not stretch
across from tip to tip of the toes.

The skin of the foot and shank (*tarsus*) is thrown into
scales, which vary in size and form.   The entire tarsus
may be enveloped in a single one, when it is spoken of as
booted, or there may be many very small scales like a net-
work, a *reticulated* condition.   The form of this scaling
is often useful in classification.

We all remember the surprise of Alice in Wonderland,
when using the Flamingo for a croquet-mallet, to find that
its knees bent the wrong way, backward instead of forward.   This curious condition, I find, has puzzled other
people as well.   The truth is that a bird's knee bends
forward like our own, but the thighbone (or *femur*) is
usually short enough to be concealed by the plumage; so
that, what Alice took for the Flamingo's knee is really its
heel!   The shank of a bird's foot (known as the *tarsus*)
really consists of three separate bones (*metatarsals*), one

for each front toe, fused into a single one, called a "cannon bone" from its long gun-barrel shape. At its lower end are the three original tips of these fused bones, to each of which the appropriate toe joins. At the other end of this bone, where Alice supposed the knee was, there are originally in reptiles and mammals, two rows of small ankle bones (the *tarsals*). In birds the nearer row has wholly fused with the shin-bone (or *tibia*) and the outer row with the shank of the foot, so that the joint itself is between these two rows of what were once separate bones. It is called therefore a *tibio-tarsal* joint. In some birds there are still to be seen traces of the three bones of the foot that are now fused into the one shank. Thus in penguins the three are partly separated by deep grooves, and in other species there is often a little hole or *foramen* left between two of the three for the passage of a certain nerve.

In carving our Christmas Turkey, we may recall that the drumstick is long and shaped like the calf of a leg, and that is what it really is; for it corresponds to the lower leg, or shin of ourselves. This joint of the leg has really two bones, the *tibia* or main bone and the *fibula,* a much more slender bone on the outer side from knee to ankle. In birds the lower end of this bone has in many species disappeared, and the fibula is a mere splint at the upper part of the tibia. It serves for the attachment of a strong muscle of the thigh or it might have been wholly done away with in the further course of evolution. In some owls, and in the Fish-hawk, of familiar birds, this slender bone is, however, nearly complete and extends clear to the heel.

The thighbone or *femur* is part of the delicious "second

joint" of the carver. In loons and grebes it is remarkably short, to give more compactness and driving power for the muscles that ply the great swimming feet with their flattened knife-edged tarsus. The lower end always has double articulating surfaces: (1) the small outer one fitting the head of the slender fibula, and (2) the main large one that fits against the tibia.

While most persons shrink from the study of bones as being intolerably "dry," the matter is really one of the utmost interest and importance, not only as throwing light on the evolution and relationships of the creatures, but also because bones (including teeth) are, with rare exceptions, the only parts preserved as fossils, and hence give almost the only clue to the nature of the animals that lived in former times.

In external form birds are more or less similar, but an examination of the internal framework affords many and significant points of difference on which to base relationships. The skull is perhaps the most important of the bony structures, for it is the seat of the brain and organs of sight, hearing, taste, and smell. The brain is the central receiving station for impressions from without as well as the despatching office for impulses governing the relations of the animal to its surroundings.

If we take a skull of each of the four higher classes of backboned animals representing mammals, birds, reptiles, and amphibians—say a cat, an ostrich, a lizard, and a frog, —a noticeable difference at once appears in the method by which the head is borne on the spinal column. In the frog and the cat it joins this column by *two* semicircular knobs, whereas in birds and lizards there is but a single round knob. In mammals the lower jaw fits into a hollow at the base of the skull on each side, whereas in the lizard it bears upon a small separate moveable bone called the quadrate. In birds the arrangement agrees with that in lizards and is another important point of similarity. Without going into too great detail, it is clear from a careful comparison that the skeleton of a bird is only a modification of that in the reptile, or, as some one has put it, a bird is merely a glorified reptile. This point of view must be kept in mind when we later consider the subject of bird ancestry.

Thomas Huxley was one of the first to make a careful study of the different types of skulls in birds, pointing out their similarity to that of lizards. The moveable quadrate bone, on which the jaw is hinged, is capable of pushing the cheek-bone or *jugal* forward and thus can move the entire beak, in such birds as parrots where it is united by a sort of hinge to the rest of the skull. In most birds, however, the beak is very little moveable. Most of the separate bones of a bird's skull unite closely in early life instead of showing sutures or boundaries, but the bones of the nose and of the palate seem to show a number of relations with each other which Huxley used as a basis of general classification. Of special interest are (1) the small bone lying in the mid-line of the skull just in front of the large orifice whence the spinal cord issues, called the *basisphenoid*. It projects forward to meet another bone lying medially in the roof of the mouth called the *vomer*. There are two other rod-like bones, one on each side, which are moveable and extend in a V-shape from the quadrate bone at the angle of the jaw forward. These are called the wing-shaped or *pterygoid* bones. In certain lizards there projects from each side of the first bone (the basisphenoid) a

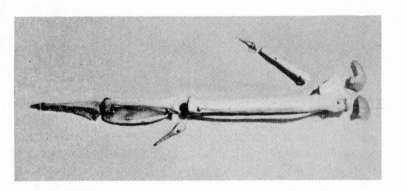

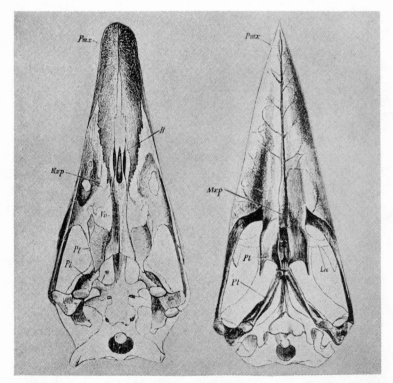

HAND BONES OF A BALD EAGLE SHOWING FUSION OF SECOND AND THIRD
METACARPALS

SKULLS OF SOUTH AMERICAN OSTRICH (left) AND GIANT KINGFISHER
(right), FROM BELOW

Mxp., maxillo-palatine; *Pl.,* palatine; *Pmx.,* premaxillary; *Pt.,* pterygoid;
Vo., vomer.

After Huxley

stout process ending in a flat surface that bears against a similar round surface of each pterygoid, giving side support to these moveable bones.   In the Ostriches, Emus, Apteryx, and related birds, collectively known as the Ratite birds— without a keel on the breastbone—the condition is practically the same, and the basisphenoid bone is continued forward to abut against the vomer, which forms the center of the palate and may separate the two palatal bones, which are relatively small forming the sides of the roof of the mouth.   This condition, since it occurs in the lizards, may be considered an ancient one inherited from reptilian ancestors.   It seems rather characteristic of these ostrich-like birds which in many other respects too are primitive, so for this reason Huxley called this type of palate *"dromæognathous,"* meaning with jaw like the Emu.   Outside of the Emus and their kin, this condition of the palate is found among living birds only in the South American Tinamous, small partridge-like species, which are primitive in this respect, though related to the fowls and grouse.   In this ancient type of skull the lower jaw has but a single head for union with the quadrate bone.   Since in all these points the skull of the ostrich-like birds resembles more that of reptiles, it is regarded as more primitive than that of other living birds.   In these other birds all six of these bones of the lower part of the skull meet; that is, the pterygoids meet the ends of the palate bones, and all come together in the middle where the two central bones (the basisphenoid and vomer) meet.   Moreover, the quadrate (that is, the bone by which the jaw articulates with the skull) has a *double* head instead of a single one, and the little processes of the basisphenoid which in the Ostrich tribe hold apart the pterygoid bones may or may not be present.   This style of skull, while essentially the same in its general structure in the birds other than the ostriches and their kin, differs in the details of the palatal arrangement, so that Huxley made three large groups for the remaining species:

(1) *Schizognathous* or split-palate birds in which the palatal bones are free from each other side by side on the roof of the mouth, so that there is a cleft down the middle.

(2) *Desmognathous* or united-palate birds, in which the cleft is closed and the palatal bones unite in the middle.

(3) *Ægithognathous* or sparrow-palated, the type characteristic of most sparrows and passerine birds, in which the central bone or vomer is broad, and the two palatal bones slender and not united.

All these types are perhaps not so different as their names might imply and are useful only in the study of smaller groups, for different types of palate may occur in birds which in other ways are obviously related. This again emphasizes the fact that the different characters of birds are widely distributed here and there among them and no one set can be exclusively used as a test of relationship.

The spine of birds differs very greatly from that of mammals. The neck in almost all mammals consists of seven bones (*vertebræ*). In whales these are often fused into a nearly solid mass scarcely a foot long even in the largest species, while in the long-necked giraffe, the same seven bones are each greatly lengthened to give the requisite reach. In birds, however, the number is more variable; the long-necked swan for example has 25, geese 19, while the ducks with their still shorter necks usually have 16 or 17. Hummingbirds have no less than 14 to 15 neck vertebræ! This greater number of bones gives the neck more flexibility, and this is aided by the peculiar form of the joints between the vertebræ which are usually somewhat convexly rounded at the sides in front, allowing much side-wise play.

At the lower part of the back a number of the vertebræ become solidly fused together and the bones of the hips (or *pelvis*) are usually firmly attached to them so that the lower back is a nearly solid piece. This is necessary in order to give stiffness to the body so that it may pivot on the legs, and particularly so since the bones forming the pelvis, which in reptiles and mammals may make a solid ring by the union of the lower or *pubic* portions of each hip, in birds *do not* unite below except in a few of the known species. That the two pubic bones, forming the front of the pelvis in reptiles and mammals, are not joined in most birds, is probably an adaptation to allow the passage of the large eggs, by springing apart sidewise. These bones have therefore, so to speak, let go instead of clasping at the midline below. It is interesting to find, however, that in the Ostrich, one of the more primitive birds without keeled breastbone, the two pubic bones of opposite sides *are* united in the middle, a retention probably of the original condition in the reptile-like ancestors. An intermediate condition has recently been made out, in the pelvis of the British Museum's specimen of that extraordinary and ancient fossil bird, the lizard-tail or *Archæopteryx,* in which the two pubic bones come quite together below, but instead of being solidly fused, are merely in contact for a considerable distance at their tips, forming a Y-shaped structure. This primitive bird will be referred to at greater length in a later chapter.

We are all familiar with the fact that reptiles such as most lizards, have long tails consisting of a series of joints, and the same is true of most mammals. The joints of the ox's tail we sometimes recognize at restaurants in our ox-tail soup. What then has become of the long tail in birds? Its primitive lizard-like condition will be mentioned in connection with the *Archæopteryx,* but it will suffice here to say that the tail of birds, so far as its series of bones goes, has become very much shortened, and this loss of length has been counterbalanced by the lengthening of the tail-feathers. In the familiar roast chicken as it lies on a platter before us, all that is left of the long lizard-like tail is the short triangular end called the "pope's nose." This is found to have within it a few separate vertebræ, and it ends in a long plate-like bone (the *pygidium*) which, if we were to trace its development in the embryo, we should find to represent a number of joints of a once longer tail, that have gradually shortened and then fused into a single mass supporting the large steering feathers.

The breastbone or *sternum* of birds is an important structure. It is so different in the ostrich-like birds and their allies from its condition in other living birds, that it forms a convenient point of departure in classification. In the Ostrich, Emu, Apteryx, and related birds, it is a simple shield, convex on its lower side and smooth, arising in the embryo as separate halves that later fuse in the middle line. Six of the ribs in the Ostrich join its upper edge on each side. This simple breast-bone is very similar indeed to that seen in many lizards, and probably represents an ancient condition beyond which these non-flying birds have not developed. Studies of the embryo confirm the view that the ostrich-like birds were probably never in the history of their evolution strong-flying birds, and never developed their wing powers to any great extent. Hence it is reasonable to suppose that

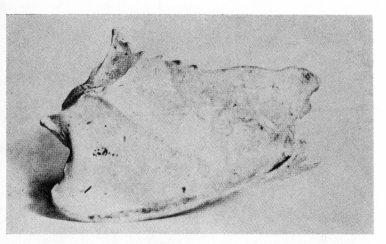

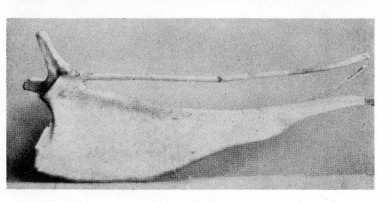

BREASTBONE OF AN OSPREY WITH DEEP KEEL AND NOTCHED BACK
EDGE (side view)

BREASTBONE OF A TINAMOU WITH LONG SIMPLE SIDE PIECES
(from above)

BREASTBONE OF A TINAMOU (side view)

their stock branched off from the main line of descent at a very early time, and that those now surviving in the southern land-masses are the last remnants of this branch.   On account of their simple breastbones without keels for muscle attachment, they have been placed in the group Ratitæ or birds with flat or raft-like breastbone, as opposed to the remainder of living species which have been called Carinatæ or birds with keeled breastbone, like a center-board boat. This division though applying to living species, is perhaps not a fundamental one for undoubtedly the two lines of descent eventually run together as we trace them back into the past.   The keel of course arises between the two great muscle masses of the breast, to separate them and give them a firm attachment.   Similar keels occur among mammals where two opposing muscle masses come together, as at the top of the skull.

Among those birds with keels, the common Fowl presents a breastbone of peculiar interest.   When next you carve a chicken, observe these peculiarities!   There is first a very short space on each side near the front where the four ribs are attached.   As compared with the same space in some ducks in which at least six ribs join this edge, the distance is much shortened.   As you carve the meat from the breast of the chicken, a high keel is exposed, arising from a broad plate.   This keel projects far backward and gives an attaching surface for the two enormous muscles of flight: an outer one that pulls the wing down on the downward stroke and an inner one whose tendon, passing over the shoulder, raises it on the up stroke.   This flat plate corresponds to the simple shield of the Ostrich in which, however, no keel has been developed.   The back edge of the shield ends in the Ostrich in a blunt point in the middle and a short projection on each side.   But in the chicken these projections have grown backward so as to be relatively very long, as long indeed as the keel of the breastbone.   In the South American Tinamous, primitive partridge-like birds, these are enormously long, extending as slender bones parallel with the long narrow keel.   In the chicken other side-projections are developed at the front corners and at half-way points on the breastbone, so that when the isolated bone is stood on its back its whole aspect is that of a curious six-legged bug.

Now in birds that are good fliers and have developed the breast muscles more than in the Fowl, the open cleft between the keel and these narrow side pieces gradually becomes filled in with bone to give more solid attachment for the great muscles of the breast, until finally there is nothing left of this slit except a very shallow notch at the lower end of the breastbone, or two notches if the second side-piece is developed.   Or even these may be wholly filled in or as in swans and the duck tribe the ends bridged across in part to leave a circular perforation.   By this method of progressive development the breastbones of the more specialized flying birds are formed, with their deep keel, long and solid sides, and lack of long projecting ends, though these are sometimes indicated by shallow notches where the clefts are not wholly filled in by bone.   These steps can be seen very clearly in the development of the breastbone in embryo birds.   The important point is that the enormous keel in birds of strong flight is merely a secondary outgrowth from the lower side of the breast-plate to give attachment to the flight muscles as these have gradually become of large size and extended backward from the front of the chest to cover the whole lower part of the body.

The breastbone is attached to the spine by a series of ribs, as in ourselves. There are a number of interesting points about these ribs. In many reptiles, especially in snakes, the ribs are numerous. Typically, as in snakes, there is a pair to each of the vertebræ or separate bones of the spine, from the head to the tail. But in those reptiles that have given up crawling, the ribs of the neck shorten and disappear except their fork-shaped end that joins the vertebra. This forms a protecting arch for blood-vessels, and in many birds these ends, or remains of the neck ribs, are perfectly identifiable as a more or less separate part. Of the ribs that attach the breastbone to the spine, there are usually in the more specialized birds, including most small land-birds, only five pairs, with additional ones in front or behind that do not reach it, though as shown by studies of the embryo, some of them *do* in these early stages, and probably once did in former geologic times. This shows that the part of the breastbone giving attachment to the ribs has become shortened at both ends in many species, while the keel, so prominent a feature in flying birds, has grown back quite independently as a long process of bone for supporting the flight muscles.

A characteristic feature of birds' ribs is the presence of a little tongue of bone on the upper third of the front pairs, that overlaps the rib next behind, helping to give firmness to the body wall. This hook-like piece is called the *uncinate process,* and among reptiles is found also in crocodiles. It is absent in the South American Screamers and in the extinct primitive bird, *Archæopteryx.* In the Rails it is sometimes but loosely attached and easily comes away.

Two other important bones, the *coracoids,* flattened, somewhat rod-like pieces, spring out from the front of the breastbone, one on each side. The same bones are well developed in reptiles, but in mammals are represented only by a little projection at the edge of the shoulder-blade. In birds, they unite by strong cartilage to the shoulder-blade (or *scapula*), and form at their point of union a shallow socket for the wing. The chief point of interest is that in primitive birds, as the Ostrich, this coracoid bone is short, pierced in the upper center by a small opening for the passage of a blood vessel, and the shoulder-blade fuses with its top, but does not make an *acute* angle, such as seen in the birds with keeled breastbone. These traits are primitive, and serve to emphasize the ancient character of the ostrich-like birds.

The wing socket formed by these two bones is strengthened by the "wish-bone," or *furcula,* which is simply the fusion of the two "collar-bones," and in birds of powerful flight is strong and helps to keep the shoulders sprung apart when the wings are raised. In some owls the two sides of this "wish-bone" no longer meet, but their lower ends are formed of tough cartilage.

We associate wings with birds just as naturally as we do with angels. A wingless bird is an anomaly, yet in the Kiwi (*Apteryx*) of New Zealand, the wings are so small as to be mere stumpy remnants nearly hidden in the feathers of the body. How this bird came to lose its wings so completely, we can only guess. Presumably its very quiet and sedentary habits led to the disuse and gradual loss of these members; moreover, the Kiwi is one of the Ratite birds that probably never were strong fliers. Yet, one asks like the child, hearing the story of Jacob's dream, "If the angels had wings, why did they *walk* up and down the stairs?" In the embryo of the Kiwi there are traces

BREASTBONE OF A FOWL WITH LONG SIDE PIECE AND SHORT AREA FOR
RIB ATTACHMENTS
BREASTBONE OF A SWAN WITH SHORT SIDE PIECE AND LONG AREA FOR
RIB ATTACHMENTS

of five distinct wrist bones and the usual three fingers of birds, but in the adult the distinctions are nearly lost and but one finger remains, proving that the wing was once better formed.   In the Emu, an ostrich-like bird of Australia, the fingers of the wing have so far disappeared that only one, the second, is left, and this has three joints terminated by a claw!

The wing of a bird corresponds to the fore limb of a lizard, or to our own arm, so that artists who fasten a pair of wings as well as arms to their angels or goddesses are making a serious mistake in anatomy.   The upper-arm bone (*humerus*) has a much flatter upper end than in mammals, lacking the round ball-and-socket joint.   It is usually hollow, and at the under side near the shoulder has a perforation (the *pneumatic foramen*) for the entrance of one of the air-sacs.   In birds that beat the wings very rapidly in flight, the humerus is very short, stout, and powerful, as in hummingbirds, swifts, and swallows, while in birds of soaring flight that do not flap rapidly, the humerus is long and well feathered to give additional supporting surface.   As Lucas puts it, if the long wing of the albatross should be moved as rapidly as that of a hummingbird, it would inevitably break.   The fore-arm has the usual two bones—*radius* and *ulna,*—the latter forming the elbow and outer side of the arm, and bearing the secondaries or smaller flight feathers.   They are usually rather similar in most birds, but in the long-toed Jaçanas—birds of lily-pad swamps in the tropics—the radius is enormously enlarged, forming a sharp-edged blade in one genus (*Metopidius*) which may give strength for a blow in fighting.   For a number of birds strike powerfully with the arm in defense or attack, as do geese and swans.   A number of birds have developed spikes, sheathed with a horny skin on the bones of the hand, which serve as weapons in fighting. In the Spur-winged Geese of Africa, this spike is on one of the two wrist bones. Several of the plovers have them on the metacarpals or long bones corresponding to those forming the back of our hand.

A bird's hand is greatly reduced from the five-fingered condition of the lizard or mammal. In all living and extinct birds—so far as known—there are not more than three of the five fingers left, though in the embryo Ostrich traces of a fourth are evident at one stage but later disappear. There has been some doubt as to which of the five fingers these three represent, but it seems most probable that the small inner one corresponds to a thumb, the second to the index finger, bearing the main quills, while the shorter outer one is the third of the original five fingers. This seems definitely settled by the recent studies of Steiner, who shows that one of the two wrist bones corresponds to a fusion of the *radiale* and its *centrale,* while the other is the fifth metacarpal of the primitive hand. The first finger in birds is always small, and the long bones (*metacarpals*) of the two others are often grown together. In the reptile these fingers bear each a claw at the end, so that we are prepared to find that many birds still retain claws on one or two of these digits as a reminder of their lizard-like ancestors.

The Ostrich has a well-developed claw on the first and second fingers, and so does the young of that curious South American bird, the Hoatzin, which in early life scrambles about easily in the branches, using all four limbs. The claws may disappear in later life. In the New World vultures the tip of the long second finger often bears a minute claw, and so does that of geese and even of swifts.

This is often hard to find among the feathers, for it is minute, or if the tip of the bone does not protrude from the skin it may not have a nail. No doubt ancient birds had well-developed claws and used them to advantage in scrambling about among branches. This matter will be mentioned again in considering bird ancestors.

Air-sacs.—In many birds the bones, instead of being filled with marrow, are hollow, or with many empty spaces, so that they appear spongy in section. These apparently empty spaces are filled more or less completely by extensions of the breathing system called *air-sacs*. The number and extent of these vary much in different birds and opinions as to their use are equally diverse. They are connected with the wind-pipe or *trachea* where this forks to send a branch (or *bronchus*) to each of the two lungs. It is a fact familiar to many sportsmen that a broken-winged bird is difficult to drown if the end of the broken wing is not submerged too; the reason being, that one of the air-sacs extends into the large bone (*humerus*) of the upper arm and air can reach the lungs that way. A recent exhaustive study of air-sacs in the domestic pigeon has been made by Bruno Müller (1908), and serves to illustrate their general relations. They form an extraordinarily complex system of tubes and are not quite symmetrical on both sides of the body. Air passing down the wind-pipe enters each of its two branches, and then before the lung is reached, a tube passes off from each of these branches into the air-sac system of its proper side. The air-sacs therefore are not directly connected with the lungs, but open into each fork of the wind-pipe just before the lungs are reached. Müller found there were five sets of these sacs on each side of the body: (1) those running as tubes along the neck to the base of the skull, with outpocketings into the bones of the neck and between its muscles: (2) the sacs between the clavicles or wish-bone, and situated on each side and below the point where the wind-pipe forks (from this set are various smaller branches lying between the muscles of the shoulders and an important one that enters the top of the humerus and so extends out into the upper-arm bone); finally (3–4) there are two pairs of intermediate sacs inside the body-cavity below the lung-chamber, and (5) largest of all, the pair of abdominal sacs, which are in the abdomen and partly enclose the intestines. They are very elastic and constantly change shape to accommodate themselves to movements of the intestines. They are not symmetrical; for the right is much larger than the left on account of the stomach occupying so much space on the left side. This pair of sacs is not present in the Ratite or ostrich-like birds. The use of these sacs is still not altogether settled. They seem most highly developed in large flying birds as vultures, swans, pelicans, albatrosses, where many of the bones are penetrated by them. They are present in some degree among reptiles as in the chamæleon. Some have supposed they increased the buoyancy of the body in flight, but, in terns for example, the bones are not penetrated by them, and they are poorly developed in many fliers; others have suggested that they serve to give suppleness to the machinery of the bird's body by filling spaces between muscles or moving parts, and so either filling or emptying as the strains require. Müller believes they are correlated with the long neck, since there is a column of air as long as the wind-pipe to be moved each time fresh air enters the lungs, so that to make up for this, these extensions of the breathing system allow a larger quantity of air to enter the body.   Finally, the most recent writer, Wetmore (1921), comes out strongly in support of the view that they act to regulate the body-temperature, so that if overheating takes place through sudden exertion the blood may more easily cool by contact with these air reservoirs, for birds cannot perspire as do mammals for relief from overheating. No doubt all these functions are in greater or less measure served.

Such very briefly are a few of the interesting points connected with the structure of birds, and particularly with the skeleton.   The value of a slight acquaintance with bones will appear later in tracing the ancestry of our present-day birds.

CHAPTER V

THE FOOD OF BIRDS

THE chief activities of an animal may be thought of as two: namely, self-preservation and reproduction, that is, the activities having to do with the perpetuation of the individual and the perpetuation of the species. For the first of these, the prime need is food of the proper sort and in sufficient quantity, for food is the fuel whence is derived the energy needed to drive the body, and the bird's body, as aptly put by Thomson, is like a high-geared engine, running at a temperature which in mammals would be fever-heat. To produce this energy, not only is the digestion of birds rapid and powerful, but their diet is usually selective according to the food preference of each species, so that there is a comparatively small amount of waste given off as excreta, even the kidney waste being more or less solid instead of liquid as with mammals. This high-geared engine therefore must be run on an air-plane grade of fuel to develop the most power with the least waste. Obviously meat, including any food of an animal nature, affords the most concentrated form of nourishment, while seeds of all kinds with their stored energy of oily or starchy matter come next in value. Vegetable matter of other sorts, as leaves or pulp, is less nutritious, requiring greater amounts and longer periods of feeding to produce the equivalent energy.

Birds doubtless inherit from their lizard-like ancestors a

predilection for animal food; indeed, most of the living reptiles capture insects, fish, eggs, and various species of amphibians, small mammals, or even birds. For example, one of the South American Bushmasters (Bothrops) is specialized for living in trees and with its poisonous fangs killing at once the small birds on which it subsists. The vegetable-eating reptiles are usually slow-moving and heavily built, and the same is true to a certain degree of birds. The many sorts of animal food utilized by birds, and their methods of obtaining it, form one of the most interesting topics in ornithology.

Turning first to the water-birds, it is surprising what large numbers of them are chiefly confined to a fish diet. The loons, the grebes, the penguins, the cormorant, pelican, and heron tribes, most of the auks, gulls, and terns are in large measure dependent on fish for a living. In sundry other groups, too, fish-eating habits are found, which perhaps in some cases are actually ancient traits persisting, while in others they are more likely instances of specialization. For example, the herons are a group in which fish-eating is a general habit; hawks are structurally related to herons, but the only familiar fish-eating species is the Osprey, which may therefore be thought of as retaining this primitive habit once common to the ancestors of both groups. A few of the eagles are also fishers, as the Sea Eagle of the Old World, and the Fish Eagle of Africa, while our own Bald Eagle will often dive for a fish, though he prefers to rob the Osprey. In thinking of the Osprey's habit as the retention of an ancient feeding-trait, it is interesting to recall that it is one of the few birds still retaining a complete fibula in the lower leg. Its long leg, too, is reminiscent of the heron's. Of birds in which the fish-eating habit has been developed as a specialization within its particular group, we may perhaps include the kingfishers, distant relatives of the cuckoos, todies, puff-birds, most of which are insect-feeders. Although the fly-catching habit of their ancestors and relatives is still retained by many kingfishers, especially the smaller species, the fish-eating custom is widespread in the group from the tiny bright-colored Alcedo of Europe to the Giant Kingfishers of Australia. The habit also crops out among the owls, whose relationships are nearer to night-jars and whippoorwills than one would at first suspect. The Barred and the Great Horned Owls are known to catch horned pout by night at holes in the ice where the fish rise to the surface for an extra breath of air; while in Africa is a group of Fish-owls that have become specially adapted for subsisting on this sort of food. Many of the ducks, especially the diving ducks, feed largely on fish at times, while the Mergansers may be thought of as specialized ducks that have become so far adapted for fish-catching as to have developed a long and narrow bill which approaches in shape the forceps-like bill of the loon, grebe, or heron as a fish-catching implement.

The methods employed by birds in catching fish are various and interesting. The herons like true fishermen make it a matter of skill and patience, standing quietly in shallow water until a fish is detected within striking distance of the long neck and bill. With the loons, grebes, most cormorants, and the snakebirds, the active pursuit of fish under water has perhaps been responsible for a certain similarity in the conformation of the bill, which in these three unrelated groups is long, slender, and forceps-like for reaching and seizing. The wings are not ordinarily used for propulsion under water in these birds, but instead the powerful hind-legs with their shortened femur and long tibia furnish the motive power. Still a third method of fish-catching is illustrated by the plungers, as the kingfishers, terns, and gannets. A species of cormorant abundant on the Chilean coasts also departs from the method usual in its kind, and joins with the gannets in plunging for fish from a height overhead, as described by Dr. R. C. Murphy. The hovering and plunging of the kingfishers and terns is a familiar sight to dwellers along our coasts. The kingfisher usually chooses a lookout perch from which to make his sally or may hover momentarily in one spot to make sure of his dive, while the tern with graceful flight patrols the rocky shores or quarters the open sea, with down-turned head, until upon spying a fish it suddenly checks with widespread tail, turns and darts directly down, presently emerging with its fish. In watching terns, one is impressed with the general accuracy of their aim. It is seldom that they miss. With the larger and heavier plungers, such as the gannets, a different method still is used. Having located a school of fish, the birds gather over it and keep up a constant bombardment of the surface, each one plunging in for its fish, coming to the surface and rising with effort *into* the wind, until a sufficient altitude is gained from which it may swing about to join once more the cloud of plunging birds. There is thus a constant circulation of the fishing birds, (1) from the summit of the plunge to the water, (2) followed by the struggle to rise from the surface *against* the wind to the requisite height before (3) the return again to the plunging position. Meanwhile, too, the school of fish may have shifted its position so that there is a gradual drift of the flock of birds after the fish.   The value of these diving terns and gannets as indicators of schools of fish is often taken advantage of by fishermen.   On occasion, too, the birds may take advantage of the disturbance made by a swiftly moving vessel, as when in the West Indies a Booby Gannet followed in the lee of our steamer for miles to plunge after the flying-fish, flushed, as it were, by the cutwater.   As with the birds that pursue fish under water, so with these plunging birds there is a certain similarity in the shape of the beak among unrelated groups, for in the tern, the gannet, and the kingfisher, the pointed·bill regularly increases in depth toward the base until it forms with the skull a javelin-like head that must largely obviate the shock in striking the water.

A careful study of the actions of diving ducks has recently been made by Dewar, who points out that they feed largely at the bottom at depths which are perhaps more or less characteristic in extent for different species. It follows that the fish eaten by such ducks are chiefly those that lie on the bottom or hide under or among stones and algæ.   He remarks that on account of their different ways of feeding the competition is reduced to a minimum between those groups of birds that like herons wade in shallow water for their prey, those that plunge for it near the surface like gannets and kingfishers, those that dive to the bottom for it like the diving ducks and those that, like loons and snakebirds, pursue it (in part at least) at intermediate depths.   From a great number of accurate determinations, Dewar has made out for diving ducks a very definite time-to-depth relation.   The length of time under water increases regularly with the depth so that it is possible to work out with a fair degree of accuracy the

THE GIANT KINGFISHER *(Dacelo gigas)* WITH JAVELIN-LIKE HEAD
Courtesy of National Zoölogical Park

depth of the water by observing the time during which the bird is down. This was found to be for the first fathom 20 seconds, and for each additional fathom 10 seconds. This implies that in ordinary dives of over 3 feet, a bird spends the same length of time searching for food at the bottom whether the distance down be greater or less, and what is more remarkable the same relation seems to hold for cormorants, grebes, loons, and auks, as well as the diving ducks, a case of "habit-convergence" in these five unrelated groups of birds. Thus, in case of a grebe feeding by diving along a seashore, the following average periods were noted over known measured depths:

12 dives, aver. 35–36 sec.	27–28 sec.	32–35 sec.
depth 15 feet	10½ ft.	13½ feet.

The habit of diving for food is developed not only in the orders mentioned, but in the penguins, among the Tubinares by the group of diving petrels (*Pelecanoides*), in the Rails by the Coots (*Fulica*) and, strangely enough, in one group of Passerine birds, namely the Dippers or Water Ousels, thrush-like birds that plunge boldly into mountain streams and walk about feeding at the bottom. Of these, Dewar points out that the Coot is an exception to the rule of 20 + 10, etc., for the time-depth relation. In this species, if one would determine the depth of water by finding the time elapsed while the bird is down, he must allow 10 instead of 20 seconds for the first fathom and *then* 10 seconds for each succeeding fathom, as before. The reason for this is that whereas the other divers spend a certain time at the bottom in searching for food, the Coot, being a feeder on water plants, merely seizes a beakful of these and at once returns with them to the surface. In other words it has no "bottom-time," but having snatched what it may of the vegetable growth, bobs again to the surface and eats it there.

Here may be mentioned an interesting habit of some diving birds of swallowing small stones, which no doubt assist in grinding up the food. This is the case for example in penguins, and it is recorded of certain recent expeditions to the ice-capped Antarctic that the chief knowledge gained as to the geological nature of the sea-bottom in certain places was derived from the pebbles retrieved from the stomachs of penguins killed there. The Great Auk apparently had a liking for small quartz pebbles—at all events in excavating for bones of this extinct bird at Funk Island, Mr. O. Bryant obtained among the bones numbers of these small polished pebbles which doubtless were gizzard stones.

From the human point of view the main interest in the fish diet of birds is whether or not it affects adversely the available supply of food fish. This matter has lately been investigated for six species of grebes of the United States by the United States Biological Survey, with the result that examination of stomach contents shows no evidence that food fish are destroyed to any extent. Most of the species eaten are of little or no value to man, though at times the Pied-billed Grebe may cause some damage in fish hatcheries. This bird as well as other grebes, however, compensates for any harm by destroying numbers of crayfish which in the South are very destructive to crops; Pied-billed Grebes also feed extensively on giant water-bugs which are said to destroy fish fry. Taverner has recently published the results of an investigation into the alleged damage done to the salmon fishery of the Gulf of St. Lawrence by cormorants. From an examination of some 30 stomachs he calculated that a well-filled one would weigh 1½ pounds and that on the basis of two full meals a day each, 700 cormorants would in the five months from May to September consume 45 tons of fish a season! The fish found in the stomachs (taken June to August) comprised, however, not salmon, but sculpin, herring, flounder, tomcod, capelin, and eel. The salmon would be in danger only while as young (smolts) they descend to deep salt water in their second year; for on their return again to fresh water as grilse they are of 2–5 lbs. weight and large enough to be safe from cormorants. The evidence is that whatever effect the cormorants have upon the salmon is likely to be beneficial than otherwise, through capturing and thus weeding out the less active or less well-developed individuals. Taverner points out that in this and other cases in general, it need not be a matter for alarm that valuable species of fish are occasionally eaten. For with most species of fish, the number of fry is far greater than can be raised and the surplus must necessarily be reduced by some agent or other. An immense number of fry could not restock a pond or stream beyond the number that can find food there. This relation has been established under present conditions of food supply and enemy factors, and the enemies need not give cause for alarm if they do not increase abnormally. An indirect benefit from fish-eating birds is brought out by Dr. R. C. Murphy who, in his account of the guano industry of the Peruvian islands, considers the Peruvian Cormorant "the most valuable bird in the world," not for itself, but for the guano derived from the multitudes of birds that congregate on these dry and otherwise nearly barren places. This valuable fertilizer is derived from the immense quanties of anchovies which swarm in these waters and form the chief food of the birds. The annual output is some 90,000 tons, and forms a great source of revenue for the government.

While living fish are prey for many birds belonging to diverse groups—as loons, grebes, ducks, auks, herons, owls, hawks, kingfishers—dead fish are eaten by but few. The larger gulls, however, have developed the taste for this sort of food to such an extent that they seldom take living prey but have become chiefly scavengers, thus filling a niche otherwise not well filled by any of our common water-birds. The advantage of a scavenger's diet is that it may at times be abundant, as when shoals of small herring or sand lance are forced ashore, and again since the prey may also be a large dead fish, it permits the scavenger to feed on bulky species that if living it could not possibly master. In hunting its prey, too, there is an advantage in the gregarious habit to the extent that an abundance of food is soon detected by the individuals within a visual radius, through seeing those nearest the prey drawing in toward it as soon as it is found by any of them.

The situation of colonies of fish-eating birds must also have a certain relation to the movements of fish. For example, of the various cliffs that might be used as nesting sites by sea birds, only certain ones are found to be in actual use. For not only must these be more or less inaccessible from enemies, but their walls must be of such a pitch that young birds in tumbling from their shelves as well as old birds "taking off" in flight, do not strike them in the nearly perpendicular drop to the water. Moreover, they must be situated not too far from shoals where fish congregate in abundance.

Altogether the relations of birds to fish are of very great interest and importance.

Of other forms of animal food available universally and in abundance, small rodents of many different kinds stand out prominently in the diet of many of the hawks and owls. Since many kinds of mice interfere with human agricultural and other interests, the destroyers of mice are reckoned among our beneficial species, though in nature they play their part no less effectively than those that help in reducing other species of mammals or birds whose existence is beneficial to our interests. A recent investigation of the food of the Australian Barn Owl has yielded some valuable results. These birds retire to some regular shelter by day to rest and at such times regurgitate as a good-sized pellet the indigestible bones, fur, feathers, etc., of their night's meal. It was found that on an average two such pellets were thrown up each day by a single owl, sometimes probably as many as three or four. On the conservative basis of two a day, this would make 730 pellets in a year, so that Lea of the South Australian Department of Agriculture collected this number of owl pellets from beneath an owl's roost, and analyzed them to find out what a single bird's diet for one year might be. The result gave the astonishing total of 1407 mice, 143 rats, 7 bats, 5 young rabbits, 375 sparrows, 23 starlings, 24 other birds, 4 small lizards, 174 frogs, 25 large night moths, 52 crickets, and a few other insects, chiefly beetles. Probably the sparrows and starlings were taken from roosts at night. The recognition of the great value of owls as destroyers of mice and rats in populated areas is very clear and the bird is carefully protected by law in South Australia, with a penalty in addition to a fine of $25 for each bird killed. Only lately have the California fruit growers learned to encourage Barn Owls about the storage-sheds for their value as killers of rats that do great damage to fruit awaiting shipment.

Among land birds, the most general source of animal food is that supplied by insects. Such is the profusion and wide variety of insects that birds of various species have become adapted for pursuing them in their several different modes of life. We are all familiar with the way in which birds of unrelated groups have acquired similar feeding habits in order to pursue insects of a given habitat. For example, tree-trunk species are pursued by creepers, nuthatches, certain woodpeckers, the Black and White Warbler, and the wood hewers of South America. Another set of birds, including woodpeckers, and such diverse types as the New Zealand Huia and the Hawaiian finch-like species, dig them out of decaying wood; another group of birds pursue the insects that frequent leaves and the smaller twigs, including warblers, many sparrows, kinglets, orioles; while yet other groups, as swallows, flycatchers, and swifts, pursue insects in the air capturing them as they fly. Again, many ground-living insects are sought by birds that frequent this type of habitat, as thrushes, blackbirds, pittas. Much has been written as to the economic value of birds as insect destroyers. They are an effective aid in helping to reduce the enormous numbers of insects that are produced and which are needed to maintain the numerical relations of these creatures. For insects have important enemies not alone in birds but in bacterial diseases which may, in seasons favorable for bacterial increase, sweep them

away in millions; other insects specially adapted for preying upon particular host species are of next importance perhaps, but these, too, may have secondary parasites which
in turn kill off the (from our viewpoint) beneficial primary parasites. As Holmes put it,

> "Big fleas have little fleas upon their backs to bite 'em,
> And little fleas have lesser fleas, and so ad infinitum."

When, therefore, a bird eats an insect, it may destroy
(1) a species neutral in value from a human standpoint,
(2) one that is positively harmful, or (3) one that is
beneficial either in killing the harmful insects or in some
other way, as in the fertilization of useful plants.

In case of serious outbreaks of insect pests, as locusts
and grasshoppers that destroy our crops, or caterpillars
that defoliate trees, it is well proved that birds are effective
in reducing their numbers.   It is also recognized that other
parasitic insects as well as diseases are even more efficacious,
so that the control of newly imported insect pests such as
gipsy and brown-tail moths in New England is to be hoped
for chiefly through the use of parasites of this nature rather
than by birds.   The same checks act to regulate outbreaks
of native species.   It must be borne in mind, as pointed out
by Fitch (see Weed and Dearborn) that it is not to the advantage of any bird or parasitic insect that it should
wholly exterminate the creature on which it feeds.   There
must be enough left to keep up the supply or the bird or
parasite will exterminate itself, too.   This no doubt happens with parasitic insects to a large degree from time to
time, should they increase so as to reduce the host species
too far.   With birds, no doubt the same is true, but in
less degree, for an insect-eating bird is seldom so specialized

as to feed exclusively on a single kind of insect. In all this it is important to bear in mind that in the course of ages the present conditions have been worked out whereby each successful species produces young sufficient not only to maintain an average representation but also to allow for a certain larger or smaller percentage of loss, as a factor of safety. If, therefore, birds are found at any time destroying useful species of other creatures, this loss may be regarded as necessary to a certain extent, as it has been allowed for in the natural relations of the species. If it prove that the loss is not compensated, the species is not successful and needs help in the way of reduction of enemies.

It would take too long to enumerate the kinds of insects used as food by birds, but their relations to the widespread and abundant ants and termites (or so-called white ants) are especially interesting. These insects especially swarm in the warmer countries and are commonly social and active the year through. In the temperate climates they are active and abundant in the warmer months. Their social habits render them in the tropics an abundant and always available source of food, so that it is not surprising to find animals of different groups specially fitted for preying upon them, such as ant-eaters of various kinds, certain carnivorous mammals, peculiar kinds of reptiles and amphibians, as well as a number of birds that feed chiefly or wholly upon them. A summary lately published by Bequaert shows that ants enter very largely into the diet of many kinds of woodpeckers in both the Old and New World. Of our familiar species the Pileated Woodpecker is especially fond of the giant black wood-ant which often attacks forest trees at their base and runs its tunnels far up within the trunk, eating out the heart wood. Such a tree may appear perfectly sound externally but prove to be riddled at the core on felling. It is to secure these wood-boring ants that the Pileated Woodpecker cuts its mortise-like holes in the trunks of living trees, and I have seen a tree with such a hole cut completely through a large trunk. Our common Flicker is probably the greatest consumer of ants among the eastern woodpeckers, and is frequently to be seen on the ground gathering them. It is remarkable that the salivary glands of the Flicker are unusually large, and I have had occasion to notice their great development among certain ant-eating mammals as well. Since the secretion of these glands is alkaline, it has occurred to me that their unusual development in these cases may be in order that the formic acid which the ants contain in quantity shall be more or less neutralized.

Many tropical birds feed largely on ants, including the family of Ant Thrushes (Formicariidæ). There are others that follow columns of driver ants and prey upon them. Many species of swifts are fond of winged ants, and at the swarming periods great toll is taken of them by many other birds. I have even seen Herring Gulls and Laughing Gulls rather clumsily catching them in mid-air during a September afternoon when millions of the insects were a-wing. So abundant were they on the Maine coast one year that the quiet surface of the bay was strewn with those that had fallen into the water, and the gulls were busy picking them up. No doubt the formic acid taste is pleasant to the bird, and the same perhaps is accountable for the liking of some species for bees or wasps. I recall seeing a Clarke's Nutcracker, one summer morning in Utah, perching beside a nest of hornets frequently picking off and swallowing one of the insects. Its movements and actions so jarred the twig from which the nest hung, that the inmates were thoroughly aroused, and buzzed angrily about the intruder, but the Nutcracker sat calmly, picking off what it needed, occasionally snapping at one of the angry horde or shaking its head now and then as if something were uncomfortable. For an early morning meal I can imagine live hornets would make a hot breakfast, and certainly the bird seemed to enjoy the sensation. In Africa we find a group of birds, the Honey Guides, distant relatives of the cuckoos, that have developed a great taste for the comb of wild bees which abound in some parts of the continent. The combs with their young bees and the honey seem to be usually more or less inaccessible to the birds, but the latter have the remarkable trait of attracting the attention of a native by a peculiar twitter or chatter, and will lead him to a bee-tree if he follow the bird. The African natives all have a sweet tooth and are quick to smoke out the bees and secure the honey, taking care to leave a portion of the comb for the bird. This I have myself seen done, though the bird had not far to lead us. Indeed, bee-trees are frequently visited by the Honey Guides, partly for the purpose of preying on the bees. It is related of a South African species that its stomach was filled with the hind legs of bees, that had been bitten off for the pollen basket carried on them. It is also related that the clever bird does not discriminate between wild and "tame" bees and may lead one to a beehive in a person's yard as well as to one in the forest.

Leaving now a consideration of animal food, we may survey briefly the vegetable food of birds. This consists chiefly in (1) the more nutritious stored matter in the seeds of various plants, or (2) it may be the soft pulp of the fruit or less often (3) the leafy tissue itself. It is natural that the seeds of plants should be most used since they contain the most concentrated nourishment. This involves a cutting open of the seed and extraction of the kernel, as we see so deftly managed for example by many of the finches. For grinding up the meat of the seeds a strong-walled gizzard is needed with the addition of a certain amount of grit picked up with the food. So largely has seed-eating been adopted by the finch-like birds that it is a habit almost characteristic of them, though found as well among other groups. An advantage of it is that it enables many birds to survive the winter climate of the temperate zone and so in some measure relieves many of these species of the necessity of migration. Seed-eating may therefore be an adaptation for surviving the northern or southern winters when animal life in the shape of insects is largely reduced. It is notable that most seed-eating birds take insects as well, and further that their newly hatched young are fed on insects until they are sufficiently grown to thrive on seeds. That is, the seed-eater returns in its early stages to this more primitive or ancestral habit. This process of adaptation is perhaps indicated by such birds as the Myrtle Warbler, a member of a typically insect-eating group, that comes to live in winter partly upon bayberries (*Myrica*) whose waxy coating is evidently nutritious, for these weak-billed birds cannot crack open the seed itself. By living largely on these berries, the Myrtle Warbler is able to spend the winter more or less regularly as far north occasionally as southern Maine, and so becomes an exception to the rule that our warblers all migrate to warm climates in winter. A similar trait in the White-bellied

Swallow may in part be responsible for its early arrival and late stay with us, matters in which it differs from our other species. The parrot family with their powerful beaks afford an example of a group of tropical birds that live on nut-like fruits in large part. In these birds we may imagine that they became nut-eaters first through becoming adapted for gnawing the oily but thin pulp which covers the small fruits of so many palms. This pulp they largely eat and one might imagine it would be only a step from this to the cracking of small nuts and bean-like pods such as those of the thorn trees on which some of the smaller species feed.

Pulpy fruits are relished by many birds and undoubtedly afford more or less nutritive sugars, salts, and acids. This seems more of a makeshift diet, however, indulged in partly as a seasonal luxury (as when robins plunder the strawberry bed) and partly when other food is scarce, as when in winter the robins eat the astringent berries of the buckthorn.

Other birds showing the transition from the more primitive diet of animal food to the derived or adaptive diet of vegetable matter are the ducks and their tribe. Very young ducks feed largely on animal matter, as water insects, and the same is true of the summer food of most of the Anatinæ or river ducks. The sea ducks or diving ducks (Fuligulinæ) also live largely upon animal matter, fish, mollusks; but in autumn some species may become chiefly vegetable feeders, such as Canvasback and Redhead. Others, however, as the Scoters and Eiders, that winter on salt water, continue their diet of animal food. This is a matter of much importance to the epicure, for those living on a diet of water plants (wild celery or seeds of water weeds) become excellently flavored for the table, while those feeding on an animal diet are more rank if not positively disagreeable to any but a stout stomach. The geese go a step farther and become largely grazers as adults.

Again among the pheasant tribe including our domestic fowls, as well as the native quails and grouse, we find species whose young probably feed chiefly at first on animal food, while the adults subsist in summer on both animal and vegetable provender. In autumn and winter as insects become fewer, the diet becomes chiefly or almost wholly vegetable. Grouse eat berries, buds, and leaves. I have seen the Spruce Grouse with its crop stuffed with fir needles in fall, and its well-known habit of eating buds has given the Ruffed Grouse a bad name in some localities where apple orchards have been too persistently visited.

It will be seen that with most birds that have adopted a vegetarian diet, there is still a return to the more primitive custom of taking animal food during the early stages, or in some species insects and occasional other animals are added to a diet chiefly vegetarian. To become wholly vegetarian is a habit apparently rare, but among the pigeons seems more nearly universal. With these really remarkable birds, the young are at first still fed on food of an animal origin, though strangely enough it is not fresh-caught, but consists of the so-called "pigeon's milk," a whitish fluid derived from the breaking down of the lining walls of the crop. Thus pigeons seem to be *entirely* emancipated from the need of catching animal prey.

Of special foods to which birds have become adapted, much might be said. Albatrosses, for example, feed partly at least by night, and this becomes explicable when we learn that they are squid-eaters, for squid are likely to be more at the surface by night than in daytime.   The same is true, too, in some degree of many species of small marine crustaceans composing the plankton of the sea. This may in part explain the nocturnal feeding habits of many petrels.   The Little Auk or Dovekie is also a plankton-feeder, rather than a fisher, and finds certain times of day best for feeding when these minute animals are nearer the surface.   In times of rough weather this floating life seeks deeper levels, so that the English ornithologists have explained the occasional great disasters that overtake the Little Auks, bringing hundreds of them inland with empty stomachs, as due to a continuous spell of bad weather resulting in the temporary disappearance of the plankton, and so depriving the birds of food and strength to stand against the elements.

Another special food is that for which the African Tick-birds have become adapted.   These black birds with yellow bills associate with rhinoceroses or large antelopes, scrambling about on their bodies to pick off the ticks which abound in tropical countries.   The huge beasts in their turn are relieved of these annoying creatures, besides profiting by the warning given when the birds suddenly take alarm at the approach of danger.   Remarkable, too, are the great Harpy Eagle of tropical America, a special enemy of the sloth, and the Philippine Monkey-eating Eagle.

A final word as to the drinking habits of birds, which have not perhaps been sufficiently studied.   We have all noticed that hens and sparrows sip from a pan, raising their head between each sip as if to let the drop trickle down their throats.   The quite different manner in which pigeons thrust in their bills and pump in the water like a horse

HARPY EAGLE OF TROPICAL AMERICA, WHOSE SPECIAL PREY IS THE
SLOTH
Courtesy of National Zoölogical Park

cannot have escaped the attention of most. We do not know much as to the amount of water birds need and how often they drink. It is said that prospectors in desert country are often able to locate springs by watching the flights of doves or pigeons which must drink daily and fly in from the surrounding country regularly for the purpose.

Most sea-birds are known to drink salt water in preference to fresh; indeed captive gulls may die without it. Land birds, however, need fresh water. No doubt some species must go long periods without drinking, as in case of certain birds that incubate continuously, for example the female Hornbill that is walled up in her nest cavity and fed by her mate. In the far north water may be unobtainable throughout winter, but it may be possible for northern birds to subsist on snow. I have known Pine Siskins to eat snow and once watched a flock of Cedar Waxwings engaged in catching snowflakes during a storm, flying up and snapping at them as if they were insects. Here is a subject on which more information might easily be secured.

CHAPTER VI

ORIGIN AND DISTRIBUTION OF BIRDS

In previous chapters we have seen that there are many points of structure in which birds resemble reptiles, particularly lizards, in the structure of the skull, the toes, the supporting portions of the breastbone, the occasional presence of claw vestiges on the fingers of the hand (or wing), in the egg-laying habits, and in other ways. If birds have evolved through age-long processes from some sort of lizard-like reptiles, we may confidently expect to find more of these reptilian traits in the ancient ancestors of our present-day birds, as represented by fossil remains, and eventually trace the two types to a common source. Let us examine briefly the evidence available. But, first, a word as to fossils. Most people are apt to think of a "fossil" as anything old, very big, prehistoric, or of an indefinite age before the time in which we are living. Indeed, we often speak of a person as an "old fossil," if he wears glasses and looks ponderous and wise. Originally, the word meant something "dug up." But these notions are quite inadequate, for in order to gain some idea of the time when the creatures lived whose remains have survived to this present, we must have a slight perspective of past ages of the earth's history and the conditions under which it is possible for fragments of animals to be kept for indefinite years and still preserve their shape and appearance.

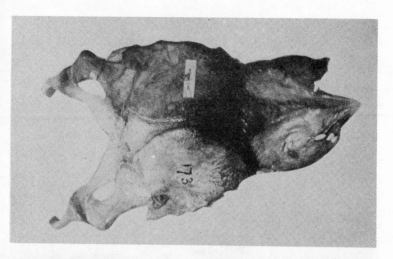

KEEL-LESS STERNUM OF YOUNG SOUTH AMERICAN OSTRICH *(Rhea)*
INTERIOR OF A PORTO RICAN CAVE WHERE FOSSIL BIRD BONES WERE
FOUND

When a bird dies and is left lying on the ground, what usually becomes of it? In warm countries decay quickly sets in, larvæ of beetles and certain flies devour its soft parts or vultures and small beasts of prey tear it to bits and eat what they can. The harder parts bleach in the weather and gradually disintegrate till nothing remains of the original structure. Sometimes by the merest chance a bird drowns in a quiet pool, sinks to the bottom, and by another rare chance becomes covered with mud before the many water creatures eat it. If by strange combinations of circumstances it remains buried, and the mud gradually gathers over it and hardens eventually into shale or sandstone, the harder parts of the skeleton or even impressions of feathers may be preserved.

In rock crevices and caves, particularly in limestone regions, bones are often preserved from going to pieces by the soaking away of moisture and gradual accumulation of soil over them, and so many become protected and mineralized. In this way bones of small creatures brought into caves by owls are often preserved. In California, there are wells of sticky asphalt whose surfaces hold water and attract animals to drink. They become mired in this natural trap and sink down to become eventually stored; quicksands, perhaps at fords or good feeding places, trap animals in the same way. Another method by which perhaps the many fossil bones of birds have accumulated at one of the Oregon lakes in the relatively recent past, was exemplified a few years ago by the death of many waterbirds on some of the salt lakes of Utah and elsewhere. Unusual drought or seeping away of water seems to concentrate the alkalis of these bitter waters, so that they poison birds which drink them; but after death so alkaline are the waters that fat birds are actually turned into cakes of soap, in part at least, and so, when subsequently cast ashore, they become covered with sand and are effectually buried before they are eaten. These are a few of the ways in which birds' bones may be kept from destruction and gradually turned to stone by the slow dissolving of the bones and their replacement by mineral matter. The chance of a bone being preserved is exceedingly small, and the chance of its being found again even after a thousand years is infinitely smaller still. Suppose that all we knew of the present bird-life of the globe were a sparrow, a loon, and an ostrich, it is obvious what a poor idea we could gather of the 19,000 species of living birds. Yet our knowledge of fossil birds is proportionately but little better.

Putting aside now all our previous ideas of age and time, let us take a glance at the past history of the earth as it relates to birds. If we look at an old family Bible of two generations back, we shall find at the top of each page the number of years that were considered to have elapsed since the beginning of the world. The calculation is simple, for Genesis gives a genealogical table of Adam and his descendants and their respective longevity. By summing these and later dates together, and adding seven days for the creation of the earth, the exact time is obtained— no less than 4004 years and 7 days B. C. But we now know that the seven days are not to be taken literally and the dates no longer appear in our Bibles.

Men have examined the structure of the globe and the forces at work upon it with the utmost skill and care; they have at last determined that there is a certain rhythm with minor pulses extending over vast eons of time that can be rather definitely made out and these rhythmic pulses of time give us a solid basis for estimates of the past.

The general processes are: first, an uplifting or warping of the continents so that large areas are raised above sea-level. The result is that the streams at once gain new velocity and wearing power as they rush downhill to the sea, so that the uplifted land starts slowly wearing down again. The final process is a leveling of land areas and a loss of barriers. A new elevation starts the whole process again, so that the surface of the earth is constantly being worn down flat and uplifted again. Small wonder then that few buried treasures in the shape of fossils should remain to us from the more ancient times! The sediment carried down by streams and dropped as they reach the level, if accumulated fast enough, may bury and preserve remains of animals, and the overlapping of the beds thus formed shows their succession in time. By making a vertical section of all these beds, an idea of the different periods may be had. Various means of estimating their age have been employed, the most nearly accurate of which is perhaps due to the brilliant work of Barrell, who made use of the radio-active minerals and by determining the quantities of helium and lead in rocks of various strata calculated the age of these by measurements of the rate at which uranium, a radio-active metal, breaks down into those elements. So now we have a time-table of part of the earth's history, in which some of the chief divisions are shown in the following scheme, and to which reference will be made as we proceed.

Subdivisions	Duration in Millions of Years	Years Ago in Millions to End of Period	Important Bird Localities
I. QUATERNARY OR PRESENT ERA			
(1) Pleistocene	1–1.5		Rancho la Brea, Calif.; Oregon; Madagascar; New Zealand.
II. TERTIARY OR CENOZOIC ERA			
(1) Pliocene	6–7.5	1.5	Greece; India.
(2) Miocene	12–14	23	
(3) Oligocene	16	39	France.
(4) Eocene	20–26	65	Wyoming (*Diatryma*)
III. SECONDARY OR MESOZOIC ERA			
(1) Cretaceous	40–50	115	England; Wyoming (*Ichthyornis; Hesperornis*).
(2) Comanche	25–35	150	
(3) Jurassic	35–45	195	Bavaria (*Archæopteryx*).
(4) Triassic	45	240	

IV. PRIMARY OR PALÆOZOIC ERA

Compared with reptiles or mammals, the remains of birds are very rare and on account of their fragile nature are seldom more than fragments of the stronger bones. It is natural that the more recent deposits should have most abundant bird remains for they have undergone less disturbance. In our own country the asphalt lakes at Rancho la Brea, California, have yielded the remains of a great many birds, and these are chiefly birds of prey and waders or other water-birds. They date from the last or Pleistocene period to the present day (for the Present is really but a continuation of the Pleistocene). The former were doubtless attracted by the animals entrapped in the pitch, and include many species, among them a long-legged eagle of a kind no longer living, as well as a large hawk of a genus (*Geranoaëtus*) now confined to South America. Another closely related species of the latter genus has lately been discovered in older deposits of Pliocene age in Nebraska, and a third in the still older Miocene beds in the same State, proving that these birds in the past lived over a wide range in North America, but now occur only in the southern continent. There are also two vultures similar to those of the Old World, and representing a different stock from ours.

A most extraordinary discovery in these same asphalt lakes of California is that of an enormous eagle-like bird, which has been named *Teratornis*. Its skull alone is twice the size of a Bald Eagle's and other bones are in proportion. In flight it must have appeared a veritable airplane! Altogether Professor Loye Miller has made out at least 25 species of carrion- or flesh-eating birds from this locality, that testify to a much larger fauna in the recent past than at present. The same is true of the mammals. For huge ground-sloths, sabre-toothed tigers, and giant wolves left their bones here and attracted these birds. Probably the gradual extinction of these large mammals was a contributing cause to the decline of this splendid company of eagles, hawks, and vultures, for large birds must have large amounts of food and it must be available in sufficient quantity. An interesting tradition of the western Indians is suggested by Merriam as a possible reminiscence of the time when the last of the enormous *Teratornis* yet survived.

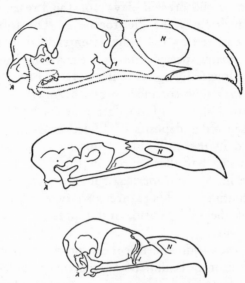

FIG. V

Skull outlines of (upper) the extinct Californian eagle, *Teratornis*; (middle) California Condor; (lower) Bald Eagle

After L. H. Miller

For these people still retain tales of a Thunder-bird that fed on bison and even carried off human beings. One such tradition relates that the bride of a certain young chieftain was carried off by the great bird, and he resolved to stop its depredations forever. So of an early morning he took a chosen band of warriors and, concealing them near, himself stood boldly forth on a rock below the eagle's eyrie and defiantly sang the death song. The terrible bird at length appeared, and swooped upon him, but as it was in the act of bearing off its prey, was shot to death by a volley of arrows from the ambush. Who knows but this tradition may relate to one of the last of the *Teratornis*?

Of other extinct birds at Rancho la Brea is one closely similar to the Old World Peacock, perhaps an immigrant from Asia at a time not so very remote when a solid land connection existed where now is the chain of Aleutian Islands, though more recent investigations seem to show it is a connecting form, near the Central American Brush Turkey.

The most famous of recently extinct birds is probably the Dodo (*Didus ineptus*), found by the early voyagers on the island of Mauritius near Madagascar. It was really an enormous pigeon which had lost the use of its wings. The first account of it is from the Dutch who visited the island in 1598, and believing they had discovered a sailors' paradise, the entire crew remained there for a time enjoying its delightful climate and feeding on turtles and Dodos. In little more than a century thereafter the bird was quite exterminated with scarcely more than a few skeletons and early figures to show to following generations. A nearly related bird on the neighboring island of Réunion met a like fate, the *Pezophaps*. On Mauritius too was a large flightless rail.

Madagascar was the home of several species of Giant-birds (*Æpyornis*), all of which seem to have become extinct in the last or Pleistocene period. Many of their enormous bones have been found and even fossil eggs a foot long. The largest species stood near ten feet high, with ponderous leg-bones but small head and degenerate wings. In New Zealand, too, was a race of large birds now wholly gone—the Moas (*Dinornis*), representing a wholly distinct type from the Giant-birds; also a flightless goose. The Moas lived till a very recent time and were probably killed out by the aborigines, for the bones are found in their kitchen-middens.

Note here that the *large* birds are among the first to go with any disturbance of their quiet island life. It is a rule of evolution that the development of large size is a final stage in growth and indicates an adjustment to certain conditions of life that, if changed, spell death for the species. Hence "giantism," as the French call it, is a dangerous thing.

In France, particularly in the Paris Basin, many bones of birds have been recovered from ancient deposits in what were probably caves and date back, according to Barrell's estimate, nearly 60 million years to the early part of the Tertiary era or Eocene time. From one deposit at Quercy over 40 species representing some 25 genera have been identified among the bones found. They include owls, a vulture allied to an American genus, a Secretary-bird or long-legged eagle now confined to Africa, as well as various storks, herons, sandpipers, partridges, sandgrouse, and swifts. Most interesting too are the remains of trogons, birds of brilliant plumage now confined to the tropics of America and with other species in Africa and Asia. There is another extinct species of trogon known from Miocene formations in France. This proof of the former extension of this type of bird is suggestive of a once continuous range from Old to New World.

Although the many remains of these early Tertiary birds

yet found are for the most part of the same general types as birds of the present day, it is likely that, if we knew more about them than what we can glean from a few bones, we should find they were in many respects different from their present-day representatives.

We must accustom ourselves to the concept that the living birds we are familiar with are the varied descendants of a yet more various company, and that in the past as now some became so specialized for particular habits that they died out long since with changed conditions. Matthew is of the opinion that, as with mammals, most of the larger modern groups were well marked at the beginning of the Tertiary era, though probably few or none of the genera and species were quite the same as their descendants. A recent and most important discovery of this early time is a nearly complete skeleton of a very large ground-bird, *Diatryma,* which from its degree of completeness really is a landmark in our knowledge of ancient birds. It comes from the Eocene of Wyoming and portions of a similar bird have been found in New Mexico. It was probably as large as an Ostrich, near seven feet high, heavy-limbed and with massive neck, enormous beak, and very small wings. This remarkable bird shows many points of resemblance to the South American Cariama, a primitive crane-like species. Very recently the impressions of long plumy ostrich-like feathers have been found in the shales of this age in Colorado, and are believed to represent its plumage. Some of the primitive points are: the imperfectly double joint of the jaw; the wide angle of the shoulder blade and coracoid bone, as in ostriches; its breadth and plate-like form, and the fact that the pubic bones nearly meet below the pelvis. The palate is of a more

modern type ("desmognathous" or roofed-over), agree-
ing with that of so-called Carinate birds (*Euornithes*).
This remarkable species thus combines characters of both
Ratite and Carinate birds, and indicates that the two types
are not of independent origin but developed from a common ancestral stock still more remote.   Let us then pass
back to the next more remote period, the Cretaceous, belonging to the so-called Secondary Era.

Few birds are known from these ancient deposits, but
those few are of utmost interest.   In addition to sundry
bones from the chalk deposits of England, there have been
found in the Cretaceous shales of Kansas considerable
portions of the skeletons of two birds which, according to
our table, lived over 100 million years ago.   They represent two very distinct types, but for the first time we find
both had simple teeth in each jaw, just as lizards do.   Here
then is another step toward the reptilian ancestor.   One
of these toothed birds was rather gull-like in general style,
and its breastbone had a prominent keel.   The wing was
well developed, with the three fingers as in modern birds.
It is called *Ichthyornis* or Fish-bird.   The other was in
general form probably like a huge grebe, with a long body
and neck, long narrow bill, with the addition of teeth, and
the same short thigh bone, long tibia, and an enormous
knee-cap for muscle attachment.   It was evidently a wonderful diver, but was flightless.   The breastplate has no
keel because of the very small size of the wing.   This is
the *Hesperornis* or Western-bird.   Thus we see that birds
in these early days had not yet lost their teeth.   The say-
ing, "Scarce as hen's teeth," would have meant little in
Cretaceous times.   We must realize, however, that even
then there were these birds of habits so specialized that

THE CRETACEOUS TOOTHED DIVER, *Hesperornis*
As restored by R. W. Shufeldt
SKELETON OF THE CRETACEOUS TOOTHED BIRD, *Ichthyornis*
After Marsh

they had lost the use of their wings, and that these are but two of the many kinds of birds that must have lived during the 40 million years of the Cretaceous period.

It is hard to push our inquiry farther back into the past. Yet by one of the greatest imaginable pieces of luck, we have two skeletons from the Jurassic period, some 35 million years before the days of the *Hesperornis*. There is a bed of slates in Solenhofen, Bavaria, of such exceeding fine grain that they are much sought for purposes of lithography. This slate was probably laid down as very fine silt in still water these eons ago. In the course of quarrying it two skeletons of a bird have been found so beautifully preserved that the outlines of the feathers can still be traced. This is the famous *Archæopteryx,* or Lizard-tailed Bird, the oldest feathered creature yet discovered and a most veritable missing link. For, while the birds hitherto noticed are clearly birds in all their points, except perhaps in the possession of teeth, *Archæopteryx* is a real connecting link with the lizards. This lizard-like bird was a little bigger than a magpie, its beak was blunt and snout-like, with 13 simple teeth in the upper and 8 near the tip of the lower jaw on each side, set in distinct sockets. The vertebræ were unlike those of modern birds in being concave or cupped at each end; moreover, it had but ten neck vertebræ , which is less than in any living bird and resembles therefore the lizards which usually have nine. The breastbone was apparently keeled, implying strong breast muscles; the tibia and fibula of the "shin" were not grown together, while the foot seems to have been much like that of modern perching birds. The bones of the pubis have been found, by more recent study of one of the specimens, to extend below the pelvis, and although they come closely against each other in the middle line, they are not fused. In this as well as in the reduced number of teeth in the lower as compared with the upper jaw, a beginning is seen toward the more modern conditions in which teeth disappear completely, and the pubic bones no longer even touch below. But most remarkable is the tail, the central bony part of which is long, slender, of many joints as in a lizard and each joint has a pair of large feathers one on each side. In modern birds the tail has become so short that its bones hardly extend beyond the general limits of the body, and the terminal ones instead of being successive joints are fused into a little knife-like piece (*pygidium*); while the tail-feathers that in *Archæopteryx* grew out in pairs all the way down this long appendage, are now represented by several of the middle pairs only, for the tip has so shrunken as to be without them.

This discovery is enough of itself to prove the reptilian descent of birds, but our thirst for more knowledge impels us to find the lizards that birds have started from. We have seen that some of the dinosaurs are rather bird-like in appearance, and certain of the smaller species are especially so. These reptiles were of several types: some walked on their hind legs, had three toes in front and one behind like birds, the tarsus was long and slender, and in walking was held off from the ground; the formation of their pelvic bones was like that of birds; and they had long tails like *Archæopteryx*. Dinosaur eggs have lately been discovered, and even impressions of their skin, but they had no feathers and their fore limbs were short and weak though like birds the hand had three fingers. Evidently, since they lived in the same times as *Archæopteryx* and flourished till the late Cretaceous time, they could not have given rise to

THE JURASSIC LIZARD-TAILED BIRD, *Archæopteryx*
As restored by R. W. Shufeldt

birds. Not long ago, however, remains have been found of reptiles so unspecialized that they might easily have been the starting-point whence the small bird-like dinosaurs as well as true birds were derived, with slight changes. These creatures were evidently common and widespread, and have the euphonious name of Pseudosuchians, which in Greek signifies "imitation crocodiles." Bones of this ancient group of reptiles have been found in the Triassic formations (240 million years ago) of localities so far apart as Connecticut, Scotland, and South Africa. Living in the period preceding that in which we find *Archæopteryx,* they seem to supply the ancestral stock of both the bird-like dinosaurs and the lizard-like birds. These "imitation crocodiles" have not yet gone too far on a line of special development to preclude such ancestry. The bird pelvis could be derived from theirs by turning the lower or pubic bone farther back. The long bones (metatarsals) of the foot were still un-united as in dinosaurs, and it seems likely that their later union into a cannon-bone as in birds occurred, as Osborn suggests, as an adaptation for strengthening the foot in walking or running on the two legs. For it is hard to see how a foot of this type could have evolved through *climbing* habits. The same point is exemplified among mammals, in which the running species have developed cannon-bones through fusion of these foot-bones, whereas climbing mammals such as squirrels and monkeys have not. Broom (1913), who has made a special study of these "imitation crocodiles," concludes that a reptile of this type "which through a bipedal habit had developed a strengthened ankle-joint and a firm metatarsus [or cannon-bone], and had lost the fifth digit from the manus [hand]" would meet all the requirements of the ancestor of birds.   Such hypothetical ancestors, for which therefore there is abundant evidence from a study of comparative anatomy, are called by Pycraft, an English anatomist, Pro-Aves, or immediate forerunners of birds.   Who knows but we may yet discover the fossil remains of some!   The critical point in their evolution came with the development of feathers from long overlapping scales.   They were doubtless quick runners on the ground, and probably very early some of them took to perching on branches.   Their slender arms ended in three long fingers each with a claw, and they probably had some sort of wing for gliding in long leaps from branch to branch or tree to tree.   They retained the sharp-pointed conical teeth of the "imitation crocodiles" but eventually lost them (as even *Archæopteryx* had begun to do) when the horny beak developed.   All the evidence points to the conclusion that the known birds were all evolved from a single line of reptile-like ancestors during a time of perhaps 200 million years at the least and that though side branches developed from time to time on account of various special habits, the group as a whole is what is termed *monophyletic,* that is, all birds are descended from a single stock that lived in the remote past and none of them has come from any second stock of reptiles of the same or another period.

Having thus briefly glanced at the birds of past times in an attempt to guess their probable ancestry, let us, before leaving the subject, once more look back across that awesome gulf of 150 million years to the days when *Archæopteryxes* hopped about on the shores of the reedy pools in Bavaria.   It is hard to conceive of so long a time.   The mind does not comprehend it.   Imagine a line 150 feet long, each foot representing a million years; ourselves a point at this end, *Archæopteryx* a point at the other. If we start moving toward the ancient bird, we shall find that by the time we have passed the days of Tut-ankh-amen's great-grandfather, we shall have progressed a distance about equal to the width of a thick pencil-line, or one millimeter to 3333 years. After going back the vast space of a third of an inch we shall have passed far beyond historic times to the early Stone Age of Man, and at the end of an inch we shall be well into Glacial times. The first foot of our 150-foot journey will have brought us only to the beginning of the latest or Pleistocene epoch of earth's history, and we shall have accomplished less than half the journey ere we reach the fauna of the Paris Basin and the giant *Diatryma* of Eocene days. And even when we at length reach the journey's end, we are still a long way from the starting-point of birds. Thus we may realize that geologically speaking a thousand years is not really such a very long time; it is only that our thoughts are small.

Distribution of Birds.—It is clear from what has preceded, that the bird-fauna of the globe has undergone very great changes during the course of time, not only in its nature but in its distribution as well. Why, for example, do we find at the present day Ostriches in Africa and their near relatives in South America, but none between these distant points? Why are albatrosses not now found regularly in the North Atlantic, and why are trogons confined to the tropics of *both* Old and New Worlds but absent elsewhere? These and like questions are hard to answer in face of our almost utter lack of knowledge of the past distribution of these birds. When, however, we find that there are fossil Ostrich remains in Asia, a fossil albatross in England, and fossil trogons in France we may conclude that in former times the ranges of these birds were either more extensive or else very different from what they are now, so that there was some way whereby they once were able to exist in regions from which they are now absent. Do not fail to grasp the concept that the arrangement of things has not been always the same as we now see it. We must look upon the present distribution of birds as the end result after many million years of slow or rapid change, not only of the earth's crust itself but of its inhabitants as well, in their endeavor to adapt themselves, whether consciously or not, to its great variety of conditions.

There are, then, two chief factors governing the distribution of species at any given time: *first,* the historical factor, that is, how and whence a particular area has been peopled; and *second,* the adaptive factor, that is, what preference each species shows for certain kinds of surroundings. To illustrate: the Golden-crowned Kinglet is a bird found from western Europe and the British Isles quite across the northern parts of Asia to eastern North America, differing locally so that minor geographic races can be recognized. It is probable that this tiny bird reached America from the eastern continent during a time when there was an extensive land connection from Alaska across to Asia. Such a connection appears to have existed, perhaps only at intervals, during much of the Tertiary era, to be broken in later Pleistocene times. Thus the historical fact of a continuous land area between what are now separate continents made it possible, we will assume, for kinglets to extend their range from Asia to America. The second or adaptive factor is that they have a preference for the northern evergreen forest rather than for open country or deserts or maple woods. For this reason, after having reached this continent, we find them devoted to its evergreen forests. If the latter were now to be burned, cut off, or otherwise suddenly destroyed, the kinglets would doubtless perish too, not being able to flourish without their chosen type of habitat. It may be that a number of birds as well as mammals reached America from Asia in geologically recent times, and being, like the kinglets, creatures of the northern evergreen forests, have also been able to range across the entire northern part of the continent. This explains why in common with northern Europe and Asia, we have a number of birds in North America that are characteristic of this type of forest. Such are the Three-toed Woodpeckers, Pine Grosbeaks, Canada Jays, Brown Creepers, Red-breasted Nuthatches, and Chickadees, all of which have close allies in the Old World. Magpies are among the birds of this invasion, but in North America have only extended part way across the western country, probably because of their preference for the sort of habitats in which we see them in our Rocky Mountains.

Birds are very tenacious in their love for certain localities and it is probable that the less migratory species, at least, are rather slow to colonize new country even when opportunity offers. Of this, however, we are in a better position to judge as years go by and we see how readily some of them adapt themselves to changes brought about by man within a century or two. Thus the increase of grass-lands in parts of the West through irrigation has caused a distinct spreading of Bobolinks to occupy the new country made available to them because of their adaptation to grass meadows as breeding places. The clearing of our

New England forests and the coming-in of bush growth instead gives a new though temporary field for the Chestnut-sided Warbler, which now certainly occurs in places where a hundred years ago it could not be found. This illustrates again the adaptive factor in distribution. Suppose now that the bushy places gradually grow up to forests of oak, maple, elm, ash, and birch, as we find in central New England, other birds will come in whose preference is for these trees, as Scarlet Tanagers, Grosbeaks, and Red-eyed Vireos. Following these trees, come in gradually a few white pines or pitch pines, and with them come the Black-throated Green and Pine-creeping Warblers, Crows, Sharp-shinned Hawks. In short, there is found to be a regular succession of faunas characteristic of the different types of vegetation that naturally follow each other in the various stages of a forest from open swamp or clearing to a thick wood. These different sets of birds, mammals, or insects that go with certain kinds of vegetation are called *associations,* and exemplify the adaptive factor in distribution. Often the relation is so very close that a particular species of bird may spend much of its life in a certain sort of tree. Our Pine-creeping Warbler, for example, is so strictly associated with pitch pines in the breeding season here, that it is seldom found far from them. The Black-throated Green Warbler is in central New England confined largely to white pines in the same way, though farther north it frequents spruces. Other instances readily occur.

These are some of the details of distribution. In a larger view, and excluding many birds of very wide or general distribution, our North American species fall more or less into two sets: *first,* birds that breed chiefly in the north, and in a general way are limited in their southward range by the southern extension of the spruce and pine forests that cross the north part of the continent and follow south along the higher elevations of the Allegheny, Rocky, and Sierra Nevada Mountains; *second,* birds that breed chiefly in the warmer, southern parts of the continent and extend north to meet those of the first group.   In the East where there are relatively low mountains and the land is not greatly varied in level, the separation of these two is not very marked, but in our western mountains with their increased altitude, it is often very obvious that the northern association occupies the high levels, the southern the lower.

Altitude is in a general way the equivalent of latitude, that is, if one ascends a high mountain on the equator, he passes from a warmer to a colder climate, just as if he had gone all the way from the tropics to the arctic region.   It is found that in general every 250 feet of elevation is the equivalent of an additional degree of latitude.   Thus it is that in our own White Mountains we find an arctic region on the summit of Mt. Washington and the nearby peaks, with a number of arctic plants, insects, and spiders, the equivalent of the Labrador coast, though there are not at the present time any arctic birds that breed on these summits.

Characteristic birds of the northern fauna are: Ptarmigan; Red-tailed, Pigeon, and Sharp-shinned Hawks; Snowy, Great Gray, Hawk, and Saw-whet Owls; Three-toed Woodpeckers, Canada Jays, Pine Grosbeaks, Crossbills, Redpolls, Siskins, Juncos, White-throated and Tree Sparrows, several warblers as the Tennessee, Black-poll, Myrtle, and Wilson's Black-cap.   Equally characteristic southern birds are: Wild Turkey, Mourning Dove, Red-shouldered and Sparrow Hawks, Yellow-billed Cuckoo, Red-bellied Woodpecker, Flicker, Whippoorwill, Kingbird, Least Flycatcher, Orchard Oriole, Cardinal, Grasshopper Sparrow, Seaside Sparrow, Field Sparrow, Yellow-throated Vireo; Pine, Prairie, Blue-winged, and Hooded Warblers, Yellow-breasted Chat, Marsh Wrens, Mockingbird, and Wood Thrush. Many others could be added. A more exact study of the ranges of these birds will show that rarely are any two exactly the same; some extend farther north, others farther south according to their special preference for different sorts of country, or vegetation, or other conditions.

Changes in distribution are even now taking place rather rapidly as we clear the original forests, transforming river bottoms to meadows, wooded hillsides into orchards, or pine and spruce woods into oak and beech woods. The rapid withdrawal of the Red-tailed Hawk from southern and central New England and the advance into our White Mountain valleys of the Red-shouldered Hawk have taken place within the last fifty years, and other similar changes could be recounted at length. In eastern China the intensive cultivation and overcrowding of population has resulted in such wide destruction of forests that at the present day, all that we know of the tree-living birds of this great area is derived from those species that still are found in places where occasional groves have been preserved, as in the sacred precincts of temple grounds.

As to the larger aspects of the problems of distribution, I cannot do better than refer the reader to Matthew's "Climate and Evolution" (1915), a masterly review of what we may deduce from the present and past distribution chiefly of mammals, for which the records from fossils are best known. The same lines of reasoning doubtless apply, however, to other groups of animals and plants. His chief thesis is that the continents have had more or less the same general outlines as those we now see for an immense period, subject, however, to periodic and relatively slight changes of level. For after an uplift there follows a long period of wearing down of the land to base-level, with slight shiftings along certain lines to equalize pressure of the material carried down by the action of streams and winds. The result of the wearing-down process is the removal of high mountains, a more uniform temperature everywhere, and overflow of large areas of land by shallow seas. The readjustment process involves an uplift along certain lines of stress, with the rising of mountain ranges, which, by drying the winds, cause desert conditions in the interior of continents, while the entire period culminates in the formation of ice-caps or glaciers at the poles and on high mountains. We have just passed through such a period, or may still be in it. The uplift may make land connection between what were before isolated areas, just as a depression makes islands out of what was a hilly or mountainous land.

If, now, we employ Matthew's method of looking at a map of the world as seen from the North Pole rather than spread out on the rectangle of Mercator's projection, it is obvious that the great land masses are in the northern hemisphere. These have been the chief centers of evolution and Asia, as the greatest area of all, was doubtless the most important. From the North Polar viewpoint, Australia, Africa, and South America are merely the outer projections of the great central land area, and by very slight elevation it becomes possible to join the northern portions together, particularly by way of Asia. The finding of related groups of birds in Africa and South America is now readily explained, if we suppose that they have spread out from a more northern center into these southern corners by way of Asia (and Europe as a peninsula of Asia). From this central Asiatic land-mass, successive waves of life seem to have spread out from time to time, finally reaching the southern remote corners. So the primitive ostrich-like birds reached opposite ends of the globe by spreading from the north, *not* by following a direct connection between Africa and South America. So too, in case of the trogons, now found in these two continents, the fossil remains from France, where the birds no longer exist, show that in early Tertiary times they ranged farther north than now and so, if they lived in northeastern Asia as well, could have crossed to North America when the two continents were joined and the climate was warmer as it seems to have been in the early Tertiary. Later, with increasing cold, they retreated southward, and so each branch became isolated, one in the Old World, one in the New. So, too, are to be explained many other apparent anomalies, such as the occurrence of a true alligator in China and in our southern states; and of tulip-trees in our southeast and again in the highlands of southwestern China. These cases but emphasize the importance of knowing the historical factor if we would explain what seem otherwise peculiar and haphazard distributions.

Another interesting problem is offered by the occurrence of species on islands far from the nearest land. Did they come by some unusual chance, storm-blown or as castaways on floating logs, or did they reach their present home at a time when the land was continuous between the continent and what is now an island? The latter ex-

THE SECRETARY-BIRD OF AFRICA—A LONG-LEGGED WALKING EAGLE
OSTRICHES ON AN EAST AFRICAN FARM, COCKS AND HENS
Dr. Wm. Lord Smith, phot.

planation seems probable in case of Australia with its remarkable fauna of so many living species whose like has elsewhere so largely died out. But here the subsequent isolation must have been of very long duration. Other cases are less clear. The isolation of tropical islands has often been favorable for the development of large and sluggish forms, as the Giant-birds of Madagascar, the Moas of New Zealand, and the Cassowaries of Ceram. For free from many enemies and with plenty of food at hand there was no hindrance to their development in size. Through the protection of this isolation, too, it has often happened that birds have survived for long periods, while their relatives on the mainland have quite died out. This we see in numerous instances in our West Indies, as well as among the Pacific Islands, so that many species are preserved to us which otherwise would long since have passed beyond our ken.

CHAPTER VII

SOME ECOLOGICAL RELATIONS OF BIRDS

THE word "ecology" is derived from two Greek words that mean the study of the "house" or the surroundings in which a being lives. These surroundings include not only the general environment but also the other plants and animals with which this being is brought into contact. The study of ecology, therefore, includes the relations of birds to their habitat as well as their relations to the other birds and animals that live with them. It includes also a study of the way in which the bird affects its environment.

We must keep in mind not only that the conditions we now see among living species are an end result of age-long processes of adjustment among a great number of beings with different requirements, but also that there is a greater or less re-adjustment constantly going on as the general conditions of life change, whether in periods of relatively few years or over a span of ages. For example, with the introduction of the European House Sparrow into this country, there was at first a great increase in its numbers and a period of years in which it struggled for a foothold to the greater or less detriment of many native species of birds. Of late years the numbers seem to be less in general than thirty years ago, and the bird is gradually taking its due place as a permanent member of our fauna subject to the factors of control that hold it from too grea an increase. There has been therefore a change or re-adjustment of relations in the space of comparatively few years. On the other hand there are adjustments that seem to proceed very slowly over immense periods of time. We know for example that most if not nearly all modern species of mammals are different in greater or less degree from the related species that occupied their territory in some past geological period, as for example the Miocene or middle Tertiary of North America with its wealth of un-familiar forms. These have gradually disappeared and have been replaced in part at least by the later species. What is true for mammals is so doubtless for birds. There has been a slow change, accompanied by extinction of some groups and the expansion of others. Time is therefore a factor in the study of ecology as we shall see presently in a smaller way in considering the succession of bird-faunas.

In a consideration of the general physical environment of birds, C. C. Adams recognizes three primary divisions: (1) water, (2) land, and (3) an intermediate ground, the shore. These in general are the surroundings in which various birds spend at least a large part of their lives, and these again may be variously subdivided. So obvious are these divisions that the birds characteristic of each are often spoken of respectively as water birds, land birds, and shore birds, though this classification is at best a rough one. There is of course nothing specially new in this, but it serves to emphasize the fact that birds have become adapted to particular modes of life, especially to certain methods of procuring their food, so that they have come to be more and more dependent upon the special kinds of environment, just as the plant or animal life on which they feed has in its turn become accustomed to a narrowed and particular set of conditions.

In more detail, the water environment may be divided into (a) salt water and (b) fresh water. Salt water implies the ocean; and the species of birds that frequent it, live by it, and obtain their food chiefly from it, are roughly of two sorts (I) those that range along the coasts (maritime species) and (II) those that range farther offshore, the pelagic species. To the former (maritime or coastal species) may be reckoned such as the auks, guillemots, cormorants, gannets, the Common and Arctic Terns, and a number of ducks, especially of the group known as sea ducks or diving ducks, species that seek their food at moderate depths along sea shores, diving for mollusks and small fish that occur on the bottom. Other illustrations readily come to mind, of birds that are out of place inland, that rear their young along the edge of the sea, returning therefore to the shore or intermediate territory for this purpose. Intermediate steps are seen in the degree of emancipation from the land, for many diving ducks, as Redhead, Canvasback, Scaup, nest on inland fresh marshes but seek the seacoast for the non-breeding periods. The second class, or pelagic birds, has departed even farther from the primeval shore life, and like the petrels and albatrosses are at home on the open sea, seldom coming within view of land except for the more or less prolonged nesting period. These two classes of water birds may be thought of as invaders into "the world of waters" just as on land we find certain species that have invaded deserts and become adapted for the sterner conditions imposed by these extreme types of environment. For a pelagic life must needs be a somewhat specialized one. Pelagic birds such

as the petrels and their allies must be able to travel immense distances, and so must have sustained powers of
flight; hence they have developed special ways of flight
such as soaring in the larger species or, as in shearwaters
and even many of the lesser species of petrels, a combination of flapping followed by a long glide. They must be
able to rest upon the ocean surface for longer or shorter
periods, a thing which some water birds, including some
terns, have been found incapable of doing. Pelagic birds
are therefore swimmers as well as birds of sustained flight,
and can rest on the water without becoming water-logged.
They must be largely surface feeders, and those that live
upon certain kinds of sea animals that come to the surface
by night, such as squid and various small crustaceans, must
become in part nocturnal.

Birds adapted to a life in or on fresh water are probably
a less varied company than those of salt water. For the
sea, except towards the poles, is always more or less open,
and even if birds are forced away from polar waters by
the oncoming of winter, they can find their way to per-
manently open areas by a continuous watery path. This
is not always the case with fresh waters. Lakes and ponds
freeze completely over in high latitudes so that birds that
have summered in such places are forced out and must
retreat by flight over land to other favorable areas of
fresh water. Even the rivers freeze in the north, so that
the fresh-water habitat becomes in the temperate and frigid
zones more or less discontinuous according to season. It
is because of this difference, I presume, that flightlessness
through reduction of the wings has not been developed in
birds frequenting fresh water, whereas among sea birds
it is common. Thus the entire order embracing the Pen-

guins has lost the power of flight through having developed the wing into a paddle. The Great Auk is an example of a sea bird that has used its wing more advantageously for flight under water than in the air, and so was able to dispense with aërial flight since the water route is uninterrupted. In the Galápagos Islands off the west coast of South America, Harris's Cormorant has reached a like condition, and though in other respects a cormorant, has such reduced wings that they are no longer available for flight. Since cormorants normally swim under water by means of the feet alone, this case differs somewhat from that of the Great Auk, for the small size of the wings seems to be due to a degeneration of the wing through disuse, whereas in the Great Auk its small size seems the better to fit it for use as a paddle in flight under water. It seems probable, too, that the extinct *Hesperornis,* the great flightless diver of the Cretaceous period, was a seabird, and though its fossil remains are found in the far interior of North America, it probably lived at a time when this area was occupied by an inland sea. The *continuity* of the sea as an environment is thus in itself a factor in the distribution of certain birds.

The precise factors controlling the distribution of seabirds are matters not easy to ascertain. In a recent account of the sea-birds of the Cape Verde Islands off western Africa, Dr. R. C. Murphy has brought out some interesting facts. The outstanding feature is the absence of gulls and particularly of terns as breeding birds. Apparently not one of the species of this cosmopolitan family (Laridæ) nests in this group of islands, although in the Canary and Madeira Islands not far to the northwestward the Common Tern breeds, and there is a gull in the Azores. The Cape

Verde Islands share with the West Indies and South Atlantic Islands, the Brown Booby and the Tropic Bird but lack the Noddy and Sooty Terns so common in the same latitude in the Caribbean Sea. Some invisible barrier, as it were, holds off the Common Tern on the north and the two latter species on the south and west. Dr. Murphy then shows that a broad belt of ocean water separates the southern nesting limits of the Common Tern (a northern species) from that of the Noddy and Sooty Terns (which are tropical species). The surface temperature of this broad belt is too high to be favorable for the Common Terns and too low for the two tropical species, whose absence therefore from the Cape Verdes as well as from the Bermudas on this side is correlated with the fact that both island groups lie within this belt. The southerly boundary of this zone is about 80 ° F. and its northerly limit 70 ° F., and covers about the distance from central Florida to Cape Hatteras on our coast. The interesting point is not that the water-temperature is of direct influence in the distribution of the birds but that it affects them in some indirect way through its influence perhaps on their food supply, which again is controlled by various factors. The temperature of the surface water therefore is but one of the ecological factors that control the breeding ranges of these terns, but its influence, though indirect, may be correlated closely.

Again, Dr. Murphy points out that the abundance of boobies, Tropic Birds, and petrels at the Cape Verde Islands is probably to be correlated with the topography of "the surrounding sea-bottom in conjunction with currents and vortices produced by the submarine slopes of the islands, . . . compelling a constant and plentiful supply of varied food organisms appropriate for these species, to approach the surface." He adds that the great albatross colony of the Laysan Island of the Pacific, may be made possible by the mere shallowing of the ocean about this island, so that a concentration is produced of the vast quantities of cephalopods needed to support these birds. For according to Fisher's estimate the consumption of these by the breeding albatrosses amounts to some 600 tons daily.

But to return to a classification of water environments. Those of fresh water include lakes and streams, whether large or small, and are characterized by a number of familiar birds. The Loon, various grebes, certain of the smaller gulls (as Franklin's Gull), Black Terns, many of the surface-feeding ducks, and the Coot are birds typical of fresh-water lakes, while others, as the American Merganser and the group of South American ducks known as Torrent Ducks, are especially characteristic of streams. The latter birds inhabit rapid waters and often climb out on to rocks, using the sharp spurs at the bend of the wings to help them. Here may be included also the Dippers of specialized habits, that plunge boldly into mountain torrents to seek food at the bottom, truly an extraordinary habit for a Passerine bird.

Shores as a distinct type of environment may be thought of as very restricted in extent, and again as of various types, but chiefly comprising sea shores or beaches and muddy shores or flats. Each type has its characteristic birds— thus the Piping and Black-bellied Plovers, the Semi-palmated and White-rumped Sandpipers are typical of the sand beach, the Least and Pectoral Sandpipers and the Yellowlegs are birds of muddy or brackish shores. Salt marshes may also be included as shores, and have been invaded by a few birds of the land as Seaside and Sharp-tailed Sparrows. Adams points out that the arctic tundra, cut up as it is into a myriad of small pools with grassy areas between, amounts essentially to a shore, so that it becomes the breeding home of many shore-loving birds, including sandpipers, curlews, and plovers.

Probably therefore *swamps* should be considered also as a variety of shore, or as an intermediate step between shore and land. Fresh and brackish swamps have each their special set of birds, the fresh swamps, however, a more varied lot, as being more nearly like the land. A good example of contrast between birds of these two sorts of swamps is afforded by the Clapper Rail and the King Rail, birds differing in little except general coloration, the former a salt-marsh species, the latter more characteristic of fresh-water marshes.

Fresh-water swamps are divisible into various kinds, as those filled by grass, those overgrown by cattails, or those grown up to bushes or trees. The cattail marsh has a specially interesting set of birds that goes with it, including Least Bittern and Long-billed Marsh Wren; while grass swamps are equally characterized by Swamp Sparrows and Short-billed Marsh Wren. Other species may occur in both as Red-winged and Yellow-headed Blackbirds, Sora and Virginia Rail.

Swamps are especially interesting as often containing relicts of species formerly more widespread, or they may offer conditions quite different from those of the immediately surrounding country. With us in Massachusetts, cedar swamps in which a dense growth of white cedars forms a continuous canopy, preventing rapid evaporation, often serve as boreal islands, where cool conditions obtain that occasionally attract such more northerly birds to nest as Canada Warbler, Winter Wren, Brown Creeper, Red-breasted Nuthatch.   Very few exact observations seem to have been made as to the precise conditions obtaining in such places.

The classification of land environments may be carried out with a considerable degree of refinement, but the outstanding features are: forested country and open country. The forest fauna varies with the type of forest cover.   In North America, the chief forest areas are (1) the great transcontinental evergreen forest; (2) the hardwoods of the eastern States, and (3) the southern pine forest.   The first of these corresponds more or less closely with the boreal zone of Merriam, and carries its distinctive fauna, many of whose members are directly related to those of the evergreen forest area in the north of the Old World. The central hardwoods or Appalachian forest has likewise its own set of species, and the southern pine woods are still different in character.   The attempt to divide these latter into climatic zones is less satisfactory.   Trotter has shown that the distribution of forests depends not only upon temperature but on other equally important factors of soil and moisture, which in turn are conditioned more or less by geological and topographical features.   Bird-life is dependent in its distribution upon these factors only *indirectly* as they affect the distribution of the forests.   The rise of the great mountain chains on the Pacific slope, with the resulting reduction in moisture-content of the prevailing westerly winds was a large factor in the disappearance of what seems to have been a much greater westward extension of forest in earlier Tertiary times than now, so that the gradual retreat of the forest from the far western United States has brought about great changes in the distribution of birds and other animals. The drying out of the winds as they come from the Pacific Ocean through the condensing of moisture on the coast ranges is the immediate cause of desert conditions in the West, while in the central United States the gradually increasing aërial moisture results in prairie and grasslands with a special set of birds adapted for this environment, until conditions are finally reached suitable for forest growth in the East.

Thus geographic distribution is not necessarily zonal, as so often thought of, but has to do quite as much with the relative amount of available water. Chapin and others have brought out this fact in dealing with Africa, whose two chief faunal areas south of the Sahara are (1) the Congo rain forest with its abundant precipitation, (2) the dry steppe or semi-desert including the eastern and southern parts of the continent and encircling the forest area. Often the transition between the two is extremely abrupt and sharply defined.

Arctic areas are ecologically a kind of desert, for plant growth is largely prevented not so much by a lack of moisture as by water being to a great degree unavailable through lack of heat and light. The similarity of the arctic to a dry- or barren-country fauna is interestingly shown by the presence in both types of country of such birds as pipit, horned lark, a grouse (Ptarmigan) and by the presence of hares, foxes, and wolves. The arctic desert is of course quite different from the torrid desert in many ways, but both agree in offering such rigorous conditions of life that but relatively few creatures can penetrate and live in them. We may think of the birds of deserts as creatures that have invaded them from some adjacent but more favorable type of country. In a hot desert the outstanding factor in the control of life is water. Buxton points out that certain birds inhabit the *fringe* of deserts but seem to be prevented from penetrating them because they cannot dispense with drinking, so that the need for drinking water becomes a limiting factor in their distribution. An example is the Desert Quail of California that wanders out to forage in the desert, but retires into the scrub along the streams since it requires to drink both morning and evening. The desert-living Sand Grouse of the Old World have an interesting habit of saturating the breast feathers with water at such times as they drink, and flying back to the nest. The young birds obtain their water supply by passing these saturated feathers through their bills, and until able to fly they receive water in no other way.

In the relations of birds to forests there is much yet to be more thoroughly studied. Many birds are typically tree dwellers, often showing preference for particular kinds of trees, a fact indicating some intimate or dependent relation with that species. Thus in southern New England the Pine-creeping Warbler shows a very decided preference for the Pitch Pine; the Black-throated Green Warbler is partial to the White Pine, the Magnolia Warbler to Red or White Spruce, so much so that there must be some as yet undiscovered reason to account for this dependence. Probably the nature of the food has much to do with it.

The fondness of the Evening Grosbeak for the seeds of the Ash-leaved Maple or Box Elder is apparently responsible for the wide extension of this bird's winter range to New England in recent years. A bird of the Northwest,

it occasionally came in winter to the Middle States, as far
east as Illinois. It was quite unknown to New England
ornithologists until the winter of 1889–90 when a considerable visitation of these handsome birds took place. Small
flocks were seen at various times in that winter in central
New England. This occurrence was looked upon as wholly
accidental and extraordinary, and no further examples were
seen here for over twenty years. Early in the present
century, however, a second flight came in 1903, and since
then hardly a winter has passed without some report of
this species in the East, often in large flocks. Very noticeable is the way in which these visitors resort at once to the
Box Elders, remaining in the vicinity of seed-bearing trees
until the supply of the fruits is exhausted. As first suggested, I think, by the late Dr. Walter Faxon, it is likely
that the extensive planting of this tree through the middle
west of the United States and Canada, as well as in New
England (to a less degree), has been the important factor
of attraction. The abundant crops of its fruit have acted
as bait to toll the birds across from their usual wintering
resorts in the West, so that as the maturing trees became
almost continuous in their cross-country distribution, the
birds followed, and having once learned the way they have
continued to come with quite as great regularity as certain of our other expected visitors of winter. Still more
interesting is the fact, recently told me by Professor Sush-
kin, of St. Petersburg, that in southeastern Russia, where
this same tree has been extensively planted, the Hawfinch,
a near relative of the Evening Grosbeak, has been similarly
tolled across the plains far from its usual winter area in
that country.

The introduction of other trees than the Box Elder has

had an important influence on birds.   Particularly, I think, the apple tree has been a large factor in the lives of many species. The readiness with which Robins, Chipping Sparrows, and other species have taken to the orchard trees is scarcely less than the avidity with which many caterpillars and other insects have done the same. The abundance of appropriate nest sites and food offered by these trees must have been a great factor in increasing the number of these birds in our rural districts. A recent writer has shown that the planting of apple orchards in Oklahoma in late years is directly responsible for the gradual spread of the Robin across that State from east to west and of one of the Kingbirds in the opposite direction. Here then is another case where tree-planting has resulted in an invasion of the birds into new country.

Birds in relation to forest succession is a matter needing further study. The gradual replacement of one type of forest or plant growth by another may take place under natural conditions or following the artificial clearing of an area. Many of our cedar swamps may easily be seen to be growing where once must have been a lake. Intermediate stages may still be found between (1) ponds in which one end is beginning to fill up with the accumulation of dead leaves and floatsam of various kinds; (2) ponds in which this accumulation is enough to form a quaking bog extending in from the shores, and supporting bush growth near the margins, to (3) final stages where the greater solidity of the portion near the original shore makes possible a ring of white-cedar growth, beyond which are tall bushes of clethra or blueberry, and beyond lower bushes, until the inner ring is reached with its sphagnum, pitcher-plants, and sedges. Each of these types of growth has its particular birds. The Swamp Sparrows are found in the inner grassy ring; Song Sparrows and Yellowthroats in the bushy border; while in the cool cedar growth the Canada Warbler locally occurs. The final condition of this process of filling up results in a large cedar swamp, which supports often a number of more northern species of animals.

The cutting off of New England forests and their destruction by fire introduces other types of succession. A white-pine forest cut off in southern New Hampshire may not reproduce itself easily. The bare ground slowly recovers and a growth of bushes and vines results, the haunt of such birds as Song Sparrows, White-throats, sometimes Chewinks or Brown Thrashers, Yellowthroats and Chestnut-sided Warblers. Usually gray-birch thickets ensue, mixed with spindling white-pine saplings, which are soon overshaded and either choked or much deformed. At this stage the growing thicket is excellent cover for grouse. As years pass and the trees become a pole forest, the shorter-lived birches gradually die out and a new pine forest may result, with again a characteristic bird fauna, including Blue Jays, Crows, Black-throated Green Warblers, and others. So a succession of forest stages means a succession as well of its bird inhabitants. This is why once-famous grouse covers, for example, gradually lose attraction for these birds and eventually hold them no more or in reduced numbers as the forest becomes unsuitable.

The Chestnut-sided Warbler is a bird quick to move into new clearings where fresh sprout-growth offers the sort of cover it needs. Perhaps some like change in our agriculture such as the giving up of wheat crops has had an influence on the Dickcissel, formerly a New England bird.

While the gradual change from one type of tree growth

to another under natural conditions results in a gradual succession of bird faunas from grass-living to bush-living types, and from small-tree lovers to forest birds, over a long period of years, we may see the different stages illustrated by separate areas here and there that are in the different transition stages. This natural succession is therefore responsible for gradual changes in any fauna, ending in what is called a climax stage where the dominant type of forest at length prevails, and as in any so-called primeval forest, becomes at length self-perpetuating. In the central-eastern States this climax forest is of deciduous trees.

Succession of floras and faunas through artificial disturbance by man is everywhere seen in eastern New England, where clearings are growing up into bushy pasture and these in turn to thickets, low woods, or high forest. One specially interesting type is produced here through repeated burning of the leaves in spring. These forest fires kill sprouting herbs and shrubs, and finally result in the death of nearly all the trees—pines first, then the less resistant hardwoods—until after repeated burnings there is left a scrubby growth of gray birch, pitch pine, and scrub oak, three species, which with the brake fern seem to be more or less fireproof and spring up again as often as the area is burned over. The birds that find this sort of growth congenial are Prairie and Chestnut-sided Warblers, Field Sparrows, and Chewinks especially, with a few Brown Thrashers and, as the growth becomes thicker and larger, Pine-creeping Warblers in the pines, Catbirds, and Cuckoos. There is much to be done in the way of a more careful study of these different types of vegetative growth and their characteristic birds, especially by series of observations covering the gradual change of a given area and the succession

of its bird faunas, the time-duration of any special asssocia-
tion of species, and kindred matters.

Birds as disseminators of seeds may play an important
part in forest economy. In Europe the large Missel
Thrush has much to do with the spread and survival of
the mistletoe. The berry includes a layer of sticky substance which hardens on exposure to air and is used in making bird-lime. When the Thrush eats the berries, it re-
jects the seeds, which often stick to its bill and have to be
rubbed off against a branch. The sticky substance then
hardens and the seed is fixed until it germinates, often
months later, when in May the temperature is sufficiently
high. Professor Keeble tells of a certain telegraph wire in
Ceylon, where every year hundreds of seedlings of an allied
species of mistletoe appear. These start from seeds
rubbed off upon the wire by birds from their bills. They
do not last long, however, as no nutriment is obtainable
from the wire, but they show how important birds may be
in the distribution of the species.

Here on the hills about Boston is found a considerable
growth of red cedars forming a characteristic feature of the
tree growth. It is noticeable how adjacent pasture-lands
and often open fields at a considerable distance from the
nearer cedar trees will be found to have a sprinkling of small
seedlings, the forerunners of more "cedar pastures."
These seedlings are undoubtedly from seeds sown in fall by
Robins that feed on the berries and then repair to these adjacent open fields and void the undigested seeds. In New
Jersey it is said that the Robins scatter the seeds of this tree
along the rail fences where they perch, so that rows of cedars grow up along the pasture boundaries. Robins eat not
only cedar berries but also those of the ground juniper.

The seeds pass through the digestive tract and this apparently is an aid to their germination. Indeed, Mr. William Brewster once told me that his attempts to grow ground juniper from seed were always unsuccessful until he discovered that in order to germinate, the seeds must first be eaten by a bird and passed through its digestive tract. Robins are also fond of eating two species of wild cherry in fall, both the Bird Cherry and the Black Cherry. After the pulp is digested, the stones are voided in a condition in which germination is probably assisted. Many of us are familiar with the fact that old logging roads in the New Hampshire and Maine woods fill up after a few years with Bird Cherries, whose seeds have doubtless been thus sown in large part by Robins that gather in fall in open places in the woods. In this way the birds help to replant the forest cover so essential for the retention of moisture and for the regrowth of the more valuable timber. They provide also for a continuation of their favorite cherries, albeit unwittingly. Other species of birds probably are instrumental in tree planting also.

On the other hand, there are probably occasions when birds do harm, as in case of those that eat poison-ivy berries and so help to scatter this noxious plant. Crossbills have been known to be a measurable factor in preventing complete reforestation of certain conifers in years when the seed crop was depended upon to replace the forest after clean cutting. Again, it seems fairly certain that the chestnut blight, whose ravages have so decimated our chestnut trees in eastern United States, may be spread in part through the agency of birds in transporting the spores on their feathers. These are but a few of the ways in which birds are intimately connected with the welfare of the forest.

There are some very interesting relations among birds with regard to size. It occasionally is found, not only among birds but among mammals as well, that there may be two species apparently closely similar in appearance and inhabiting much the same general area, but chiefly differing in size. A familiar case is that of the Hairy and the Downy Woodpeckers, birds which differ chiefly in size but have similar plumage. In this case the under side of the tail in the Downy is barred with black, whereas in the Hairy, the tail is usually unmarked below. Another case is that of our two species of Yellowlegs, the Greater and the Lesser. In Europe, the Herring Gull and the Lesser Black-backed Gull are two familiar species of the English coasts, which are practically alike except in size and in the tint of the mouth and the feet, yet they live harmoniously together for all that we can see. In all such cases I believe that some difference in habits goes with this difference in size, though the distinction may not be very great. Of the Downy and Hairy Woodpeckers, both obtain much of their food, especially in winter, by searching the crannies of bark in trees, but in a large percentage of the cases it will be found that the Downy extends its forages to the smaller branches, even to the twigs of trees or of bushes, whereas its larger relative is more confined to trunks and large limbs. Thus the smaller bird has the advantage in a larger range of search, for it can hunt over the bark of large trunks and branches and then extend its search even to smaller twigs among which the Hairy would be less at home. Here, then, we see a beginning of a specialization which results in a restriction of the larger species to a more limited feeding area. Further increase of size would limit the field of action still more, as we see in case of the Pileated Woodpecker which is characteristic of large timber. Too great a specialization in the direction of increased size, therefore, becomes ere long a decided disadvantage unless it can be compensated by an ability to reach a more abundant food supply. This the Pileated Woodpecker may perhaps have done in part, for its large size and increased power enable it to cut great holes in the trunks of forest trees in order to reach the tunnels of the big black wood-boring ants which often attack live trees from the root, boring their galleries in the heart-wood far up into the stem. To become dependent upon food of this sort, however, is in itself a specialization, and implies a reliance upon more particular conditions, the failure of any one of which may spell disaster. Thus large trees in New England, for example, are more and more becoming reduced in our forests, and not every tree is suitable for the big ants. The range and abundance of the Pileated Woodpecker may therefore depend in part upon the supply of these ants and in turn the supply must be sufficient and widespread, which means a large number of trees, a certain proportion only of which may be suitable for the maintenance of this supply. So, in this increasing ratio of size between Downy, Hairy, and Pileated Woodpeckers, we may have an increasing degree of specialization, or of limitation to certain requisites for food getting. These facts in turn may help to explain why the Downy is commoner than the Hairy, and the Hairy in turn outnumbers the Pileated, while the last is rare and with changed conditions of forest finds itself in danger of being wiped out.

Size differences in the two species of Yellowlegs may be correlated with feeding habits in a similar way. The Lesser Yellowlegs is shorter-legged and shorter-billed than its larger relative. Its feeding habits, however, are similar in that both frequent marshy places, and the edges of pools, wading in often up to their depth and picking at food particles in the mud or in shallow water. The Greater Yellowlegs by reason of its longer legs, however, can wade into deeper water than the Lesser and its longer bill and neck additionally increase its potential feeding range. It should follow that the larger species, conversely to what we saw with the woodpeckers, would here have a slight advantage, on account of its ability to obtain food from a wider range of depth in the pools which it frequents. It may be therefore that this is a factor in the usual greater abundance of the larger species, its longer stay with us in the fall migration, and its regular presence in spring. For the Lesser Yellowlegs is rare here as a spring migrant and in fall has passed by late summer, whereas the Greater stays till late in November. Thus it appears that comparatively small matters of size may be of great influence. Yet a further large increase in proportions of the Greater Yellowlegs might prove a disadvantage, requiring so much more food to maintain a body much larger that the advantage of a greater feeding radius would be lost. There are thus factors tending to limit the extent to which one species may profitably exceed another of similar feeding requirements.

Among the group of birds called Tubinares (Procellariiformes), including the petrels, shearwaters, and albatrosses, we find birds of very great diversity of size, yet all pelagic species obtaining food under more or less like conditions. Nichols, who has studied these birds in a long ocean voyage to the southern seas where they most abound, has brought out some interesting points. He plotted the body-lengths of the various species of the group, with the exception of the Diving Petrels whose habits are different, and found the resulting curve to show three well-separated peaks, which indicated the three chief groups of sizes—the first including the smaller Mother Carey's Chickens, the second the medium-sized shearwaters and fulmars, the third, the larger albatrosses. These birds are all pelagic and constitute practically the whole aërial population of the southern seas below the Tropics. Nichols says that to one "familiar with their breeding and feeding habits, it is perfectly obvious that the great range in size relieves pressure of competition" for food in this vast population. Thus the "small Wilson's Petrel or Mother Carey's Chicken, the medium-sized Cape Pigeon, and the large Albatross collect at one time to partake of scraps from a ship, and the smaller birds are satisfied with the crumbs left by the larger ones." In their breeding habits these birds show further the result of this size relation. For they seek relatively small land areas such as islands or the edges of the antarctic continent. Here again the extremes of size are brought together in close proximity where competition for food is keen and where a smaller species is exposed to danger from a larger through having its eggs and young eaten or itself killed for food. So we find the smaller forms making burrows where they will be safely out of reach of the larger predacious species or seeking clefts or cavities among rocks; while the large and powerful species build in the open. It is found, too, that the sexes relieve each other in nest guard and brooding. In this way small and defenseless species are able to live in comparative safety among a host of larger and more powerful birds.

There are other size relations in birds that need explanation through a study of their habits and behavior. For example, the significance of the often greatly superior size of the female over the male in hawks seems to have received very little attention. The disadvantage of being small or the advantage of being larger was brought out by a recent note in "The Auk," recounting a scene witnessed in Florida. The small male of a pair of Bald Eagles nesting near the seacoast had just swooped upon a Fish Hawk causing it to drop its prey, a fish, apparently of unusual size. With unerring aim the Eagle darted after it, seizing it in mid-air. So heavy was the fish, however, that the Eagle was unable to rise with it, but was forced to a gradually sinking course. Presently it dropped the fish with a peculiar cry, to which its larger and better half at once replied, left her perch and dove like an arrow after the fish, snatching it when it had nearly reached the water, and with superior strength bore it away to the eyrie—apparently a fine case of coöperation between the two sexes.

CHAPTER VIII

EGGS AND NESTS OF BIRDS

In all vertebrate (back-boned) animals, the reproductive organs are paired glands, which in early life become differentiated into *testes* (in the male) or *ovaries* (in the female). In the chick this difference can be detected as early as the fifth day of incubation. Curiously, in birds the development of the ovary on the right side presently halts, leaving the ovary of the left side to reach full maturity and give rise to the eggs by the budding-off of the germinal cells. In no other group of animals is this known, except in case of certain sharks. It is supposed to be correlated with the large size of birds' eggs, and the necessity for room inside the body to contain them. As some one has remarked, a Guillemot with more than a single egg within would surely burst (though more likely the egg would)! Very recently, Gunn (1912) has shown that in spite of this general rule among birds, it is nevertheless not at all uncommon to find *both* ovaries well developed among certain hawks and falcons. This investigator found double ovaries in 56 out of 98 of these birds, and in birds of other groups he found 14 cases out of 112 in which both ovaries were present—including owl, Crested Grebe, Red Grouse, Bewick's Swan, Woodcock, and Little Gull. Additional observations on this matter are desirable and can easily be made by those having to prepare specimens.

The eggs of birds are first given off by the ovary, and

consist each of a single enormous cell, the germ from which the chick develops. The size is a result of the quantity of yolk or nutritive material with which the cell is filled. On being given off by the ovary, the egg is caught by the trumpet-shaped end of the oviduct, a tube-like organ down which the egg is passed by a series of wave-like contractions, until it comes out or is "laid." On its journey down the oviduct, it passes by certain sets of special glands, the first of which covers it with the gelatinous albumen or "white," the next covers it with a double skin or membrane, and the final set with a limy shell, which may or may not be colored.

We have all seen occasionally the so-called "double eggs" laid by hens. There are two chief sorts (see Parker, 1906) : those in which there are two yolks enclosed by a single shell, and those in which an egg with yolk and shell is enclosed inside another complete egg. Sometimes three separate eggs have been found, one inside another. Where an egg has two yolks, it seems that these are two separate eggs given off together or nearly so, that have traveled down the oviduct side by side, to be enveloped by the albumen, skin, and shell as one mass. Where two complete eggs are found one inside the other, the case is different, for obviously the inner one must have reached the lower end of the oviduct where the shell-glands are, before the outer one. Observations on such eggs seem to prove beyond doubt that after the first or inner egg has been completed a peculiar reversal of the wave-like contractions of the oviduct takes place so that the completed egg is carried back to the upper end of the oviduct whence it started. Here it meets a second egg commencing the journey and the two go together past the albumen-, skin-, and shell-glands, so that the first egg is completely enclosed by the albumen, skin, and shell of the second.   Sometimes eggs on such a reversed journey do not meet a second one on its way down but are turned out inside the body cavity itself, and may cause the death of the hen.   It is a curious fact that the majority of double-yolked eggs are laid during the warmer part of the year, from May to August, while inclosed eggs are produced in the winter and spring (see Parker, 1906).

An anxious lady during the Great War once came to me to inquire about some eggs she had received from the market.   They were longer and narrower than usual, and having seen in the papers that the eggs of alligators were being sold for those of hens, she feared she was being cheated in this way.   I assured her they could not be other than extra-long hens' eggs, for alligators' eggs could not be had in quantity, and she seemed satisfied.   But eggs of lizards, alligators, and crocodiles are as a rule much longer in proportion to width than in birds, though those of some large turtles are nearly spherical.   Eggs of dinosaurs, ancient reptiles related probably to the ancestors of birds, have recently been found fossil in Mongolia, with even the unhatched embryos inside them.   These eggs are very narrow and long in proportion to width.

The shapes of birds' eggs are more various than one would at first suppose.   Those who have read the Cruise of the Kawa recall Captain Traprock's discovery of the bird that laid square eggs!   But though his tale is discredited, there are nevertheless many variations from the simple oval that we know so well in the hen's egg. This itself is subject to much fluctuation in size, for some hen's eggs are long or pointed, others nearly spherical.   In

the times of Horace, epicures chose for eating the long
pointed eggs, for these were believed to be more delicate,
with a clearer "white." It was also supposed that such
eggs would produce males, the short and rounded ones females, though we now know that this is not of necessity so.
Certain types of eggs are more or less characteristic of
particular groups of birds. Thus it is usual among the
sandpipers to have four eggs of a distinctly pear-shape,
that is the small end is almost conical. In the nest the
pointed ends lie at the center, and the shape is perhaps an
adaptation to allow the bird to cover so large a nestful in
incubating. For they fit closer together than if they were
oval or elliptical like the eggs of hens or loons respectively.
The eggs are large for the size of the bird to permit of
storing a quantity of yolk on which the embryo may feed,
for the young of these birds are able to run and leave
the nest very shortly after hatching. The affinity of the
murres and auks to shore-birds is indicated in a similar pear-
shape of their egg. But murres lay only one, and instead
of a nest, merely select a spot on the ledge of a cliff, whence
often the egg rolls off if the birds are suddenly disturbed.
Yet, as has often been pointed out, the very shape is an advantage here, for, if slightly moved, the egg tends to re-
volve upon its smaller end instead of rolling away, and so
no doubt is often prevented from going over the edge to
destruction. Dr. Chapman has aptly termed these "diplo-
matic" eggs, as their shape allows them to move without
going far.

Most owls lay nearly spherical eggs, and in this respect
are supposed by some to be primitive. Yet the lizard,
which might be considered still more primitive, lays a long,
elliptical egg. Beebe has suggested that the spherical

shape aids in keeping the eggs all together, if laid in a cavity. But probably this is only an incidental matter, for woodpeckers, which have probably nested in cavities longer than owls, have elliptical eggs.

Eggs and Vigor.—Recently a very interesting relation between the form of the egg and the extent of migration in the bird laying it, has been studied by Averill (1923), who confirms a previous statement of Coues in 1884, that the short diameter of the egg, since it corresponds to the caliber of the oviduct, is less variable than the long diameter, and since an increase in the amount of stored food, that is the amount of yolk and white, varies with the vigor of the individual, it follows that the greater the amount of food or the greater the vigor of the individual, the longer will the egg be, to make room for the surplus. For if an increase in size is needed, it takes place most easily in a lengthwise direction. The converse also is true that the less the amount of stored food, or the less the individual vigor of the bird, the shorter will be the egg.

Averill (1923) has applied this proposition to eggs of certain birds to test the idea that a migratory species is more vigorous than a sedentary or non-migratory one. By dividing the length by breadth he arrived at a ratio which may be used to express the relative vigor of the species. In four warblers that breed in the northern United States and northward, and winter in South America,—namely, the Black-poll, the Bay-breasted, the Blackburnian, and the Yellow Warblers,—this ratio averaged 1.37 (ranging from 1.35–1.39) ; in four other species whose length of migration is much less,—namely, the Pine-creeping, the Myrtle, the Prairie, and the Yellow Palm Warblers, that winter in part within the United States,—the ratio averages 1.32, the lowest being the Yellow Palm (1.29). For the Black-throated Blue it is 1.37, which, however, is as great as the average in his first group. With a second set of egg measurements, his results are 1.36 for the first group of species and 1.31 for the second. Five western warblers whose migration is short—Audubon's, Black-throated Gray, Townsend's, Hermit, and Golden-cheeked—average 1.26 for one series of eggs, and 1.32 for additional eggs, which accord fairly with those given for the other set, and are much less than that (1.37) of the long-distance warblers. Other species of birds seem in general to conform to this rule; thus in the Northern Water-thrush, a bird of long migration, the ratio is 1.30, in the Louisiana Water-thrush, of shorter migration, it is 1.24; for the Baltimore Oriole, 1.48, for the Orchard Oriole, 1.38, the latter with the less extensive journey having the smaller ratio. Among sparrows, it is found that those breeding in high latitudes have a different shape of egg from those breeding in more southerly latitudes, as expressed in this ratio of width to length. Thus, the Savanna, White-crowned, White-throated, Lincoln's, and Fox Sparrows—all northern breeding species—show a general average of 1.38, while Grasshopper, Henslow's, Seaside, Pine-woods, and Bachman's Sparrows (southern species) show an average of only 1.27. As an example of this same relation, the ratio in the Great Blue Heron is 1.66, whereas in the Florida form,—Ward's Heron, which is not migratory,—the ratio is 1.43.

Birds greatly differing in size cannot well be compared, for in the larger members of a group the length of egg seems to be proportionally greater; thus in the Great Auk and the Razor-billed Auk, the ratio is 1.60 and 1.63, while in the smaller Black Guillemot and Dovekie it is but 1.45

and 1.47 respectively, and all of the species have about the same migratory range.

Averill adds further that in certain birds of great power of vigorous flight, as swallows, swifts, and hummingbirds, the eggs are relatively most elongated. Among the owls, many of which are very little migratory, the eggs are most nearly spherical.

The colors of eggs are not especially varied. Reptiles (including lizards, turtles, crocodiles, and snakes) all lay white eggs with a shell that is only partly limy. The white bird's egg is therefore primitive in being like that of the ancient reptilian ancestors of birds. It seems more likely that the white eggs of many hole-nesting birds simply retain this ancestral trait rather than that the eggs are white because they are hidden from view, as some have suggested. This trait is found universally within such relatively primitive groups as owls, woodpeckers, and hummingbirds, none of which is known to lay speckled eggs. A great many of our small birds lay white or bluish eggs with fine brownish or lavender spots often arranged in a wreath about the larger pole. Most of our flycatchers lay such eggs. It is interesting to see, however, that the Phœbe's eggs are normally white, though very rarely with a few speckles. The question arises, then, is the Phœbe *losing* the spotted type of egg, and is it developing a white egg because of nesting under dark ledges?

Birds whose nests lie open to view are apt to lay eggs with more or less color. Those of sandpipers are mottled on a brownish ground that must aid in their concealment when the bird is away. Yet there are many contradictions to this, for pigeons, nearly all of which build open nests, all lay white eggs. The Nighthawk lays a speckled egg that closely simulates its background and so is not conspicuous when exposed; yet its close relative the Whippoorwill, with a similar habit of nesting on the bare ground, lays nearly white eggs with a few pale blotches only. It may be that this is correlated with a difference in habits, for the former often flies by day, but the latter is, I think, much more strictly nocturnal and sits closely all day, concealing its tell-tale eggs.

Curious are the dark-brown eggs of the Loon, the greenish ones of the Cassowary, and the blackish egg of the Emu.

The number of eggs laid is more or less characteristic of a species or of a group of related species; though there is, as usual with birds, no rule without its exceptions. Auks, some penguins, albatrosses, and petrels lay one egg. Two is the normal number in most pigeons, the hummingbirds, loons; four in sandpipers; while many small birds lay from three to five. The Ostrich and the Emu stand near the head with about 15 and 13 respectively, and Ruffed Grouse and Quail may lay as many. By taking away an egg as soon as it is laid and leaving one only for a "nest egg," birds may sometimes be induced to lay a great number. Probably the record is held by a Flicker that is said to have reached nearly 70 in this way, a remarkable example of the action on the body of an unfulfilled instinct.

A large number of species lay but two eggs, and there are some singular relations among certain of these birds. In the Antarctic there is a large species of Skua Gull (*Megalestris maccormicki*), a bird which in those regions takes the place of hawks in preying on its inoffensive neighbors. This bird lays two eggs, but it seems that only one chick ever lives to grow up, for almost invariably one of them gets gobbled up by one of the neighboring old Skuas who seem not to discriminate between the eggs and chicks of their own and other species of birds.

The Adélie Penguins that live in close proximity also lay but two eggs, and it is interesting to know that very soon one of the two chicks outstrips the other in growth since it succeeds in getting more than its share of the food brought by the parents. Whether or not the weaker brother invariably fails to grow up would be interesting to ascertain.

Dr. F. M. Chapman notes that some of the species of Boobies or Gannets lay two eggs, but often only one of the young survives, for the first chick hatches several days ahead of its twin and seems to require its parents' attention to the neglect of the other. Bent says that in case of the Common Loon that lays but two eggs, one egg is often found to be addled, so that only one hatches.

Among pigeons, two eggs form the usual complement, though there are exceptions to this. The Passenger Pigeon, for example, laid but a single egg, and there is doubtless some significance in this breaking of the rule, perhaps to be connected with the fact that the bird was social in its habits, living and nesting in associations. We shall never know if there was a low rate of mortality through this flocking habit, but such was probably the case, and it allowed the species to economize by reducing the number of eggs and young needed to maintain normal numbers. The quickness with which the species disappeared when its breeding colonies were broken up illustrates the danger of too close an adaptation to particular conditions, for with any considerable change the species must succumb.

The Domestic Pigeon normally lays two eggs and there is a very widespread belief, even among pigeon fanciers, that these are invariably male and female. So careful a worker as the late C. O. Whitman, after considerable observation, came to the conclusion that "the first egg is smaller and is a male, the second is larger and usually a female, while as the season advances the smaller ones also are female-producers." The whole matter has lately been carefully studied by the French zoölogist, Cuénot, and by Cole and Kirkpatrick (1915) in this country. The last two, working together, made a long series of careful investigations as to the time of laying each egg, the proportion of sexes, the rate of mortality, and kindred matters. They confirmed the results of Cuénot, that in the long run there is a slightly larger number of male than of female birds produced, in the ratio of about 105 males to 100 females. This is a slightly smaller disproportion than reported by the French worker, who, however, had but 136 birds in all, while the conclusions of the American authors were based on over 1600 birds. This discrepancy in proportion of the sexes is doubtless a normal one and is found in other animals, though in different ratio. There appeared to be a practically equal death rate in both sexes, so that the disproportion is not due to any factor causing the females to die before hatching. In later life, between the age of one and two years, there is, however, a higher death rate among the females. As to the current belief that the two eggs produce a male and a female young, it was found that there is no basis at all for the view that the first egg is usually a male and the second a female. The entire matter is purely one of chance, for the number of males to females hatching from the first of the two eggs laid is about the same as the relative proportion of the sexes and was actually 103 : 100 instead of 105 : 100. The number of cases in which the two eggs produced either two females or two males is about the same as the number in which there was one young of each sex, a result quite in accord with the expected if it were a matter of chance.   It would seem, therefore, definitely disproved that the sex of the hatching brood can be controlled by the breeder.   The time of hatching averages 16.5–17 days, but it is interesting to note that if for some reason the eggs fail to hatch the bird usually continues to sit for a varying time, but on an average about six days more—as a sort of factor of safety—before the sitting impulse dies out.   A pair of Mourning Doves continued to sit on eggs substituted for their own four days after the latter had hatched in an incubator, indicating that this "factor of safety" exists in other species and disproving the assertion of Raspail, a recent French investigator, that wild birds have an exact notion of the time required for their eggs to hatch.

Ingersoll has pointed out that the number of eggs laid by a given species of bird undoubtedly bears some relation to the normal death rate, so that the bird may maintain its average numbers under the conditions to which, in the long period of its evolution, it has become accustomed.   It is not to be supposed that this adjustment is a perfect one, or that it is capable of a quick readjustment in different species if they become exposed to new factors of peril.   The subject offers an attractive field for speculation as well as for careful observation of the causes of normal destruction of birds.

A recent very able contribution to this subject has been made by Dr. Joseph Grinnell (1920), who regards the small number of eggs laid by sea birds as proof that their

life is a comparatively safe one. Of the various albatrosses, petrels, shearwaters, auklets, murres, and puffins
of the North Pacific, but one brood is raised yearly, and
this consists of but a single young. These birds typically
resort to islands for breeding.

The Pigeon Guillemot and the Kittiwake Gull usually
lay *two* eggs. The former nests in clefts of rocks, the
latter on shelves of precipitous cliffs. With other gulls,
however, three eggs are usual and these birds nest often on
shores of the mainland. On the supposition that the number of eggs laid is on the average sufficient to maintain the
population of a given species at a certain normal, Dr.
Grinnell assumes that in the case of the Fork-tailed Petrel
(closely resembling our Leach's Petrel) the single egg
hatched increases the total population of Petrels by 50%
at the beginning of the breeding season—this of course if
all the birds pair and all hatch their young. In fact, the
actual number is doubtless less, since not all the birds are
necessarily paired, nor perhaps do all the young hatch.
Thus each two birds become three, and the number of
Petrels is 150 where before it was 100. But by the following spring the population is presumably back again to its
former normal average number, so that the mortality for
the year nearly equals the annual hatching but is distributed
over the entire colony, old and young. The age distribution of those birds that annually die would be an interesting
thing to study, and it may be that, by bird-banding carried
out over a series of years on particular nesting colonies, we
may eventually arrive at positive knowledge. It may be
said parenthetically that among a flock of tame pigeons kept
for experimental study it was found that there was a high

mortality of both sexes during the first two or three years of their adult life, and this was especially high in females between the ages of one and two years.

But to return to the comparison of sea birds and land birds. Dr. Grinnell compares the assumed mortality of the Petrel in which one-third of the total population at hatching-time dies in the course of a year with that in the land birds. The Song Sparrow, as an instance, lays say four eggs and raises on an average two broods, so that the pair of Song Sparrows becomes ten birds if all hatch. By the following spring eight of these will have died if the population is to return to its normal number. Again it may not be eight of the young that die, but perhaps both parents and six young, or some other combination. At all events, the mortality would be, on these assumptions, 80% instead of 33⅓% of the total population at the close of hatching. The active enemies of sea birds we know little of, but they seem certainly fewer than those of land birds. Occasional accidents or catastrophes during heavy storms there must be, but the conclusion is doubtless correct that in general the sea is a safer place than the land. And this any sailor will tell you.

There is another factor that may come in, however, that does not seem to have been considered in the accounting. For in the case of many birds that lay one or two eggs and are thus able to maintain a normal population, there is not only the fact of a relatively low mortality on account of the nature of their habitat, but it is possible, if not likely, that their natural term of life is longer, so that if a pair of land birds and of sea birds lived out their normal number of years the latter would not only count for a longer time as part of the population, but would be able to breed over a longer term of years, and in this way partly make up for the fewer number of their eggs.

But precise facts as to the length of days in a bird's life are not so easily obtained. This is one of the matters on which much light may be thrown by banded birds, especially those banded as nestlings. It will be interesting, therefore, to review briefly some of the facts already known as to the age attained by different birds. These are gleaned from two sources of unequal value: *first,* from observations on wild individuals that have been marked or are otherwise recognizable; *second,* from observations of captive birds kept in zoölogical gardens or as pets. Observations on birds living naturally in the open are the only ones that really indicate the normal term of life under usual conditions. It seems to many naturalists that few animals ever die a "natural" death, they are so constantly exposed to dangers from other animals that prey upon them, as well as from storms, times of cold, hunger, drought, or other accidents of Nature. At first sight it would seem that birds kept in a zoölogical park, where food and shelter are regularly provided, would be most favorably placed for living out the natural period of existence. But to this it must be replied that captivity is very likely to upset the natural processes of the body, and disease is much more apt to seize the captive. Perhaps, however, the dangers of the free life are counterbalanced more or less by the luxury of confinement, so that the comparative value of the figures is nearly the same. But this remains to be proved.

Of the few good cases relating to wild birds, one of the best known is that of the Herring Gull "Dick," which for twenty-four winters came regularly to the Brenton Reef Lightship off our coast. It appeared usually in October and left in April, and though tame enough to come to the deck to feed it never could be handled.   Its identity seemed well established by its familiar behavior, though it was not otherwise marked.   There are records of captive birds living for 21 and 44 years.

An instance of a Black-backed Gull is reported by Steenstrup.   It was taken from the nest in the Faroe Islands and reared by one of the peasants, given its liberty at all times. It became so tame that it would eat from its owner's hand, but was more wary of the other members of the house. Eventually it sought a mate and the pair chose a nesting place on a cliff of the island.   For many years this bird returned to the peasant's home for food, eating freely from his hand, but the mate never became so daring.   This bird was still living, sixty-three years from its birth, according to Steenstrup who had personally verified the facts.   In captivity this species has been kept for 19½ years.

Swans have been known to live long periods in domestication; one in St. James Park, London, was known to be at least seventy years old, and a Domestic Goose eighty years.

A Chipping Sparrow, identified by its having lost a joint of one toe, as well as by its great familiarity, nested for nine successive years at Annisquam, Massachusetts, and another identified by its loss of the claw from a middle toe came for three years to a locality in Virginia.   Banded Chipping Sparrows have been taken in Georgia over as long a period.   Many cases of Robins identified by some individual peculiarity have been reported as returning for a series of years to the same place, but usually for periods of about three or four years.   A captive Robin has been known to live ten years.

From records of birds in captivity, several extensive lists have been compiled (see Mitchell, 1911) from which a few of the long-lived species are the following:

Raven: 50 and 69 years.
Sulphur-crested Cockatoo: 50 and 80 years. There is a record of
    an Amazonian Parrot reaching 102 years, and a Gray Parrot 93
    years.
Eagle Owl: 53 and 68 + years.
Condor: 52 years.
Eagles of several species: to 56 years.
Pelican: 40 years.
Collared Dove: 30 to 40 years.

A good many of the smaller birds will live from 15 to 20 years. Merriam records a male Cardinal kept by his grandmother for 21 years. Its colors faded noticeably several years before its death, till finally it looked very like a worn female. Another was at least 13½ years old in captivity. The same author knew of a Rose-breasted Grosbeak that lived 18 years in confinement. An English Song Thrush lived 16 years and finally turned quite black, and a similar peculiarity is known in case of captive Robins (which is of unusual interest in connection with the fact that the European Blackbird is really only a black thrush, related to our Robin). Compared to the three or four years or thereabout for known cases of wild Robins, the 13 years in the London Zoo is much greater, and despite the lack of specific knowledge I am inclined to regard it probable that for these smaller birds a natural term of ten years in free life is near a maximum, though under the protected conditions of captivity nearly twice as long a life is possible. Lankester has recognized such a distinction and terms the average longevity in the wild, "specific" longevity, in distinction to that in captivity, where the bird can with good care reach the utmost limit possible until the bodily mechanism breaks down. This he calls its "potential" longevity.

Owls do not stand captivity well and are relatively short-lived in confinement. Ten years is a long term for them, though they have been known to reach five or six times that in certain cases. Hawks and eagles are potentially long-lived, and with ducks and geese can exceed 50 years. The gallinaceous birds (fowls, pheasants, grouse) are lower in relative viability, ranging to about 20 years, the Ostrich tribe under 50.

As a whole there seems to be no correlation between size and potential longevity. An Ostrich does not exceed a crow or a parrot. There seems some support for the theory advanced by Metchnikoff, that those forms having short hind-guts tend to be longer-lived, for with these species waste food products are not retained so long and there is less chance for putrefaction by bacteria. There does, however, seem to be some ground for believing that within a group of related birds as the hawks, or the eagles, the owls or the woodpeckers, the larger species live longest, but this is not universal. As the study of individual birds by means of banding continues, we shall eventually acquire important and accurate data on this subject.

Some recent extensive studies of eggs show that the weight of the newly hatched young averages about two-thirds that of the fresh-laid egg. There is thus a loss of nearly a third the original weight, and this is due partly to evaporation and partly to chemical changes of the yolk and albumen involved in growth whereby part of this stored food goes off in gases.   For the shell of an egg is porous and allows a certain amount of passage by gases.

There is an interesting relation between the weight of the yolk or more nutritive part of the egg and the condition of the young on hatching.   It is found that in those birds whose young are well feathered with down and leave the nest almost as soon as they hatch, the yolk varies from 22 to 50% (⅕ to ½) of the weight of the egg, while in those that spend a considerable time as nestlings, the yolk is proportionally smaller, only 15 to 25% (⅐ to ¼) of the egg's weight.   The result is that these "nest-fleers" or large-yolked birds are much farther developed at hatching from having a larger store of food to draw on, while the birds with little yolk are proportionally less advanced.   Such young birds, that at hatching are almost at once active and able to feed themselves, are called "præcocial."   They include the ostrich-like birds, tinamous, fowls, gulls, shore-birds, cranes, ducks, geese, grebes, and loons.   Since in tortoises' and crocodiles' eggs the yolk is likewise large, from ⅓ to ½ the weight of the egg, and the young are able to fend for themselves on hatching, we are probably safe in inferring that this "præcocial" condition is the primitive one and that it has gradually been lost in those that have smaller yolks and whose young hatch in a less-developed condition as nestlings.   The obvious advantage of this latter process is that the eggs hatch sooner and the parents are not obliged to incubate for so long a time; on the other hand the mortality of the young is probably greater and the labor of feeding them increased.   This nestling or helpless condition of the young is spoken of as "altricial" (or nursery) and is exemplified in the penguins, cormorants, petrels, and albatrosses, herons and storks among the water-fowl, and is seen in all pigeons, owls, hawks, parrots, swifts, woodpeckers, and passerines. It is not necessarily a sign of relationship to be of one or the other class, but merely marks the degree of emancipation reached by different groups of birds, from the long incubation period.

For some of the incubation periods are really long. That of the Albatross is said to be nine weeks. For the Emu it is 56 to 58 days (nearly two months); for the Cassowary two months, and for the Ostrich a little less or about six weeks. One of the large vultures incubates 57 days. For most ducks this period is from about four weeks to as much as 32 days; while shore-birds take three weeks more or less; the domestic hen 20½ days. Contrast this long period with that of the Cardinal or the English Sparrow, 12 days, one of the shortest.

Finn believes that a bird must derive considerable satisfaction from a long period of incubation, and particularly such a one as the Eider which in some cases at least is said not to leave her nest for the entire period. One cannot but think, however, that for an active species it must become intolerably dull, and that the shortened period of the more evolved groups is an expression of their greater restlessness.

Nests.—The nests of birds and the manner of their construction have not been so carefully studied as they deserve, and there is much yet to be learned as to the steps leading to the development of many complex processes concerned with nest building. In attempting to reconstruct something of their ancient history, it is natural to see if there may not be some birds that still retain traces of reptile habits in the care of their eggs. We know that most lizards lay their eggs singly among dry rubbish or slightly buried in loose earth. Turtles bury their eggs in a hole excavated for the purpose.   There is no such thing as parental care thereafter, but the young on hatching crawl forth and make their way alone, reminding us of the "præcocial" birds. But the alligators and crocodiles seem to show slightly more interest in their children.   They prepare nesting mounds in which the eggs are laid all together.   The Florida alligator gathers a quantity of reeds and grass, flattens it all down, and after laying its eggs in the center, covers them with more reeds and grass.   The male seems to take no part in all this, but the female stays about and is reputed even to attack persons disturbing the nest, though this seems to be a trifle dubious.   When the eggs are about to hatch, it is said on good authority that the young can be distinctly heard squeaking inside the eggs (and this is true also of some of the water-birds).   The watchful parent then opens the mound and assists in the release of the young.

To find among birds a parallel to these first instincts of nesting, we naturally turn to the groups of birds considered the least advanced of those now living and discover a habit so similar among the Megapodes, or so-called Brush Turkeys, of Australia and some of the East Indies, that it seems too good to be true.   For this reason perhaps some ornithologists have supposed the habit of this bird is not a survival of primitive methods, but instead a degenerate process on the part of birds that once knew better.   Be that as it may, these curious birds, which are distantly related to Fowls, scratch together a loose heap of leaves, earth, and other rubbish, lay their eggs in the midst of it, cover them, and leave them to hatch by the even but not excessive warmth of the mass.   A recent careful account of this process in captivity appeared in the *Ibis*.   Eventually the young hatch and either make their way out or are said to be unearthed by the male birds, who assume the care of this incubator. Several hens may lay their eggs in one of these heaps, and it is recorded that a very large mound was near 150 feet around. Here then is at least the method of the alligator and it certainly meets the requirements for a primitive one among birds. In any but a warm climate it would probably not work. It is said that the temperature within the mound reaches 90°–96° F. Among some of these Megapodes a different expedient is found: they dig a hole in warm sand, bury the egg, and leave it to hatch after the manner of turtles. It is most interesting to find the same habit in a bird related to the plovers, the Black-backed Courser of the river banks of North Africa, the bird that runs about among the dozing crocodiles and even picks food from between their jaws. This bird buries its eggs in the sand, and they hatch by its warmth. Such a method is available for eggs requiring a moderate warmth over a considerable period. It would not do for the more evolved species that hatch in shorter time at higher temperature. It may therefore be supposed that these methods, if not actually relics of an ancient habit now largely abandoned, are at least similar to those used by the primitive ancestors of our present-day birds. Traces of the same thing are perhaps the habit of grebes of covering their eggs with the damp weeds of their nest when they leave it for a longer or shorter time, and the similar habit of ducks in covering the eggs with the down of the nest lining on like occasions. Possibly the habit of some birds of bringing green leaves as part of the nest lining is a reminiscence from a stage when they hatched eggs by the aid of green and fermenting leaves.

It is difficult to see other earlier stages in the development of parental care among living birds, for most of them seem to have gone far beyond such primitive ways. Among the less-evolved species, including the various water-birds, there are, however, very primitive attempts at actual nests: many make no nest, but merely lay their one or two eggs on the bare ground and incubate them there. The penguins of the Antarctic gather pebbles into a mound for lack of anything else, and one species, the Emperor Penguin, living where there is even less promising nest material, actually holds the single egg on the backs of its feet and covers it with a loose fold of feathery skin. Here it hatches, and so is the baby carried.

Finn suggests that the desire to withdraw into a safe shelter during the period of incubation may be the next stage, and induces the bird to seek a cavity, a hollow tree, or a deserted burrow in the ground. From the last, it is not a long step to the clearing and enlarging of a cavity or burrow, and finally to the actual construction of a burrow; such steps as this are found for example among the Puffins and Pigeon Guillemots that enlarge or hollow out burrows, or seek deep clefts among or under rocks. Petrels do the same. Dr. R. C. Murphy has pointed out that among antarctic petrels, the large species nest *on* and the smaller *in* the ground, partly no doubt because the larger kinds are strong enough to defend their nests against each other and the marauding Robber Gulls, while the smaller kinds unless they sought shelter in burrows would be constantly in danger from these larger birds.

It seems reasonable to suppose that with most of the less-evolved types, birds in which the young are able to run about shortly after hatching, the important factor in the development of the nest-forming habit is safety to the parent during the long process of incubation. This is accomplished among many birds that nest on the ground, either by choosing inaccessible places such as ledges on island cliffs or by seeking a burrow or cavity. Among land-birds, the same result is often attained by the development of concealing patterns as in grouse, quail, woodcock, shore-birds, nighthawks, and others. There are of course birds whose size or habits preclude much concealment, as ostriches, albatrosses, cranes, swans. They must instead guard their nests from attack by themselves being aggressive. In all these species the nest construction is not elaborate, often there is none at all, or at most a few feathers and bits of rubbish brought from close at hand. Again, however, as in many ducks, a thick layer of down is made as incubation proceeds. This is plucked from the breast of the sitting bird, and Finn has suggested that it may be a relief to the parent as a counter irritant to the wear of the eggs against its breast, rather than a thoughtful provision for keeping them warm.

An extraordinary protective habit is that found in the horn-bill family of the tropics, in which the male bird actually plasters up the entrance to the nest cavity in a hollow tree, leaving only a hole for the protrusion of the female's beak, for while she is thus immolated he regularly feeds her.

The sandpipers and plovers as a group make a simple nest on the ground that may vary from a bare depression to a grass-lined hollow. There is, however, an exception to this rule in our Solitary Sandpiper and its near relative in the Old World, the Green Sandpiper, both of which utilize the old nests of other birds built in trees. Sometimes the Green Sandpiper will use a squirrel's nest, or a mossy tree-limb. This habit, though long known in the Old World bird, was not discovered in our Solitary Sandpiper till recent years. It is an exception to the rule and may have been a habit developed in comparatively late geological times. Yet it shows a desire not seen in the other water-birds considered, to nest in trees. It is this habit of tree-nesting, or at least of nesting above ground, that has become characteristic of most of the so-called "higher" groups of birds and in connection with the helpless state of their newly hatched young has perhaps been responsible for the extraordinary development of nest architecture.

We find a suggestion of the tree-nesting habit in several of the water-fowl, that come to it more or less from necessity where their ground nests are in danger from rising waters or ground-living mammals and reptiles. Thus the Brown Pelicans of Florida, when their nests have been destroyed by unusual tides, have occasionally taken to building rude nests in the mangroves. Herring Gulls sometimes build in trees on inland waters where the isolation of small islands is not available. Cormorants will usually build in trees in the tropics, making strong compact nests of twigs. Young cormorants, as well as young pelicans, are helpless at hatching, so that it would perhaps be expected that they should have some sort of nest to rest in during their earlier days, but gulls leave their nests very soon after they appear.

It is not until we come to the herons, storks, and pigeons that we leave the ways of the more primitive water-birds and come to those that regularly construct nests of some pretense in trees. It is true that herons often make nests on the ground in regions where trees are not available, and some of the pigeon family are ground-nesting, for we shall constantly find that in nearly every group of birds there will be exceptions to any general rule. Storks make very solid nests and the Hammerhead Stork of Africa, a small bird about the size of the Night Heron, makes a huge affair in the fork of a tree, resembling two bushels of twigs with an entrance at the side.

Excluding for the moment some groups of birds such as woodpeckers and barbets, that excavate nest-holes in dead trunks, and such groups as todies, kingfishers, and bee-birds, that nearly all dig holes in banks, the tree-nesting birds include most of the more progressive species, such as hawks, flycatchers, warblers, thrushes, starlings, and finch-like birds. No doubt in many cases some of these birds have gone astray in seeking other kinds of nest-sites. Thus among flycatchers, though the open nest is the usual type, as with Kingbird and Wood Peewee, there are the usual exceptions, for the Great-crest has taken to holes in trees and the Phœbe makes a mud foundation on ledges or under bridges near water. Among swallows there are those that nest in holes not of their own making, as the Tree Swallow, others that dig their burrows either in the face of a sand bank or in level ground, while the Cliff Swallow constructs a retort of clay pellets and lines it with feathers and soft grass. The Red-winged Blackbird belongs to a tree-nesting family—the Orioles and Grackles are its relatives,—and it is perhaps due to previous ages of tree-building that its nest among cattail flags is so firmly made. Among sparrows and tree-warblers there are many that have perhaps returned to ground-nesting in a similar way, as the Junco and White-throat among the former, the Ovenbird and Golden-wing among the latter.

Most interesting of all is the development of the social

NEST OF AFRICAN OSTRICH
Dr. Wm. Lord Smith, phot.

NESTING COLONY OF WEAVER FINCHES IN EAST AFRICA—THE NESTS
ARE SUSPENDED FROM THE TWIGS OF A THORN-TREE

instinct that brought about colonial and finally communal nesting.   Among the South American Black and Yellow Orioles or Cassiques, a single tree will often contain many of their long hanging nests, so closely placed as to be almost if not quite in contact.   The African weaver-finches have carried this farther.   Many species nest in colonies, hundreds of birds placing their hanging baskets along the tough branchlets of a single thorn tree.   In nesting time the constant jargon of their cries is an extraordinary sound. It can be imagined that continued crowding would bring the nests into contact so that entire branches would be covered, and we do actually find in South Africa a species that makes a vast tenement of nests in some thorn tree, with nesting compartments opening out on to little passages along which the birds move.   A species of parrot in Argentina has gone nearly as far, building great community nests, in which, however, each chamber is separate, and to which more are added till the mass weighs a quarter of a ton or more, and may eventually fall of its own weight.

Such in brief are some of the steps by which we may suppose that the more specialized birds with tree-living habits and helpless young seem to have been led to construct substantial nests for holding the eggs securely and affording a safe platform for the young during their first stage.   A recent very interesting review by Herrick (1911) of nest structures is suggestive of many further questions.   He specially emphasizes the idea that a first purpose of the bird in making a nest is with the desire of building a rampart about the eggs.   It seems to me further that the primitive incubator method is perhaps an original factor, and that tree-nesting habits have been largely responsible for the development of the more complex structures.

CHAPTER IX

SOME PARASITIC HABITS OF BIRDS

A PARASITE is usually defined as an organism (be it plant or animal) that gets its living at the expense of some other plant or animal, and is thereby saved the need for itself undertaking this labor. But there are many degrees of parasitism, ranging from mere highway robbery to actual extermination of the host species. Many birds play the highwayman in varying degree. I have seen Herring Gulls close in behind a fish-laden Osprey and, by their mere inquisitive presence and eager feints at his booty, finally make him drop his fish and hurry away. The gulls circled over the spot where the fish struck the water, but evidently lost their plunder. On the Pacific coast, Finley tells of watching Brown Pelicans fishing at Santa Monica. The birds had been attracted by a school of small fish, among which they dove, coming to the surface with their catch. "A bevy of twenty gulls were fluttering around to pounce on every pelican that dove. The instant one dropped and came up with fish he was surrounded by the gulls, each scrambling to get a nose in the pelican's fish bag." Another observer, Gifford, has seen Noddy Terns fluttering excitedly about a pelican while it was fishing, and often sitting on the long-suffering bird's head while it swallowed the fish. He adds that the solemn pelicans never seemed to be annoyed, nor did he ever see the Noddies get any fish. Even the Laughing Gulls, I am told, will sometimes so harry terns coming in with fish for their young that relatively few may pass the gauntlet and reach their nests without being forced to drop their loads for the benefit of the gulls instead of their own young.   This condition, however, must be unusual, though it has been observed in the breeding colonies of these birds at Muskeget Island.   The Bald Eagle, too, is often a buccaneer.   Its love for fish frequently prompts it to pursue a Fish Hawk after a successful dive, and when the latter at length drops its prey, the eagle darts like an arrow after the falling fish and seizes it before it reaches the water. The eagle, however, can catch its own fish and will feed on dead fish washed up on the shore.   It is not difficult to imagine that from an occasional practice such robbery would become an established habit, until, as in case of the Jaegers or Robber Gulls, it is a characteristic trait of the bird.

In the tropics the forked-tailed Man-o'-War Bird is well known for its piratical habits.   For although it can and does fish much for itself, darting down to the water to pick something from the surface, or even snapping up a flying-fish in mid-air, it is nevertheless a constant tormentor of the species of gannets with which it is associated in the warmer parts of the globe.   W. Alanson Bryan recounts a visit to Marcus Island where a nesting colony of the common Brown Booby was the center of attraction for numbers of Man-o'-War Birds.   These were usually to be seen sitting watchfully on the tops of trees or patrolling the air high overhead awaiting the return of the boobies from the fishing.   Presently one or more would come in, bringing fish for their young.   At once a half-a-dozen of the Man-o'-War Birds would leave their ambush, under full sail to engage the returning fisher.   "Swooping down upon it from every side, buffeting it with their wings, snapping at it with their long hooked beaks, flying now above, now before, now below it," the menacing pirates so confused their victim that it let drop its fish which then the robbers would swoop upon, one of them catching it and carrying it off ere it could reach the water.   Just how many young boobies starve to death as a result of the Man-o'-War Birds' robbery has not been definitely estimated, but no doubt an appreciable burden is laid upon them.   Nor does this winged privateer hesitate to turn cannibal, for it has been seen to snatch up and fly away with a nestling of its own species whose parent had been frightened off the nest.

This habit of preying upon the helpless young while the parents are temporarily off guard is mentioned by explorers in case of the big Antarctic Skua, a relative of the Jaegers or Robber Gulls.   In South Polar lands these birds harry the penguin colonies, devouring eggs or chicks that are momentarily left unwatched.   So great is the menace from these powerful birds that the penguins (Adélie Penguins) have developed an interesting habit to foil them.   For the amount of food needed by the growing young of a colony is large and requires the efforts of a large part of the adults for its supply.   Consequently a communal method has been evolved, whereby the young birds are herded into little groups of from 20–30 each, protected by a few old birds who stand guard against the skuas while the other parents are engaged in fishing for the younger population.   The voracious habits of the skuas seem also to react upon themselves, for Wilson says that although two chicks are always hatched, not more than one of them is ever reared, because one of the pair is almost sure to be gobbled up by some other skua nesting near.   This must be an unusual condition and serves to emphasize the keen competition for animal food in these inhospitable regions.   It is interesting to see that in nearly all these cases in which adult birds of one species rob others of food, the "bone of contention" is fish.

Among vegetable feeders, however, some of the ducks so frequently appropriate part of the water weeds brought up by diving Coots as to have earned for themselves the common name of Pochard.   It seems probable, however, from a study of the stomach contents that the duck is more interested in the seeds while the Coot is especially fond of the succulent roots and stalks so that there is seldom any antagonism displayed.

Another way in which one species of bird becomes parasitic upon another is in the matter of using the nest of some second species.   Not infrequently an old squirrel's or crow's nest is fitted over by an owl for her own use, or the first-comers to a desirable nesting site may be driven out and their home appropriated by a more aggressive species; but actual parasitism hardly obtains until we come to cases in which one species lays its eggs in the nest of a second and leaves them to be hatched and the young cared for by the foster parent.   This habit has been independently acquired in several groups of birds particularly by some of the cuckoos and some cowbirds.   In a slight degree we find it among ducks also.   Where many ducks are nesting in the same marsh, the females seem to become somewhat careless in depositing their eggs, and often lay in each other's nests. It is common to find a single nest containing more eggs than one bird usually lays; as if two ducks of the same species had deposited their eggs in a common nest.   Many such instances are noted by Dr. J. C. Phillips in his work on this group.   Thus with Mallard in which ten eggs is an average set, as many as 18 have been found in a nest, and the same is true of the Green-winged Teal and others.   Bent records finding eggs of the Mallard in nests of Canvasbacks and Redheads.   Nests containing eggs of both Mallard and Teal are also recorded.   The Redhead is notoriously careless in this respect.   Bent records finding its eggs in nests of Ruddy Duck and Canvasback, in one case the latter species incubating the combined batch.   He adds also that both Redhead and Canvasback seem to have the peculiar habit of building nests in which both species deposit eggs but do not incubate them.   One such nest found in Saskatchewan contained 19 eggs apparently belonging to Redhead, Canvasback, and Mallard.   Another found in California contained no less than 27 eggs (2¼ dozen!), 17 of one type and 10 of another.   The Lesser Scaup Duck sometimes lays a few eggs in nests of other ducks.   Thus Bent found an egg of this species in a Gadwall's nest and another in the nest of a White-winged Scoter.   It is noteworthy that all these are marsh-nesting ducks, and we may suppose that the birds either are forced to deposit their eggs when at a distance from their own nests, or that the chance sight of a nest of eggs of some other bird acts as a stimulus to cause the newcomer to settle upon them and add to the set.   It is unfortunate that the subsequent history of these nestfuls of eggs has not been followed, to see if more than one female bird takes part in bringing up the mixed brood.

In the case of species that nest in tree cavities, the scarcity of suitable nesting sites frequently induces competition. Thus in localities where the Hooded Merganser and the Golden-eye Duck occur together, their hole-nesting habits often result in two females trying to use the same cavity.

The Wood Duck likewise comes into competition with these species. One writer mentions finding in a single desirable hole no less than 30 eggs of the Wood Duck and five of the Merganser. The hollow of the tree was not very large and the eggs were several layers deep!

It must be said, however, that none of these cases quite fulfils the conditions of parasitism, for each species commonly makes its own nest and rears its own brood. Yet there seem to be degrees of frequency with which the different ones lay in other ducks' nests, the Redhead being perhaps the worst offender. It is easy to see, however, that among hole-nesting species, when proper nest sites were few and birds more common, a parasitic habit might be developed simply through one species being prevented from regularly occupying a chosen cavity.

There is a South American duck, however, in which a state of actual parasitism seems to have been attained. This is the Black-headed Duck (*Heteronetta*), a species found in the marshy parts of southern South America but one that appears to be nowhere common, or at any rate very little is positively known about it. A recent writer, however, has published some notes on its habits in Argentina which confirm previous suppositions that this duck commonly lays its eggs in the nests of other marsh-nesting birds, including the Rosy-billed Duck, the Limpkin, the Coscoroba, Gull, Coot, Ibis, a large Rail, the Spur-winged Screamer, and even a species of Kite (*Milvus*). It is difficult to imagine how the young ducklings are cared for by such foster parents, but perhaps they are able from the first to fend for themselves. Possibly, too, the apparent scarcity of the species may have some relation to the parasitic habit and the precariousness of this mode of labor-saving.

Among land birds the habit of laying eggs in other birds' nests and leaving them to the care of strange parents, has been independently developed in several unrelated groups.

In the Icteridæ, the family to which our orioles and blackbirds belong, parasitism is well known in our common cowbird, as well as in some of the South American species. Our species lays its eggs in the nests of other, usually smaller, birds, apparently only one in any particular nest, though some of the cases in which two or three eggs have been found in a nest may be the laying of a single bird, perhaps, however, of more. The young cowbird on hatching speedily outstrips and generally crowds out his nest-mates and alone survives, a provision perhaps made necessary by his larger size and consequent need for more food and space than the rightful young. By ruthlessly eliminating competition he is thus able to usurp the entire efforts of the foster parents and so profits by a more plentiful food supply and speedier growth to maturity. It is strange that so little is accurately known of the methods whereby the female cowbird finds the nests of her dupes and imposes her own egg. And our ignorance of the way by which the grown young regains the parent flock is equally great. Hudson records that the young of a South American cowbird seemed quite indifferent to the warning calls of its foster parents, that would at once have caused their own young to crouch motionless in the nest. Even after the young cowbird has left the nest, it is still, he says, stupidly tame, and more than once has he seen one carried off from its conspicuous perch by a hawk when it might have escaped had it heeded the warning of its foster parents.

Hudson is the authority usually quoted in regard to the cowbirds of the Argentine Republic. The Bay-winged

A THREE-STORIED YELLOW WARBLER'S NEST PARASITIZED BY
COWBIRD
Courtesy of Charles Macnamara, phot.

Cowbird (*Molothrus badius*) is said to be victimized by another species, the Screaming Cowbird, for the Bay-winged makes its own nest and performs its parental duties in a proper manner. A third species is again parasitic. Apparently the males far outnumber the females, although Azara's statement that it is 10 to 1 may well be doubted. Nevertheless, this may have a bearing on the origin of the habit. Hudson found that the South American cowbirds would place eggs in old forsaken nests or even in old nests he put up in trees for the purpose, showing a lack of discrimination not found apparently in the European Cuckoo. He believes further that the same female will lay several eggs in the same nest, and he has known several cowbirds to lay in a single nest so that incubation was impossible for the very number of the eggs. Thus in ten nests of the Scissor-tail Flycatcher, with a total of 47 eggs, only 12 were the flycatchers', but 35 were cowbirds'. So frequently is this species parasitized that it is believed a large percentage of flycatcher nests are abandoned as a result of the confusion caused by the cowbirds. Moreover, it is said by Hudson that both male and female cowbirds destroy many of the eggs in the nests they visit, by breaking or devouring them.

In this same family (Icteridæ), parasitic habits have been developed in one of the South American orioles known as Hang-nests (*Cassidix*). According to Goeldi, one species in eastern Brazil (*C. oryzivorus*) places its egg in the nest of another Hang-nest of the same genus (*C. persicus*), while farther south, at Rio Janeiro, it is even known to victimize other related orioles of nearly its own size, as *Ostinops* and *Cassicus*.

In Africa is found the peculiar family of honey guides

that haunt the neighborhood of wild-bee trees and appear to lead people to these for the purpose of claiming their share of comb and larvæ. Most of the species are inconspicuous dull green with whitish breasts, and seem to be nearly all of them parasitic, although much is yet to be learned about them. Sparrmann's Honey Guide of South Africa has been seen to leave the nest of a White-throated Swallow, which on examination was found to contain two small white eggs of the swallow and a third larger oval one, presumably of the honey guide. A second species, the Yellow-throated Honey Guide of South Africa, is known to lay its eggs in the nests of the Black-collared Barbet, and of the Drongo, a black flycatcher. Stark and Sclater relate an instance of a honey guide of this species being pursued by a pair of Drongos in whose nest close at hand were seen three eggs of the Drongo and the nearly transparent one of the honey guide. Still a third species, the Lesser Honey Guide, has also been shown to be parasitic. Layard states that its eggs have been found in nests of the Olive Woodpecker and of the Pied Barbet; and it is said that two other species of barbets are also thus victimized, all therefore hole-nesting species. Stark and Sclater relate an incident in which the honey guide was at least partially frustrated. The bird had flown to the nest-hole of a barbet, but was opposed by the male, whose efforts were presently seconded by the female's with such effect that the impostor was hustled out and chased away by the female barbet, chattering and fighting the while. In about five minutes the honey guide reappeared, however, and the same scene was enacted. This continued for upwards of an hour when all three birds were shot. The honey guide was found to have an egg ready to be laid, indeed actually protruding

SECTION OF THE THREE-STORIED YELLOW WARBLER'S NEST SHOWING
A COWBIRD'S EGG BURIED IN EACH OF THE TWO LOWER STORIES
Courtesy of Charles Macnamara, phot.

from the vent, while the barbets' nest contained two fresh eggs. In another case a pair of the same species of barbet was found feeding a young Lesser Honey Guide nearly full-fledged in a similar nest-hole of which he was the sole occupant, having no doubt eliminated the rightful young.

It is noteworthy that the eggs of these honey guides are white and those of the birds mentioned as parasitized by them are also white, while, as we shall see, with the cuckoos the eggs are speckled as are those also of its host species. That is, the eggs of the intruder bear a general resemblance to those of its host, though whether this is enough to deceive the latter we cannot tell.

It is among the cuckoos of the Old World, that the parasitic habit is best known, and here it is found in several of the species. Apparently the American cuckoos have not developed the trait to any extent, though there are occasional instances wherein a cuckoo's egg has been found in an open nest of some other species. In the Philippines lives a cuckoo called the Koel (*Eudynamis*) which is parasitic upon a large Starling known as the Myna (*Eulabes*). Sharpe points out that in this cuckoo, contrary to the usual rule, the young bird in its juvenal plumage is not colored like the adult female (that is, black above and streaked or barred below) but is entirely black like the *adult* male of its species and in this stage is therefore colored like the black Mynas, its foster parents. Sharpe believes that this similarity helps it the more easily to pass as the young of the Myna by which it is thus reared. The true cuckoos of the genus *Cuculus* seem to be generally parasitic, and are widely distributed in the Old World. A South African species (*Cuculus gularis*) is parasitic as also the Red-chested and the Black Cuckoo. The last species is known to place its eggs in nests of the Wren-warbler (*Prinea*) but since the nest of this species is very small and domed over, it is apparently a physical impossibility for the cuckoo to lay its egg in the nest.   It is therefore believed that she lays it on the ground and then carries it in her bill to the nest selected.   Some of the African Golden Cuckoos (of genus *Chrysococcyx*) are also parasitic and apparently remove an egg from a nest to replace it with one of their own. One of these birds, Klaas's Cuckoo, is known to have laid in a kingfisher's nest, and another in a woodpecker's hole. A second species that frequently parasitizes small birds has actually been twice shot in the act of carrying its own egg in its bill to place in the nest of the host species.   A third genus of cuckoos (*Coccystes*), larger birds about 14 inches long, has at least four species in South Africa, all of which are parasitic, some on the shrikes, while two Indian species parasitize Babbling Thrushes, laying blue eggs like those of these latter.   The Spurred Cuckoos (*Centropus*), however, all make their own nests.

The European Cuckoo—the Cuckoo of the poets and of childhood tales—is most famed and has been most carefully studied.   The eggs of this bird are deposited in the nests of a number of species of which, however, the Meadow Pipit, Hedge Sparrow, and Pied Wagtail are among the most frequent.   It is believed that individual Cuckoos habitually lay their eggs in the nests of a particular species, and that their offspring in turn parasitize the same species that were their foster parents.   Thus a certain Cuckoo may lay its eggs in nests of the Hedge Sparrow and its young later, from constant association with Hedge Sparrows in youth, may in its turn lay eggs in nests of this species. Sharpe even records a case of a young Cuckoo that was kept alive through the winter in the Zoölogical Gardens at London, and by the following spring was to all intents an adult bird.   At that time a number of British species were introduced, including a Hedge Sparrow when at once the Cuckoo, "which had lived for months in the Gardens, and was perfectly able to feed itself, fluttered down to the little Hedge Sparrow, and began with open mouth to clamour to be fed." It seemed as if this Cuckoo must have been reared by Hedge Sparrows and had recognized the foster species, an interesting case of memory.   The eggs of the Cuckoo are relatively small for the size of the bird so that they are not greatly out of proportion when placed with those of the smaller victims.   They vary greatly in color and apparently each individual Cuckoo lays a more or less identical style of egg, so that the eggs of a single bird are more or less the same in pattern of markings or in ground color. A careful study, "The Cuckoo's Secret," recently made by a British ornithologist, Edgar Chance, has confirmed and extended many previous observations on this bird.   Chance kept watch of a certain area where several pairs of Meadow Pipits bred, a species commonly parasitized by the Cuckoo in his neighborhood.   His method was to discover all the nests of the Pipit in this area and from blinds or in other ways make continuous observations on these and on the Cuckoo that frequented the meadow.   He found by patient watching that a female Cuckoo would control so far as possible a given area, keeping out other females.   Such a bird he called a dominant Cuckoo, for in some instances there were Cuckoos that seemed to have less nearly complete control over their chosen meadow.   Such Cuckoos have favorite perches from which they can command a view over their domain, and actually spend much time watching the nest-building operations of their intended victims. In this way the Cuckoo discovers the situation of the nests some time in advance of their readiness, and even flies down from time to time to examine or to locate them more exactly. Chance believes that this watching of her dupes in the nest-building process acts as a stimulus to ovulation so that the egg is ready for laying some five or six days afterward, an assumption that seems certainly very probable. It also incites the Cuckoo to a feeling of proprietorship that results in her driving off other Cuckoos from the territory. He further believes that the number of eggs laid by a single Cuckoo depends in part upon the number of such nests available within the preëmpted territory and may be even as many as 21 in a season. There is thus a certain synchronism established between the time when the nest of the victim is to be ready and the time when the egg of the Cuckoo is to be laid. Any upsetting of this relation, as for example if the completion of the victim's nest is delayed or stopped, results in the egg being ready for deposition too soon, so that in such emergency cases it is laid in some other nest ready at hand. Chance believes that this accounts for the laying of an occasional egg in a nest other than that of the usual host. That Cuckoos may even be "fooled" seems occasionally to be shown, for if the intended nest be exceptionally well concealed and difficult to find the Cuckoo may even lay in a dummy nest placed conveniently near. Having located the nests of her intended victims, the female Cuckoo by occasional visits discovers when they are completed and the fresh eggs laid. When all is ready she leaves her observation post, glides softly to the nest, removes one of the eggs in her bill and lays one of her own, presently flying away again. The entire process is short, and occupies but a few seconds.   A photograph was taken showing the adult Cuckoo laying her egg in a Meadow Pipit's nest, while at the same time holding in her bill an egg of the Pipit's that she had removed to make place for her own.   This seems to be the general habit of the bird, but instances are given in which this instinct had apparently become exaggerated and *two* eggs of the host species were removed.

It is well known that the streaking or marking on a Cuckoo's egg is variable but with a given bird the eggs are fairly true to a type and have thus an individuality.   This fact was in many cases demonstrated by Mr. Chance in his study of the various layings of the same individual Cuckoo. That the general similarity in pattern of the Cuckoo's egg to that of her victim's may have a bearing on the choice of species parasitized has been further suggested.   Chance quotes the observations of Swynnerton who made a number of experiments in interchanging and substituting eggs of several species breeding in South Africa.   Some birds showed a decided ability to detect the fraudulent eggs, while others seemed quite indifferent, and accepted nearly any substitute.   Chance suggests that a possible explanation may be seen here of the fact that Cuckoos are mainly parasitic upon certain species "for the less discrimination and resentment shown by the dupes, the greater is the chance of the young Cuckoo being hatched and reared" by the foster parents.

Among the many interesting notes by this observer is an account of the courtship actions of a pair of Cuckoos, the male pursuing the newly arrived female, and calling all the while.   The interesting point was that the female was carrying a twig or straw about six inches long, which she held for over a minute during this performance.   This act of picking up nesting material is a common one in the courting actions of many species that build nests and may thus be reminiscent of the time when Cuckoos built their own nests.

The origin of the parasitic habit may long be obscure. Several facts, however, seem to point suggestively to possible ways of origin. Thus among the cases mentioned, it will be recalled that many of the ducks occasionally lay from one to several eggs in the nest of another species, or two of the same species will frequently lay in the same nest. In case of the honey guides, the eggs are laid in nests of hole-nesting species, as woodpeckers and barbets, which have white eggs like those of the parasitic species. Of two species of cowbird in South America, one is frequently parasitic on the other or lays in nests of other birds that have, like itself, a dotted egg. The smaller of two Hang-nests lays in nests of a larger Hang-nest. There is thus in these cases a certain closeness of relationship between the parasitic bird and some at least of its victims; and thus a certain resemblance between their eggs as well as in the style of nest both originally constructed. Now in birds it is well known that in certain species ovulation and egg-laying may be induced by proper stimulus. Thus Craig found that Doves could be induced to lay eggs in response to several methods of stimulation; in one case a young female reared in isolation, who knew only human companions, responded in the typical way to constant caressing of her head and neck and laid an egg at the usual interval from the beginning of the experiment. Hens are very different in their method of laying. With them egg-laying comes at a definite time of year and, as with such birds as the Flicker, the presence of a nest-egg seems to encourage them to keep on laying as if to attain a number whose contact stimulus would satisfy the brooding instinct. It may be that in case of those ducks whose eggs seem so often to be laid promiscuously in nests of their neighbors, the mere sight of a nest with eggs resembling their own may act as a stimulus inducing them to add to the number. The same suggestion may explain the occasional laying of an egg in the nest of a different species, as recorded of various birds; and from such habits parasitism may possibly have arisen. The case of the Cuckoos seems different, for their victims are not near relatives of theirs. Herrick has suggested that the habit may have started from a lack of "attunement of egg-laying to nest-building" such that the eggs were ready for laying before a nest was ready for their reception. The fact that the habit is found in so many species of cuckoo seems to prove that it is a trait of ancient origin, so ancient that it had become characteristic of the genus *Cuculus* before the various species of the genus had been marked off from their parent stock. With the cowbirds, however, the trait is not quite so fixed, for there are some species that still make their own nests. Should these become exterminated in years to come and the parasitic species be preserved, we should have a case similar to that of the Cuckoo in that the remaining species into which the stock has now developed all have this habit.

Still another possible way in which we may imagine the parasitic habit to have started is shown by the peculiar nesting habit of two of the sandpipers. The first is a European species, a frequenter of fresh water, known as the Green Sandpiper (*Totanus ochropus*). This bird has the remarkable trait of laying in the abandoned nests of other birds, usually of the European Blackbird and the Missel Thrush. Their nests are found near the shores of ponds in trees sometimes as high as 35 feet from the ground. Hintz, who found many such nests in Germany, seems to have been the first to publish much about this singular habit. He records one case where he found eggs of the sandpiper in a Missel Thrush's nest from which the young thrushes had flown but six days before. Sometimes the same nest is used in two successive years. This writer has also found the Green Sandpiper nesting in old half-ruined nests of Jays, Wood Pigeons, or even on a squirrel's nest. The young as soon as hatched jump to the ground and flutter down without harm. Cases are recorded by Dresser of seven and of eight eggs in such a nest, instead of the usual four, probably the combined effort of two birds, and indicating a scarcity of desirable second-hand nests. In this country a similar habit is found in case of the Solitary Sandpiper whose method of nesting was till recent years unknown and its nesting place a mystery until the discovery of its eggs in an abandoned Robin's (?) nest in Canada. Since then, this bird has been found nesting in Alberta and elsewhere in abandoned nests of the previous year. It seems to evince no special choice of nest, using those of Bronzed Grackle, Brewer's Blackbird, Cedar Waxwing, Kingbird, Robin, Canada Jay, in situations up to 200 yards from water. A dearth of nesting birds noted one season in Alberta may have resulted in a dearth of sandpipers through a lack of sufficient abandoned nests for their use. In one case a Robin's nest of the year before had not been fitted over in any way, but eggs were deposited on the original mud lining.

If we suppose the acquirement of a similar habit in such

a species as the Cowbird, it is easy to imagine that the bird might not discriminate between a newly completed nest and one recently abandoned. The result would be that if the intruder laid in the new nest, its rightful owners would resent the intrusion and prevent the repetition of the act, even though they had themselves to bring up the unwelcome addition. It is likely, too, that the greater abundance of new than of deserted nests would favor the frequency of such mistakes until the parasitic habit would have become established.

One must therefore be prepared to find that this habit has been acquired in more than one way, and independently in these different groups mentioned.

CHAPTER X

THE SENSES AND BEHAVIOR OF BIRDS

It is a failing perhaps not peculiar to the human race, to think of ourselves as a center about which the rest of the universe revolves, and to impute our own feelings and desires to other animals that differ greatly from us. It is only in very recent times that we have gradually learned to take a different view of the matter. In our observation of the habits of birds we must therefore be cautious in assuming that they will act just as we would under given circumstances, and in our interpretation of their actions we must ever be on our guard against substituting our own minds for theirs. So it becomes necessary to test as we may the senses and mind-working of birds in order the better to understand how they are affected by the impressions they receive from without and how they respond to these stimuli. The study of bird behavior is a wide and fascinating field. Each species and individual proves to have its characteristic traits, and there is much yet to be learned by careful and critical observation of individual birds. To do this in the natural state, there must be some way of identifying the particular bird, and this difficulty is met by marking them with the numbered bands now so familiar.

In studying the senses of birds great difficulty is met in eliminating possible sources of error. There are always so many other things that might affect the result that we

CINEREOUS VULTURE *(Aegypius monachus)*, A KEEN-SIGHTED
SCAVENGER
Courtesy of National Zoölogical Park

cannot always be sure of our interpretations. This is why tests in the laboratory where the conditions can be controlled are usually necessary as collateral aids. Hitherto comparatively few species of birds have been studied under laboratory conditions, for even tame birds seldom lose their instinctive quick response to unusual sounds or movements or surroundings, so that we are not always sure that their actions are deliberate and normal.

Sight.—The eyesight of several species of birds has been somewhat tested in the laboratory. From field observations we receive the impression that in most day-birds sight is fairly keen. The height at which hawks, eagles, and vultures quarter the ground in their search for food is apparently to be interpreted as a proof that they can *see* as well as *distinguish* small objects at considerable distances. Yet there is doubtless great variation among different birds in the keenness of their vision. For example, some of us may have had the experience of sitting motionless by a river bank and allowing a company of American Mergansers to pass a few feet distant without taking notice as they swim along, feeding as they go. A Black Duck, however, is of so much more discriminating vision that he would veer off long before reaching gun-shot range.

Birds' eyes are somewhat different from our own. In most species they are quite at the sides of the head so that instead of looking forward in the same way that the head points, birds often "cock their heads," as we say, in order to bring one eye particularly to bear on something they wish to scrutinize. In our own eyes there is a place on the retina or sensitive surface where the focus is sharpest, called the "yellow spot" on account of its distinctive color. In many birds it is found that there are *two* yellow spots, that is, one of the spots is at the best focus for seeing at the side with one eye, while the other is at the best focus for seeing with both eyes something directly ahead.   The side position of the eyes gives command of at least three-fourths of a circle, instead of half a circle or thereabouts, as in ourselves.   Moreover, the eyes of birds are relatively nearer the top of the head, so that they can see above them to better advantage than most mammals.   Dr. J. C. Phillips has recorded in his observations of tame Canada Geese that he believes they have very far and keen sight.   For he has often, while concealed in a blind near tame decoys, seen them cast an eye aloft and call out to a flock of wild geese passing high overhead that no human eye would have noticed save by the merest chance.   In the Woodcock the eye is so large and placed so high that it seems as if the bird must easily be able to look behind as well as ahead.   Probably the large size of the eye is an adaptation for dusk- or night-feeding.

On account of the speed of flying birds their eyes must have power to adjust their focus quickly, so that we find in birds that there is a special muscle for changing the shape of the lens of the eye by its pull, thus at the same time changing the focus.   There is a peculiar structure in the interior of the eye, called the *pecten* from its comb-like or folded shape, which helps to increase the blood supply of the eye.   A similar structure is found in a few reptiles, thus emphasizing once more the close relation between birds and reptiles.

A few species of birds have been tested to see if they can discriminate the different colors of the spectrum visible to human eyes, and, as may be imagined, the matter is one difficult of convincing proof.   One recent investigator,

Hess, using the Domestic Fowl, scattered white rice grains on a black-matt background in a dark room and then illuminated the area with light through a prism so that the food was covered by broad bands of the rainbow colors: red, orange, yellow, green, blue, indigo, violet. A hungry hen, brought in from the light (light-adapted, as the psychologist calls it), was then placed before this meal, and at once started picking up the rice grains. Curiously, it was found that each time it would begin picking from the orange through the red areas, then coming back, it would start in the yellow light, and pick the rice grains through to the limit of green, but never in the blue, indigo, and violet, which seemed to act as dark or blind areas. When the same experiment was tried with hens that had been kept in the dark just previously ("dark-adapted"), they acted much the same, except that they began pecking in the orange-yellow instead of orange, then came back and pecked a little farther into the blue-green, but never into the blue. Pigeons used in similar experiments behaved in the same way. Hess concluded that for day-birds as exemplified by these two species, the spectrum was shortened at the violet end. Yet he might have concluded as well that birds do not recognize blue rice as good to eat. A more recent investigator, Watson (1915), has repeated the work and carried it farther, but finds that the Fowl *is* sensitive to the full set of spectrum colors, though there are perhaps certain differences in comparison with our own eyes. Nevertheless, he concludes, it appears safe to assume that day-birds *do* see colors in about the same way that we do, which, after all, is a comforting thought, for in observing mammals we have to keep in mind that some may be color blind.

We see therefore that care must be used in making deductions from what seem perfectly obvious premises.

The sensitiveness of birds to light-intensity would seem from field observation to be very keen, but laboratory proof of this is difficult. I have supposed that it was a factor of this sort that caused birds to wake in the morning, as by an alarm clock. While living in Boston one winter, I noticed that the House Sparrows, which roosted regularly in a vine near my window, began to awaken and start chirping at approximately 15 minutes before the sun rose. As the days grew longer, and the sun rose earlier, the Sparrows awoke correspondingly sooner, until as spring came, they were off and away before my own awaking time, which seems controlled by some quite different stimulus, though regular enough too. Those of us who have lived in summer near Whippoorwills have remarked upon the punctuality with which they begin their nightly serenades; cloudy nights have the effect of starting them somewhat earlier, as though their routine depended more or less closely upon the degree of light-intensity. The late Horace W. Wright published the results of very systematic observations on the time and relative order in which many of our commoner birds start to sing in the morning and cease at evening during the breeding season, from which it is clear that there is a considerable regularity in these times and that nearly every species has its characteristic place in the schedule. The matter is one of common knowledge, though its careful study is yet to be completed. The crowing of the Chanticleer is of such regularity in the morning that people who live in or near the tropics, where sunrise does not greatly vary in time, make the cock-crowing equivalent to a rising bell.   You recall the lines from Omar the Tentmaker:

> And, as the cock crew, those who stood before
> The Tavern shouted—"Open then the Door!
> You know how little while we have to stay,
> And, once departed, may return no more."

Experiments made with small chicks, however, in an attempt to see if, other factors being equal, they could learn to discriminate between two lights of different intensity, seem rather negative, and it was not until one light was made ten times as bright as the other that they seemed to notice a difference.   Very likely there are other factors of a mental nature involved.

Our familiar Robin seems to be one of the earliest of the common birds to rise and sing in the mornings, but whether it is the change in the intensity of light with the approach of day, or whether other matters of habit are involved, we are as yet unable to say.   That the "pale gray light of dawn" may affect Robins so that they are prompted to sing, seems likely, and we have often noticed that in daytime hours during the breeding season, the sudden clouding of the sky with an approaching shower is enough to start a burst of melody.   So apparent is this that in the country it is considered a sign of rain when the Robins carol "More wet, cheer up."   There is room for a good deal of accurate observation, using a photographer's machine for testing light-intensity by exposing a strip of sensitized paper, to see what apparent effect the coming daylight has as a stimulus to song.   It is likely that other factors of habit are intimately connected with the awakening actions, and that much difference will be found among different species of birds.

The ability of animals to discriminate details seems to vary very much. Dogs are found to be very deficient in their ability to distinguish between various shapes. Monkeys, however, are much more clever, and so are even chicks.

Some work carried on with tame Crows, and partly published (Coburn, 1914) showed that they learned very quickly to distinguish the correct exit door when placed in a dark box from which there were translucent and lighted exits, each of the same area and light-intensity, but of different shapes. In this way it was shown that they distinguished with very little practice between a circle, a triangle, a square, and a hexagon. In this and in other tests, the experimenters were convinced that the Crow's reputation for brains is quite deserved, and that Henry Ward Beecher was correct when he said that if men could be feathered and provided with wings, very few would be clever enough to be Crows!

A recent writer (Lewis: Emu, vol. 15, p. 217) considers some birds to have a sharpness of vision 100 times greater than that of human beings, as is attested by various cases, such as that of the Sparrowhawk which spies out and catches small beetles though hovering 200 feet from the ground above them. Meinertzhagen tells of watching swifts feed about a mountain summit, and though their turns and twists seemed to denote an abundance of food, he himself could not see the flying insects. On shooting a swift, however, he found that they were feeding on minute beetles about as large as a pin's head. Imagine the power of sight, if such it be, that enables them to pick out these insects while traveling at 80 miles an hour.

A suggestive note by Dr. J. Grinnell (1921) on what he calls the "principle of rapid peering," may explain in part the quick active method of searching for small prey in the twigs of trees, as employed by warblers, kinglets, and others. For just as we, when standing still, see more clearly the movement of an object, so conversely the bird more readily detects the motionless insect or egg cluster by rapidly changing the angle of sight, as by moving its head from side to side or hopping quickly from one twig to another to scan a leaf surface. Kinglets for the same purpose often hover momentarily before a cluster of leaves. These movements serve to bring the small object into better relief so that it may be perceived by the eye if the level of sight be constantly changed, on the same principle that if an object is dropped on a mixed carpet it is easier to see it if we stoop down so that the eye is nearly at the floor level, —"looking Indian-fashion," as we used to call it. Grinnell, therefore, divides birds that seek living prey into those that sit passively waiting to see it moving by, and those that actively move about and perceive still objects by their own frequent change of attitude.

Hearing.—The hearing of birds is probably next to sight the most important sense to them and appears to be very keen. The ears of birds differ from those of mammals not only in having no outstanding portion for collecting sound, but also in the structure of the transmitting portion. In ourselves, for example, there is first, slightly inside the outer opening, the ear-drum, which vibrates to the waves of sound like a telephone diaphragm. This drum is slightly concave and connects with a series of three small bones, named from their shape in the human ear, the hammer, anvil, and stirrup.   The innermost of these covers a minute opening in the inner ear or *cochlea,* which is shaped somewhat like a snail-shell and is filled with a fluid.   The auditory nerve extends to this, and its inner wall is carpeted with a layer of sensory cells, each of which has a little filament projecting into the fluid.   The vibrations of sound are received by the ear-drum and transmitted by the chain of three little bones to the fluid of the snail-shell, where they are picked up by certain of these little filaments.   At the base of the spiral are the long filaments which vibrate to sounds of lower intensity, and at the summit are the shortest filaments corresponding to those of highest pitch.   Now in birds, the ear-drum is convex, like a plug in the tube of the outer ear, while instead of a chain of three bones there is a single rod-like bone, the *columella,* which acts like the dasher of a churn to transmit vibrations to the fluid of the snail-shell or inner ear so it may be that by this more direct form of transmission birds are able to hear sounds that we cannot.   There seem to have been rather few attempts at an accurate study of birds' hearing, though there are many recorded notes of interesting observations.

During the Great War, parrots kept in French fortresses and on the Eiffel Tower gave warning of the approach of aëroplanes that they could not possibly have seen, before they were discovered by human beings.   A recent authority on earthquakes, Dr. Charles Davison, in discussing the distances at which great explosions may be heard, brought out that pheasants during the War often showed evidence of being disturbed by air waves from explosions or naval battles which were not heard by human ears, and their be-

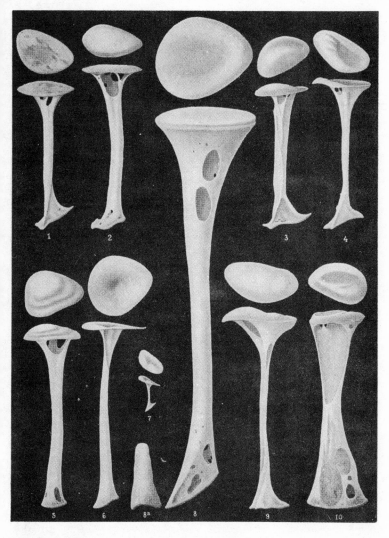

THE COLUMELLA OR SOUND-TRANSMITTING BONE OF THE BIRD'S EAR
(greatly enlarged)

1, 3, 4, Crows of three species; 2, 5, Hawks; 6, Capercaillie; 7, Least Sandpiper; 8, Bearded Vulture; 9, Raven; 10, White Stork.

After Krause

havior has helped to throw light upon the problem of the so-called "zones of silence" around great detonations, which after skipping these zones, again become audible. These inaudible sound waves were evidently perceived by the pheasants, for they acted as if greatly frightened. This action was noticed, for example, on January 24, 1915, during the naval battle on the Dogger Bank, when at a distance of 216 miles from the action, pheasants "shrieked themselves hoarse," as it was said, and smaller birds were terrified, though no sound was heard by persons present. In like manner birds reacted to the explosion of Zeppelin bombs, 80 miles away, which was beyond the range of human earshot. In some cases, people did hear cannonading 200 miles away. If this were heard on the *far* side of a silent zone, the pheasants were affected a little before persons heard it, as if the inaudible vibrations arrived first, but if it were on the *near* side, the audible waves arrived first. It is supposed that the inaudible sound waves travel across the silent zones close to the ground, while those that are heard farther on make a detour upward and so arrive later. It is also suggested that the inaudible waves are of long wave-length, and set up vibration in loose articles, so that the birds are frightened by the strange quivering of their perches or other things.

It is well known that geese, tree ducks, or peacocks are of acute hearing, and in case of alarms are often the first to give warning, which the watch-dogs then take from them, thus getting the credit rather than the birds! Few can have failed to notice the peculiar reaction of pigeons to loud sudden noises. On our Boston Common, where there seems little chance that the many pigeons can ever have been hunted or known the meaning of a gun-shot, an entire flock will spring into the air as one bird at the sudden *bang* of an automobile.

A special study of hearing in owls should be made. It is untrue that owls cannot see by day, for they are often given to basking in sunshine and are quite as able to see as other birds. But it seems likely that in their nightly prowlings they hunt in part by hearing. At least their structure points that way. Not only are their feathers so softened as to muffle every sound made by the bird itself in flight lest it should not hear other noises but the ears of many owls have some very strange peculiarities that suggest special uses; but concerning these, good field observations alone may perhaps inform us. In the Brown Owl of Europe, allied to our Barred Owl, as well as in the Barn Owl, there is a curious flap of skin in front of the large ear opening by which the opening may be closed. When raised, however, this flap would greatly help to catch sounds. The peculiar feathers which cover birds' ears are much less dense than the usual plumage, and may be useful as sound catchers. In some owls the ear region of the skull is greatly enlarged, with a peculiar blind pocket outside the ear openings covered by the flap. This pocket, as Mr. Austin H. Clark has suggested to me, may act as a resonance chamber to intensify small sounds. More strange still, this pocket may be quite unsymmetrical on the opposite sides of the skull. Thus in Tengmalm's Owl of the Old World (like our Richardson's Owl) the blind pocket is *above* the ear opening on the right side, and *below* it on the left, causing a considerable distortion in the shape of the skull. Why this is, we do not know. May it be that it gives a means for locating more exactly the source of a sound? Or does the owl hear better on one side than on the other?   Here is a matter for more observation.   Perhaps too the curious peering motions of owls help to give more accurate sound location, just as the Eskimo test wind direction by turning their heads till the force is equal on both sides.

No doubt different species differ much in their sensitiveness to sound.   Close observations on breeding Hermit Thrushes (Hussey, 1917) seemed to indicate that sounds alone, such as loud whistles or taps from an observation tent but a few feet away, had little effect on the adult bird, but if accompanied by a slight visible motion as of a finger at the observation hole, the bird was at once alert.   Young Hermits up till ten days old were unaffected by loud noises close by, though they thereafter soon learned to associate certain sounds with feeding.

Smell.—There has been much conflicting testimony on the sense of smell in birds, in which apparently the evidence on the negative side is large.   Yet the organ of smell is well developed in some birds.   It consists of two lobes at the anterior part of the brain from each of which the so-called olfactory nerve extends to three small scroll-like projections known as turbinal bones on the bony wall within the beak.   In many mammals these bones are remarkably well developed.   They are covered with a sensitive membrane which receives the scent particles and the nerves transmit the stimulus to the brain, producing the sensation of smell.   In birds these bones are small, and sometimes but two are present, the one nearest the brain, often but a mere projection, being then lost.   In the flightless bird known as the Kiwi or *Apteryx* of New Zealand, the organ of scent is very well developed and the turbinal bones large. Turner, who studied the organs of smell in over forty

American birds, concluded that the more primitive birds, such as water birds, had these structures least reduced. They are smaller in marsh birds, and least of all in the more highly evolved groups, as sparrows.

A great many field observations have been made as to sense of smell in vultures, most of them, however, inconclusive. It will be instructive to review a few of these. Darwin in 1834 recounts his experiments with Condors in Chile. Several were tied by a rope in a row at the foot of a garden wall. Darwin then walked back and forth past these birds at three yards' distance, carrying in his hand a piece of meat wrapped up in white paper. The birds paid no attention to him, even when he threw it on the ground before them. At length with a stick he pushed it close till one of them touched the package with its beak. "The paper was then instantly torn off with fury, and at the same moment, every bird in the long row began struggling and flapping its wings." The trouble with this experiment is that Darwin does not state if the meat was wholly concealed, or if there were an opportunity for an odor to escape from the package; nor does he mention if there was a breeze to carry scent to or from the birds. Audubon tried a few experiments which, too, were inconclusive. (1) One was that of placing in a large field a well-dried deer skin, including the hoofs. It was stuffed with dry grass and provided with artificial eyes. The observer concealed himself not far off, and presently a vulture sailed down, tore open the hide and scattered the grass about. No doubt, however, the watchful bird had seen something going on from afar and merely came to investigate "on a chance." (2) A large hog was hauled to a ravine and covered with canes. In the warm weather it soon became very offensive, but though dogs found and fed on the carcase, the vultures failed to discover it.   (3) In another case a young pig was killed and its blood scattered about on the ground, while the body was hauled into a ravine and covered with leaves.   The vultures found the blood and followed it down the ravine to the carcase which they then found and devoured.

Bachman about the same time tried several experiments with similar negative results, in South Carolina: (1) A load of offal from a slaughterhouse was dumped on the ground at the foot of his garden, and a brush-covered frame raised above the pile at some 12 inches from the ground.   Though hundreds of vultures passed over it in the next 25 days, none noticed the meat.   (2) He then took a rough painting on canvas of a sheep skinned and cut open, and placed this upon the ground 15 feet from the pile.   The vultures observed it at once, walked over it and tugged at it with their beaks, yet never noticed the pile of offal.   (3) The most offensive parts of the offal were next placed on the ground, and covered by a thin cloth on which were placed a few pieces of fresh beef.   These last they ate but did not discover the offal underneath until a rent was made in the canvas, whereupon it was seen and eaten.   Here again we have no information as to air currents, and the final trial proves little, as the birds may have connected the scent of the offal with the sight of the fresh meat they had eaten, and so have searched no farther.

These bits of negative evidence seemed fairly conclusive, until of recent years the entire subject has been reopened.   Beebe, in 1909, tried the following experiment with Turkey Vultures and Black Vultures.   Three inverted boxes were placed on the ground in their cage and allowed to remain there so that the birds became used to them. Then after several days of fasting a piece of tainted meat was placed under the central box, and care was taken also to go through the farce of placing something under each of the three boxes, lest any visual hint be conveyed as to the location of the meat. The vultures watched intently but made no move to come to the ground; the keeper then re-entered and threw down a few small bits of meat, at which every vulture swooped to the ground and started to struggle for the morsels. Twice the Black Vultures walked close about the meat box without appearing to notice the odor, though it was clearly perceptible to persons outside the cage. Next a Turkey Vulture walked to the *lee* side of the box, then instantly turned and started to examine the box closely on all sides. He was soon joined by two others of the same species, all three standing close to the source of the odor. Two of the Black Vultures later came up, apparently from imitation, and for a long time all five stood close to the box, now and then going up to examine it carefully. Did this indicate that the Turkey Vulture smelled the meat and recognized the odor; and did it indicate that this vulture's sense of smell is better developed than that of the Black Vulture? Did the other vultures assemble because the first acted as if food were near? Unfortunately the experiment was not repeated nor were the conditions carefully controlled, so that we do not know what chance elements were present.

Another recent writer (Gurney, 1922) has gone at some length into the matter of scent in birds, marshaling an array of observations drawn from many sources. He considers most important a case related to him by a doctor of

repute in Jamaica, who, while making a post-mortem examination, found presently that the roof of the house was
studded with vultures, attracted, as he implies, by their
olfactory sense; while on another occasion, an old patient
of his at a distance having died, he found on arrival at the
house 36 hours later, that a number of vultures were
perched on the ridgepole and in the neighboring trees.
But he overlooks the possibility that there may have been
a dead pig in a neighboring yard.

Experiments carried out on the Kiwi or *Apteryx* in the
island bird-sanctuaries off the coast of New Zealand
seemed to indicate that this bird has a sense of smell. This
species is peculiar in having its nostrils at the tip of its
long bill, and strange to relate they open on its *under* surface. One species lives largely on earthworms, and a number of tests were made using this natural food. The experimenter used earthworms in the bottom of buckets,
covering them with four inches of earth and found the
bird much excited, probing eagerly for the worms, but
when he put down a bucket containing earth and no worms,
the birds would not even try it. On using a bucket of earth
that had been searched the preceding day, the bird again
disdained it, but on putting two worms at the bottom of the
earth and again presenting it, the bird promptly probed
for them "as if it knew they were there." All these experiments, though suggestive, are nevertheless too few and un-
certain to be conclusive, and tests made by Dr. R. M.
Strong on a captive *Apteryx* in the London Gardens were
negative.

Dr. Strong (1911) later devised an experimental chamber, square in shape with a small entrance door, and in the
middle of each side a small opening to a food chamber.

Carefully planned mechanism for controlling the air currents within the chamber allowed the scent to be drawn out from the food chamber toward the center of the larger box, and out through a hole in its roof. Tame Ring Doves were used for the experiment and at first trained to look for food without the use of any odor, so that they became quite used to looking at once in the food chamber, of which a different one would be used in each trial. Over a period of nine months, however, using scent with the food, the doves never learned to find their food with perfect accuracy, yet it seemed evident that of the various substances used, the oil of bergamot *did* stimulate them in a definite way, so that they seemed to associate it with food and entered the correct food chamber more times than would happen if their choice were governed by chance alone. This seems like fairly positive evidence, deduced from so large a series of well-controlled experiments as to be really conclusive.

Experienced duck-hunters often affirm that ducks can detect the sportsman's presence by scent, and that pheasants can do the same. A French experimenter is certain that pheasants can discover water by the sense of smell. Ravens are firmly believed by many to have keen powers of scent. The only general conclusion that at present seems warranted, is that many birds probably do have a certain power of scent, but that they are little dependent on it. Their quickness of vision is of much surer service. It should be borne in mind that the sense of smell is one very difficult to experiment with. The perception of an odor depends upon a contact of very minute particles with the sensitive membrane of the turbinal bones. If these particles are blown in the wrong direction, or lie in a lower layer of air, or for some other reason do not enter the nostrils, there can be no response. Some scents may attract, others repel, or again be of indifferent effect; if a scent is not associated strongly with an attractive or a repellent object, it might be ineffectual. The whole matter is one for the most careful experiment.

Taste and Touch.—I often wonder how much sense of taste those birds have that swallow hard seeds quickly and in quantity. Probably there is very little discrimination or enjoyment of flavors with many of them; nor can we expect there to be much in many fish-eating birds whose tongues are exceedingly small, and whose prey is instantly gulped down. With ourselves "taste" is largely a matter of smell after all, as any child will tell who has held its nose while gulping down a dose of castor oil. Our own sense of taste by the tongue is confined largely to the sensations of salts, sweets, or acids. Probably birds recognize by sight or touch what is their proper food. Finn (1919) mentions a case where a toad was swallowed and then rejected by two large gulls in succession, and then by a third, which after retaining it a while, itself threw it up and stood looking at the strange morsel, but seeing another gull coming to investigate, again swallowed it and retained it as long as watched. He concluded that during the previous killing and swallowing processes most of the irritating mucous secretion of the toad's skin had been washed off so that in its final disappearance, the unpleasant effect had been much lessened. He thinks that the vigorous bill-wiping movements we sometimes see birds make, are indicative that the last swallowed morsel did not seem so good as it looked. Probably it is often not until the food arrives in the stomach that the bird can tell whether or not it "agrees," and this is sometimes true with ourselves.

While sight in the discrimination of food is doubtless the usual guide, it is likely that many birds do not see their food. This applies to the probers and sifters especially. We have all seen the characteristic feeding habit of the Semipalmated Sandpipers as they run along the edge of a sandy beach, making short quick probings several in succession in the wet sand and water. Woodcock and the Kiwi of New Zealand probe soft earth for worms and doubtless catch them in part through a sense of touch. The horny tongues of most small birds are probably of much more use as organs of touch in manipulating and judging of food than as organs of taste. The complex nerve endings in the bills of ducks have been carefully studied and indicate the sensitiveness of their sifting-plates at the edges of the jaws. The finely divided brushes of honey- or sap-feeders perhaps are in part feeling organs. Many birds are provided with stiff hair-like feathers which probably act as organs of touch, such as the bristles about the mouths of flycatchers and the nighthawk tribe. The bristly tuft covering the nostril of crows and ravens may be of use as an organ of touch, but observations are lacking to help our interpretation of them.

Life Histories.—Just as there is a certain rhythm in the succession of the seasons with the earth's revolution, so there is a corresponding series of yearly activities in animal life, especially marked outside the Tropics, though none the less evident there. The round of events comprising a bird's life, its hatching from the egg, nutrition, bringing up and final growth to adult life, with its own yearly succession of mating, nesting, flocking, migrating, comprise the general background of the life history. Few more sug-

YOUNG BROWN PELICAN FEEDING WITH ITS HEAD INSIDE PARENT'S THROAT

Courtesy of George Nelson, phot.

gestive and careful studies, attractively written and illustrated, are to be found on the behavior of some of our common birds than those published by Professor F. H. Herrick (1905) in his "Home Life of Wild Birds." He concludes that much of the activities of birds in mating, nest-building, egg-laying, hatching and rearing the young, form a cycle of more or less instinctive acts which come on one by one, reach their climax and give place to another set of acts in a somewhat automatic fashion. As soon as one instinct is satisfied, another seems to possess them with resistless force until it too wanes and gives place to another. In other words there is no planned action in selecting a time for house-building, laying eggs, and so on, but the start once made the entire train of consequences is set off and followed through. If, however, something happens to interrupt this chain, the birds go back and start anew. In this way, Professor Herrick supposes, when a Yellow Warbler's nest is invaded by a Cowbird and one of the latter's eggs is added, the warblers, if the chain of instincts is sufficiently disturbed, start over again and build another nest on top of the violated one, thus, as it happens, effectually burying the strange egg together with their own, and laying a new set in the added story. The whole matter is merely the making of a fresh start because the peaceful course of events was unduly interrupted; not that the clever warblers foresaw that the hatching of the strange egg would result in their own young being elbowed out, for apparently they are quite as willing to hatch and raise the young Cowbird as their own children. It would be interesting to discover by careful observation what difference it would make whether the Cowbird were discovered by the rightful owners when she lays her egg; or if the Warblers are less affected if she lays it *before* incubation starts or after. All these things are matters of importance. The two-storied nest of the warbler is not often seen and very frequently no attempt is made to outwit the Cowbird. It is often the case that at first birds show very little feeling for their eggs. Indeed many birds can easily be fooled by substituting other eggs for their own. Hens will sit cheerfully on china eggs, and pigeons will do their best to hatch one of their own eggs hard-boiled without seeming to notice anything amiss. But these birds are not very intelligent species. Hume tells of an Indian Kite that, when its egg was removed, contentedly sat upon a pill-box in its stead until this was wrecked by rain, and Finn mentions a pair of cranes nesting in captivity, but unable to produce eggs, that fished up a couple of pieces of brick from the bottom of their pond and made believe these were eggs. Such facts make us careful in assuming that birds are able to tell if their eggs are touched or if one is taken from the nest. Yet some birds seem very sensitive to disturbance, as the Indigo-bird. What interpretation, then, shall we put on a case mentioned by J. H. Bowles, who found a Virginia Rail's nest with nine eggs, but did not disturb it in any way. Yet on chancing to pass back near it five minutes later, he saw a Rail standing among the eggs, stabbing them with its bill. He interfered at once but not before three had been quite thrust through. Bowles assumed that the female bird was destroying her own eggs on account of his discovery of the nest, but there are other possibilities, such as that the bird he saw was a male of another pair, eagerly eating the morsels. At all events, it is not safe to assume that the parent bird was worried about the eggs.

FLICKER FEEDING YOUNG BY INSERTING FOOD IN ITS BILL
Courtesy of George Nelson, phot.

As the incubation period lengthens there is a greater attachment for the home site and its treasures, and an increasing desire to guard the young. With the hatching starts the process of feeding, in the manner of which there is great variation among different birds. Stephens (1917) has pointed out that there seem to be progressive steps in the development of this duty as we proceed from the less highly organized water birds, to the more specialized small land birds. Thus gulls feed the little ones by throwing up for them partly digested food. Others, such as pelicans and gannets, do not keep the young ones waiting for this, but allow the young to thrust their bills into their parents' throats to feed on the predigested food, raised from the stomach. In small land birds just the opposite process takes place, for the young, at first blind, merely lift their heads with open bills and the parents place food well down into these, or in some cases seem to pump up predigested food from their own stomachs into the gullets of the young.

The development of instincts in the young follows a regular cycle. In the small land birds, the sanitation for example is at first performed by the parent, who carries away the excrement of the young and drops it at a distance. As the young grow and the nest becomes too small, there comes a time when they all leave it more or less at the same period. The sense of fear seems to be another instinct that soon begins to appear. In the birds that leave the nest soon after hatching, it is developed almost at the same time, so that they are quick to run and hide if disturbed. But in the small land birds that spend a good while as nestlings, it comes later. Most of us have had the experience of watching a nest till the young were well fledged. They were perfectly fearless and opened their bills for food as readily as if we were their parents or they surveyed us calmly as they sat in the nest. One day this is suddenly changed. We come as usual to the nest but at the first jar every bird springs up and flutters away. Fear has come. So other instincts follow in their gradual unfolding, and in regular order with the growth of the young to maturity.

It is with the nest-life of birds in their relations both as young and as parents that much of their emotional life centers, and there is much yet to be learned from careful and intimate observation of this part of their lives. Professor Wallace Craig's (1908) excellent discussion of the use of the voice in pigeons as a means of social control, points the way to further studies. He shows that the young dove on hatching begins to exert control over the parents by its very movements stimulating them to secrete and feed to it the pigeon's milk from their crops. If the young one is hungry his voice has a similar strong effect on them. When old enough to leave the nest, his insistent squealing as he follows the old bird begging for food insures that he will have due attention. The parents, unconsciously of course, show toward the young the body-form, colors, gestures and sounds of the species, so that the young bird learns to recognize his kind. This effect has been many times proved by letting pigeons' eggs be hatched by Ring Doves, with the result that the young pigeons ever after associate with the Ring Doves and try to mate with them; so it seems that they come to know their own kind through their association with their parents. In the same way they learn to distinguish individuals. For at first a young pigeon will beg food from any adult that chances to be near, and by

HOODED WARBLER FEEDING YOUNG BY INSERTING FOOD IN
ITS BILL
Courtesy of L. W. Brownell, phot.

constant rebuffs, comes to distinguish its parents. It is shown by Professor Craig that at weaning time the mother becomes unwilling to feed long before the father does, so the young one learns to tell its two parents apart. It was found that if two young birds be allowed to mate, their inexperience seems to delay the nesting process and causes a lack of precision in the various actions of mating, nest-building and incubating. If, on the other hand, an inexperienced bird be paired with an old experienced mate, the result is very different, for the older bird takes the lead in many of the operations, and in this the voice seems to play an important part as a controlling or suggestive factor. Thus tradition is seen also to be a means of social control.

CHAPTER XI

FLIGHT AND SONG

WITHIN the last two decades Man may be said to have solved the problem of flight, even if only by aid of that extension of himself, a machine. But long ago the problem was solved in part at least, not only by two groups of fishes (one long extinct, the other including our flying fishes), but also by reptiles, various mammals, and birds. There is an entire order of extinct flying reptiles with true wings, which were probably thin extensions of skin stretched on the enormously elongated fourth fingers; these were the pterodactyls or wing-fingered reptiles which died out with the era preceding the last or Tertiary. The largest known of these strange creatures, the *Pteranodon,* had a long narrow beak, no teeth, and a wing-spread of eighteen feet. Among flying mammals, the most familiar are bats, of which there are a great number of species. Birds must have developed flight very early, for *Archæopteryx,* the oldest known fossil bird, had strong wings.

The beginnings of flight are seen in many animals. Those which glide or volplane from one tree to another afford perhaps the first stage. The flying lizards of the East Indies that spread a wide fold of skin by opening the long free ribs like an umbrella, and so glide from one tree to another, as well as our familiar flying-squirrels that spread out the loose fold of skin along the sides of the body are good examples, and this form of flying or gliding has been independently acquired not only by certain squirrel-like African rodents, but also by a very small Australian opossum, hardly six inches long, and by still another Australian marsupial (or pouched mammal) as big as a large squirrel. In these species the tail is long and feathery and aids in steering during the glide. In all, gliding or actual flight has been independently acquired in at least seventeen groups of vertebrates.

We do not know how birds first became fliers, but it is supposed that their early ancestors ran on their hind legs, leaving their fore limbs free to develop as wings or as sails by the aid of which they glided from bough to bough or from tree to tree. In this the wings were probably held outstretched and the legs were extended behind. In many bats additional support is gained by the growth of a membrane which stretches between the extended toes and the tip of the tail. This is called a "patagium." It has been argued that if the ancestors of birds had learned to glide before their feathery covering had become evolved, they would probably have had a thin membrane of skin stretching between the fingers and from the sides of the tail to the feet just as there is in bats and in the extinct flying lizards or pterodactyls. Since, however, this "patagium" is lacking, it is believed that some of the feathers on the hand had already become large enough to sustain the bird in the air. That ancient birds extended the legs *behind* in flight is rendered probable not only from analogy with bats, but also because most of the more primitive birds still do so. For example, ducks, loons, herons, cranes, sandpipers, gulls, as well as grouse, hens, hawks, owls, pigeons, and the cuckoos all fly with the legs out behind when under way, in contrast to many of the more specialized or perching birds which fly with the feet drawn up in front ready to grasp a branch on alighting; such are the crows, sparrows, warblers, thrushes.   In connection with this posture of the legs in flight should be mentioned the so-called "pelvic wing," recently described by Beebe (1915).   This author finds in the young of pigeons, jaçanas, Great Horned Owls, that the feathers along the hinder edge of the feather-tract on the thigh are much stouter and more strongly developed than their neighbors, so that at an early stage they seem to be as strong as the regular flight feathers of the wing.   He advances the theory of a primitive condition in which there were wing feathers on the hind legs as well as on the fore, so that the ancient ancestors of birds were originally four-winged though they probably used the front pair of wings for flapping and those of the hind legs solely for additional supporting surface.   Such a supposed four-winged bird Beebe calls a *tetrapteryx,* and suggests that the pelvic wing is a vestige of this tetrapteryx stage, the remnant of the once functional flight feathers of the leg. In the early gliding stages of flight, these long feathers of the thigh were not of course used as flapping wings, but extended out behind to serve as an additional parachute instead of a fold of skin.   More recently this pelvic wing has been found in young chicks and turkeys, and in these early stages is apparently better developed than in later life.

After the gliding stage, flight was perhaps acquired by a laborious process of alternate flapping and sailing, much as we see in the Sharp-shinned Hawk when not in direct flight. The primitive flying birds were probably small species and by gradually increasing the rapidity of their wing beats, they developed swifter flight.   Observations made in Europe on birds harnessed to automatic registers showed in the pigeon about 480 wing beats to the minute, in a duck 540, and in the sparrow 780. Dwight's observations on Herring Gulls showed an average of about 180 strokes a minute in free flight, while in such birds as swifts and hummingbirds it must be very many times that. In these birds the humerus of the upper arm is a very short bone. Once the art of sustaining the body in air was acquired, we may suppose the more expert forms of flight followed, such as soaring, or poising with delicate adjustment on air currents. Such a form of poising is seen in the Rough-legged Hawks which have learned to hang in the air nearly motionless by balancing on an upward current coming over the brow of a hill. Passengers on steamers have often admired the beautiful flight of gulls which, taking advantage of the wave of air forced upward by the advance of the vessel against the wind, are able to poise on motionless wings in this current and yet keep pace with the steamer as it advances. Once outside a certain zone, however, the force of the air current falls, and they cannot maintain their position except by flapping. These two cases indicate a very delicate adjustment of forces in the poising bird.

The most complex and interesting type of flight is true soaring, by which is meant the ability to glide through the air, to rise or descend, to increase or check speed, to circle or go straight away, all without flapping the wings, or greatly varying their general outstretched position. In a recent book, "Animal Flight," Dr. E. H. Hankin (1914) has published the record of his long and minute observations carried on in India concerning this type of flight in vultures, kites, and marabous (or Adjutant Storks). That there is much yet to be learned about its mechanics, he makes abundantly evident. It is interesting, too, that this form of flight is found chiefly among large birds, and in the Tropics can be studied more easily since there vultures, kites, and eagles abound. In our own latitude, studies of gulls, eagles, and one or two species of large hawks may be made (indeed have been undertaken by Miller on the Pacific coast) to see if Hankin's accounts may be corroborated, while their bearing on human flight in engineless planes, as of late successfully undertaken in Europe, is additionally valuable. Hankin began his study by making accurate tracings of the courses taken by soaring birds. This he did by using a mirror and with a stylographic pen containing copying ink, following the track of the bird's flight as reflected on the glass. After the record was complete, a piece of paper was placed on the glass and rubbed, thereby producing a permanent copy. A metronome ticking at half-second intervals supplied the time, which he indicated by a dot or cross line, marking the tick.

Among the many interesting points brought out was the fact that in circling in calm air or with light wind the horizontal speed is less on the *windward* side of the circles, which indicates that the gain in height comes here. In calm or nearly calm air there is very little drift down wind, but instead the successive circles overlap. There may be circling *without* gain of height—or "ease-circling." With an increase of wind or often without wind the circles many overlap less and less, making loops to leeward, and there often comes a sudden increase of speed at the commencement of the down-wind glide, following a slight adjustment of the wings. In circling, the time required to make a complete circle is closely the same in a given species, but differs in different species.

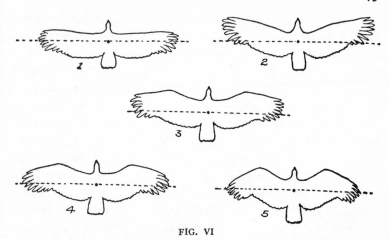

FIG. VI

Diagrams of a soaring Vulture showing relation of center of gravity to
supporting surface in circling and flex-gliding
After Hankin

In "ease-circling" without gain of height the wings are
held straight out from the shoulder. In gliding straight
ahead, however, there is a slight bend at the wrist which
advances the primary feathers of the wings nearly to the
level of the beak. This gives greater speed and is called
"flex-gliding"; the speed is increased by still further flexing
this part of the wings so that their tips are turned backward, though the wrist is well advanced nearly to the level
of the bill. On perfectly calm days, hundreds of vultures
could be seen near the meat factory where Hankin's studies
were made, flex-gliding at all speeds and at various heights.
In general, of the five species of birds studied, the heavier
the bird the greater the height at which it more commonly
flex-glides. This flex-gliding is the most important and
specialized form of soaring flight.

This soaring flight does not occur at any or all times.

On the contrary, in calm air, soaring flight may not be possible in early morning or late afternoon, but as morning advances its occurrence depends upon the presence of upward currents of air due to the heating of the lowermost layers of the atmosphere. In other words, the air becomes "soarable" at a more or less particular time, and this "soarability" gradually increases, as proved by the fact that the lighter birds first start circling and the heavier ones follow in the order of their weight. An interval always occurs between the time of commencement of circling and the time of commencement of flex-gliding; also slow flex-gliding begins before fast flex-gliding. As the day wanes the "soarability" of the air decreases, or the development of cloud shadows may cause flex-gliding to cease while still allowing the circling form of flight. In our latitude (44° N.), true soaring birds seldom are seen, and it is likely that the air does not constantly possess the properties necessary for this form of flight. My recollection is, however, that the towering of flocks of Herring Gulls is seen on bright days and in noontime hours, as if it were perhaps dependent on this same effect of the sun which is so much more evident in the Tropics. With us, soaring is more often seen when there is a steady breeze, but this "wind-soarability" is a quite distinct phenomenon; for the force of the wind is the effectual supporting power.

We have rather little definite knowledge of the height that birds may attain in flight, but there is little doubt it has been much exaggerated. The supposition of Gätke, the famous ornithologist of Helgoland, that migrating birds attain a height of between four and five miles and make their long flights at tremendous speed, is not now accepted.

Observations made in this country on birds crossing the field of a telescope trained on the moon have made possible several fairly accurate measurements. Scott, at Princeton, estimated the altitude of birds thus seen at from 5000 to 10,000 feet, or under two miles. Dr. F. M. Chapman in similar manner records observations of over two hundred birds at various altitudes of from 1500 to 15,000 feet, among these being five Carolina Rails, the highest of which was estimated to be at 13,500 feet or about two and one-half miles. Measurements by Carpenter gave lower figures, from 1400 to 5400 feet.

More recently the airmen in the Great War have supplied a certain amount of definite information, and Colonel Meinertzhagen (1920) of the Royal Air Force has summarized answers received in reply to his questionnaire. Though some of these replies were facetious (one airman reported surprising a flock of forty cock Ostriches at 17,000 feet, attacking them and so effectively breaking up the formation that one nose-dived on to the general's tent), yet on the whole pilots were agreed that birds were seldom seen at altitudes above 2000 feet, and with their constant and sharp lookout it is unlikely that many birds would have escaped observation if in range of vision. In his summary of the more accurate records, there are notes of Lapwing and Golden Plover at 6500 feet; two flocks of plover flying north at 1400 feet above a dense and continuous layer of cloud, and a flock of eight ducks at 7500 feet in a snowstorm. The highest record was of a flock of 60 to 70 Rooks at 11,000 feet in England, and a single large vulture in France at the same altitude. The general conclusion from a large number of careful observations is that the bulk of even migratory flight is at altitudes less than 3000 feet whether by day or night and that it is exceptional to meet with birds above 5000 feet, that is, about a mile. It is obvious, however, that at even 3000 feet the country must appear to them spread out like a map for, at that altitude, the visible horizon is 67 miles distant and at 5000 feet it is 86 miles.

The same author (1921) has published an account of extensive observations on the speed of flying birds, which help to reduce previous rough estimates and guesswork to some fair degree of accuracy. Similar observations could easily be made by two observers working together at opposite ends of a carefully measured baseline, and by stop-watches timing the flight between two points aligned by posts. In many cases Meinertzhagen used flying birds for practice in stations. Other observations were made from airplanes following birds and using the figures of the air-speed indicators. From the summary of these and other records of over forty species, the swiftest was perhaps the Lammergeier, a large vulture, which, when chased by an airplane made a nose-dive at the rate of 110 miles an hour by the air-speed indicator. The next fastest record was of swifts in Mesopotamia which easily overtook and circled around an airplane going at 68 miles per hour. Various ducks and geese fly at from 40 to 59 miles an hour in calm air; pheasants are slower, from 34 to 38 miles, and Golden Plover when pressed made 60 miles per hour; Lapwings 40 to 45 or 50 and the same for curlew and some of the sandpipers. One's general impression that most land birds except swifts and swallows are not so fast ordinarily is borne out by various observations. Rooks and Jackdaws average about 40 miles; crossbills, pipits, and wagtails from 37 down to 20 miles per hour. The Starling, how-

FLOCK OF WILD SWAN AT CURRITUCK IN V-FORMATION
Courtesy of Albert F. Bigelow, phot.

ever, is a swift-flying bird, with a speed of nearly 50 miles
an hour (43 to 49), an impression which one readily gets
from seeing them in our region of late years, for their
flight is remarkably direct and strong.

Birds in general are found to have two speeds: (1) a
normal rate for every-day purposes, including migration,
and (2) an accelerated speed, that is, they can "hurry"
if pursued or frightened so as nearly to double their normal
speed in some cases, though with certain of the heavier
birds it seems that the degree of "hurry" of which they are
capable is but little more than the normal rate.

There is opportunity for some interesting studies on the
formation and behavior of birds in flocks.   There are many
sorts of flight-formations—from the scattered, rather
loosely associated companies of Robins to the soldierly pro-
cessions of geese and pelicans.   Robins flying to a distant
roost at sundown illustrate a form of flock in which there is
little coherence.   The birds may be widely and irregularly
spaced and though flying at about a constant elevation, the
successive detachments are larger or smaller, farther apart
or nearer, or occasional birds may suddenly leave the company and dart down for a moment's halt in the trees.   One
would hardly expect anything different from such a scatter-
brain as the Robin.   A contrast is seen in the dense compact flocks formed by Cedarbirds that dash by in a solid
phalanx at speed, the entire company turning or shifting as
a unit, implying great quickness in adjustment of the individual to its neighbors.   The same thing is seen in many
of the African weaver-finches, that live in great flocks for
much of the year.   I recall seeing thousands of these birds
leaving the great river marshes on the Blue Nile in the
morning after the night's rest and whirling away to the

inner country to feed.   They formed a long narrow column of perhaps ten feet front, stretching for near a quarter of a mile and in this dense formation dashed by with a roar of wings.   It may be that such dense flocks in which birds move with great speed, are found more often among species that, like Cedarbirds and weaver-finches, are in close association for a good deal of the year.   Flocks of sandpipers in migration are often quite as dense and swift. They add a feature in their maneuvers which seems different from anything in the flocks of the species mentioned, which may be called "streaming," a twisting and turning all in unison, so that one moment the entire company flashes white in the sun and then darkens again when, to a bird, they turn their backs toward the observer.   In alighting, too, those that follow are apt to pass over those already down and alight farther on, so that their whole action is like the waving of a great scarf.

Some birds never fly in such long columns but spread out abreast.   This is noticeable in parrots, many species of which habitually fly back and forth in platoons between feeding and roosting grounds.   I remember watching for their nightly flights in East Africa, as they came in from the plains where they were feeding.   Every bird seemed to be screeching at the top of its lungs; and they flew all abreast, company after company, spread out many yards wide but with very shallow lines, disappearing in the distance on swiftly moving wings.

With many of the larger water-fowl, the procession or file-formation is common.   Pelicans are apt to fly in single file.   I recall one early morning seeing a flock of nearly 200 coming down the Blue Nile, one behind the other at regular short intervals and at even height, some 25 feet

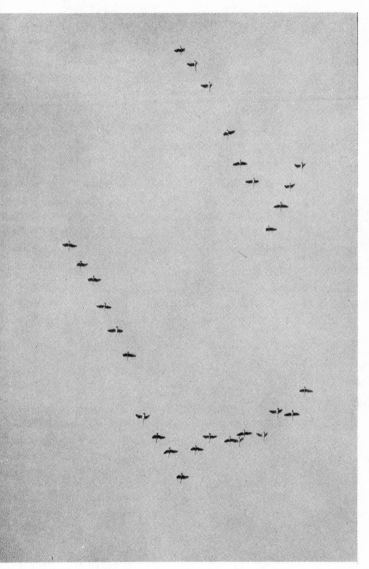

FLOCK FORMATION—CANADA GEESE IN A DOUBLE V
Courtesy of Albert F. Bigelow, phot.

from the water.   At one point the leading bird apparently
saw something that for a moment startled him.   At once
he rose in air a foot or two but immediately resumed his
former course and kept on at the original level.   Every one
of the birds following as they deliberately winged their way
downstream, upon reaching this spot rose in air the same
way as the one before it, so that there was a continuous
hump in the line at that spot until all had passed.   This incident is rather instructive as showing perhaps how far they
played the game of "follow your leader" and that each
bird's responsibility, while in file-formation, was to watch
the one in front and follow his actions.   With the Herring
Gulls, traveling birds often drop into a short file, not one
directly behind the other, as with pelicans, but with each of
the following birds a little to one side of the one in front.
A further development of this same type of flock-formation
is seen in the faster-moving ducks, geese, and cormorants,
which often maintain a V-shape, each bird slightly overlapping the one in front.   For faster-moving birds there is
perhaps an advantage in this arrangement, allowing each
bird a clear view ahead, so that there would be no occasion
for such a hump in the line as was noted in the slower-going
pelicans.

With some birds a particular type of flight is used in display before the female or afterward as a continuance of
this action during the nesting period.   Such in simplest
form is perhaps the Kingbird's towering flight accompanied
by occasional tumbling and many twitterings.   The pursuit-
flights of Chimney Swifts as they career through the air
in close groups of three or more, chippering as they go, and
the arrow-like dives of the Nighthawk with the extraordinary *twang* of air rushing through the wings as he turns

up again at the bottom of the downward course, are familiar examples of special forms of flight in display. Some of our western hummingbirds have also been described as performing in this way by swiftly rising and coming down again in a vertical course of over 75 feet, or there may be several back-and-forth darts before the rise.

Voice.—The voice of birds is so often associated with flight that it may be appropriately touched upon here.

With ourselves and in mammals generally, the voice is produced by the vibration of the vocal cords or membranes stretched on the firm cartilages of the *larynx* or "Adam's apple" at the *upper* end of the windpipe. In birds, however, this is not the case. The vocal organ or *syrinx* is at the *lower* end of the windpipe (*trachea*) where it forks to send a branch (or *bronchus*) to each lung. In general three different sorts of syrinx may be distinguished, though there are many variations in details. In the majority of birds this organ includes the lower end of the windpipe (or trachea) and the beginning of the two bronchi, and this type is therefore called (1) a *tracheo-bronchial* syrinx. Briefly, several of the lowermost rings (bony or of cartilage) which compose the windpipe fuse to form a more or less solid tube, while the first few rings of the two bronchi, instead of being complete, are open at the upper side and the gap is filled by a membrane (the tympanic membrane). A more or less bony bar arising from the last ring of the windpipe stretches across to the fork of the Y formed by the two bronchi. This bar is called the *pessulus* and gives support to a tough crescent-shaped membrane (the semilunar membrane) directed upward between the two sides of the fork. It is the vibration of these membranes that produces the voice. A pair of slender muscles arise along

WHITE PELICANS IN SINGLE FILE
Courtesy of National Zoölogical Park

opposite sides of the windpipe and go one to the upper part of each bronchus. These are called the *intrinsic* muscles, because they are wholly attached to these tubes. There is also a second pair each of which runs from the windpipe to an outside attachment and is therefore called an *extrinsic* muscle. Such is the common simple type of syrinx.

In some birds the lower part of the windpipe only is specially modified by having its bony rings of some particular form. This is called therefore (2) a *tracheal* syrinx, and is characteristic of a large group of South American passerine birds, and is found too in storks. The other extreme is found in birds such as the Oil-bird (*Steatornis*) and the Ani (*Crotophaga*), in which the windpipe is not modified, but part way down each bronchus the bony rings become incomplete and a membrane is stretched between their ends, with the intrinsic muscle attached here to tighten or loosen it. This type is (3) a *bronchial* syrinx, because the modified rings are confined to the bronchi. In the Ostrich the syrinx is very simple indeed, with no muscles or pessulus and but a rudimentary vibrating membrane. The voice is equally simple, a sort of bellow. At the other extreme are certain song-birds and parrots with three or four pairs of intrinsic muscles, instead of one, associated with great power of modulating the voice. Unexpectedly we find the Crow has a very full set of voice muscles. It is these muscles that give parrots and certain passerine birds such a variety of vocal modulations so that they can mimic other birds or even the human voice.

Much has been written as to the origin and meaning of song in birds. No doubt the diversity of views on this subject indicates that song arose in more than one way and serves more than one purpose.

Some birds, such as the Common Stork of Europe, seem to have no voice at all, but with them a clattering of the beak is used instead to express various matters. With many of the water birds, as some ducks, the voice is little used or its expression is chiefly reserved for the breeding period. With others there are special notes for use during the mating activities. It is possible that among some birds song may have developed as part of the mating display which so many male birds go through before their intended mates. These displays are often very complex and in the nature of particular ceremonies performed in a given order, which, however, may not always be adhered to strictly. They are indulged in not only before and during the period of active mating, but are kept up after pairing and even until after the young are hatched and well grown. Among most water birds the part played by the voice during these actions is a minor one. The display has been well described by Julian Huxley in grebes, in the ducks by many writers, and in the Laysan Albatross by Fisher. The latter author has published excellent photographs showing that the mated pair (the sexes are alike in color) face each other, going through bowing and dancing motions till finally one or both throw the head up to the full extent of the neck and utter a curious groan-like note. The actions of the grebes are different in the two sexes, and Huxley suggests that differences in behavior therefore preceded differences in plumage. In the Mallard Duck the male is the chief performer. In displaying before the placid-looking female he at first (1) swims about or floats with neck drawn in; (2) then rears abruptly on the water, at the same time passing the bill rapidly up the breast and giving a curious note, part whistle, part groan; (3) next the breast is depressed in the water, tail raised, and a series of short notes uttered, followed by (4) an upward throw of head and tail, then (5) by swimming rapidly about with head and neck held out straight.

A peculiarity of many ducks is the development, in the male, of a bony enlargement of the syrinx as a rounded chamber, which seems to have the effect of reducing the voice to a faint wheeze, while that of the female is louder.

These displays before and during the period of mating become stereotyped and are at length carried on by the male from a given post of vantage instead of directly before the female. In the grouse and pheasant tribe they are accompanied often by particular wing-movements. Thus the rooster flaps his wings before crowing, for the crow corresponds to the song. It is said the Javan Jungle-fowl, a related species, claps the wings *after* crowing, as do pheasants. In some pheasants the vocal part is omitted and there is a flapping or even a rumbling flutter of the wings instead, while our Ruffed Grouse has developed the instrumental part alone, making his well-known drumming.

In some groups of perching birds there is a similar display of wing action and voice. Thus, among the oriole family the Bronzed Grackle and the Cowbird slightly expand wings and tail and puff up the plumage in giving vent to their unmusical song-note. The Red-winged Blackbird acts in a somewhat similar manner, spreading the wing to show the red shoulder-patch, but in this species the song-note is more prolonged and musical. In the Oriole and Meadowlark there is ordinarily no display by wing-movements in giving the song (though both do occasionally sing on the wing, with a tremulous fluttering flight) while in the Bobolink both song and display-flight are present and highly developed, for the song-flight is often performed by peculiar short wing beats. Thus among the birds of this single family we have at least three types of display: (1) wing- and tail-spreading with an explosive note; (2) a song usually without spreading of plumage, though sometimes given on the wing, and (3) a combination of flight and song. It may have been that in such species the song developed as part of the combined display of plumage and voice, as seems so often the case in the water birds and eventually the song element became the dominant one.

Among many other birds, particularly the smaller land birds, I imagine that song arose partly through the development of call-notes for keeping mates in touch with each other. This may have been especially the case among tropical species that live the year around in a closely circumscribed area, and in which mating is more or less permanent. I recall the case of several species of African Bush-shrikes, haunters of dense thickets, and of one especially, with black back and scarlet breast, that is common in the Sudan. In the winter season the two birds of a pair continue to keep much together, and seem to delight in each other's company. Several times I noticed a male bird give his loud whistled *o-wheé-o,* to which his mate instantly would reply from the depths of the thicket with a harsh *churr churr,* and presently join him. A male would reply in similar instantaneous fashion to the note of the female. From this habit of quick reply must have developed the remarkable responsive song of one or two other species of East African bush-shrikes. I recall one in which the male bird uttered a series of ringing notes like measured beats of an anvil, while the mate replied with a series of double notes exactly timed to fill the interval between the anvil strokes. This pretty duet lasting several seconds was done with such

precision as to give the impression of a single bird singing.
Sometimes the measured notes of the male were heard but
no response came from the mate, and one can readily imagine that the male bird could still further develop his performance into a coherent song in which his mate would
gradually take a less active part.   Such a song, if frequently indulged in, would still serve the original purpose of
keeping the pair in touch by proclaiming: (1) the species,
(2) the sex, and (3) the individual.   The female could
respond or not as her caprice might be.   This song would
also serve to notify neighboring pairs of the location of the
first pair and so to preëmpt for the latter a certain territory
which they might regard as their home ground.

This home idea is a matter of great importance.   Nearly
all species of birds and mammals have the feeling of possession or right to a certain territory, which at least during the
breeding time forms for each pair a focus or home, to be
guarded against violation by others of their own or different species.   The song as a proclamation that a given territory is already occupied, is no doubt of value in producing
the proper spacing of breeding pairs so that each may have
its own sufficient domain and hunting-ground.   In the case
of social or colonial birds, such as murres that nest close
together on a narrow ledge, or weaver-finches that hang
dozens of nests on a single limb, the occupied territory is reduced to the actual nesting spot itself, and in such cases as
occur to me, it is noticeable that the search for food is conducted at a distance on common hunting-grounds.   So it
results that in bird colonies the parents travel considerable
distances, as with terns, puffins, and murres, for fishing,
or as with the colonies of weaver-finches in which there is
a stream of birds coming and going into the neighboring

area for food; while with species that are not so fond of company, each pair defends a certain established domain. This matter has lately been elaborated by Howard (1920) in the study of various British birds, and in America by Mousley (1919) who shows that with many warblers a particular tree is chosen by the male as a singing station near the center of the domain.   Moreover, it is suggested by the latter author that in the process of mating, the unpaired male selects first his domain and attracts to himself a mate by proclaiming his presence from such a singing station. Further careful field studies of these matters are very desirable, but there is already much evidence for believing that in this way the female may actively be led to a mate, while the male plays the more passive part in the search, by merely advertising himself.   Perchance the male Mockingbird that for several years sang all the spring in a certain part of the Arnold Arboretum was an illustration of this method of mating.   At all events he appeared regularly at his station, season after season, but in spite of his singing seemed never to have attracted a mate.

Another bit of evidence that this method of mating is common among singing birds is the experience of canary fanciers, who, according to Finn (1919), in their attempts to mate certain females to certain males, are constantly troubled by finding that a female is so attracted or affected by the song of a particular male that she will not pair with any other bird as long as that singer is within hearing.

It would be interesting to trace the development of complexity in bird songs, but only a word or two can be said here.   The songs of many birds probably arose as a repetition of one of their ordinary call-notes with the later addition of special modulations.   A familiar case is perhaps that of the common House Sparrow whose best effort is merely a louder and more liquid utterance of his ordinary *chirrup;* another is our Chipping Sparrow, whose simplest song is a quick repetition of the *chip* call-notes run together as a sort of trill.   There are several modifications of this song, however, for one hears often the *chipping* style in which the separate *chips* are distinguishable and another in which they are more run together.   A third variation is heard before daylight in the breeding season, a succession of modulated runs.   A special twilight song is also heard from the Wood Pewee in which a refrain is added to its usual utterance, and other birds, including Kingbird and Robin, sing in somewhat different strain before daylight.

The simple type of repetitive song, which is based on the repetition of a single note, may develop into a trill by more rapid utterance, as we see in the Chipping Sparrow or the Field Sparrow.   The next stage of complexity might be the addition of another and different note, as in some barbets whose song is like a cuckoo clock striking twelve.   Or the simple notes may be grouped in twos (as the *peet-weet* of the Spotted Sandpiper), threes or fours (as in the *peabody* song of the White-throated Sparrow).   From this to the division of the song into bars as we find in our thrushes is perhaps not a far cry and there may be a succession of bars, each different, repeated again and again, as with the Hermit Thrush or Indigo-bird.   Even the bubbling song of the Winter Wren may be resolved into a series of trills with different musical values, while of our common species it has often seemed to me that the Warbling Vireo has one of the most complex little songs of all.

CHAPTER XII

WE marvel at the restless activity of many birds, particularly the smaller species, but it is far less often that we think of their resting periods, or where and how the diurnal species pass the night, and the nocturnal the day. It is a familiar fact that we see more birds in early forenoon hours or in the latter part of the day than at other times. With most species those hours are their periods of greatest activity when they are busy procuring food after the night's rest or before the end of day. The reason for their apparent absence at other times of the day is in part a result of lessened activity or in part of actual rest. In spring and summer the songs that so readily declare the birds' presence are often hushed in the warmer hours and the result is that birds are harder to find. Many birds become more or less still at these times or move about quietly in restricted haunts. This is perhaps particularly the case at times other than the breeding season when the parental cares are over and life is at a less fevered pace once more.

The habits of even so commonplace a bird as the Domestic Pigeon are rather instructive in this regard. In late summer I have frequently watched these birds enjoying a morning's rest in chosen spots. One pair daily frequented a cosy corner formed by a window-ledge and a rainwater pipe outside my fifth-story window. One or two other pairs as regularly resorted to generous window-ledges on

the floor below. My notes show that in August, for example, the first pair reached their sunny nook very promptly
about eight or slightly thereafter each morning, usually arriving separately, but each evidently awaiting the other.
They then squatted side by side or at least close together,
apparently delighting in the comfort of companionship, and
settled for two or three hours of continuous rest. Yet
they were alert, seldom closing their eyes for more than a
few moments at a time, but ever and anon blinking or changing position slightly, standing to preen each other's head
feathers, and once more settling down for another nap.
They seemed to enjoy the full sunlight and basked contentedly till near noon. The characteristic posture in dozing is squatted flat on the roof, the neck drawn in so that
the head sinks close in upon the shoulders, the bill buried
in the feathers of the upper breast, but never have I seen
the head laid back upon the shoulders, a posture so frequent
among sleeping birds of other species. The morning's
nap over, they would rouse themselves toward noon and
presently set forth to feed. Small flocks gather in street
or on lawn to feed and seem to wander about a good deal
in the afternoon, for seldom do they return to the resting
place again save for a momentary pause. It seems to be
true that the daytime resting places are different from the
night roosts, for invariably they retired at evening to a narrow ledge under the eaves on the inner or sheltered side of
the court, on the same building. Here some twenty birds
nightly slept, squatted in single file along a narrow projection barely wide enough for safe foothold, under the eaves.
As in their daytime sleep, their heads were drawn well in so
that their bills rested on their breasts as they slept. In
early winter the resting part of the forenoon was spent on

the more sheltered parts of the building, particular pairs resorting to their chosen window-ledges, and they came in early to the roosting ledge, often by half-past two or three o'clock of November afternoons; and I have known them to be gathered for the night by two o'clock on a dark rainy day in that month.   The hours of rest have a fairly definite relation to the time of sunset and sunrise at these seasons: the earlier the sun sets the earlier do the birds come in to roost.

There is a good deal of resemblance between Pigeons and Herring Gulls as regards daytime rest.   In the lower Charles River basin since it has become a permanent body of water, these birds come with considerable regularity to rest and bathe during the middle hours of the day in that part of the basin most distant from surrounding shores. Just as pigeons on the Boston Common will sometimes gather to the number of a hundred or two, standing or lying down in a close company, so the gulls "bed down" in numbers often reaching hundreds.   If there is ice with open water, they stand along its edge or lie flat down quite like the pigeons.   They visit the larger ponds to rest in the same way, but apparently they never pass the night in any of these places.   Dr. C. W. Townsend states that they sometimes sleep in flocks on the upper beach above high-tide marks.

Herrick notes that in a nesting colony of Herring Gulls the birds are more or less active throughout the night, but the old birds take frequent naps at all hours whether perching or on the nest.   Occasionally they will doze with head drawn in and eyes closed, but usually the head is turned back with the bill among the scapular feathers.   He adds that "some of the Pheasants sleep with the head either

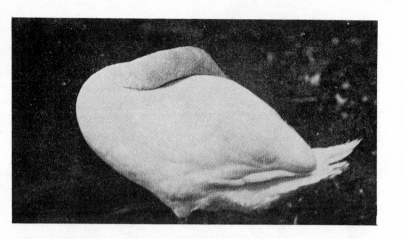

TRUMPETER SWAN ASLEEP, STANDING, WITH HEAD AND NECK LAID
BACK ON SHOULDERS

Courtesy of L. W. Brownell, phot.

COMMON PIGEON ASLEEP, SQUATTED, WITH HEAD DRAWN DOWN ON
BREAST

drawn in on shortened neck, or turned back and concealed."
In these two groups, therefore, we have birds in which
both postures may be assumed in sleep, that is, with the
head drawn in upon the breast or laid back between the
shoulders. It is therefore of special interest as affording
a stage intermediate between the more usual one and that
seen in the domestic pigeon which seems invariably to sleep
with head drawn down. This resemblance is the more interesting in connection with the possible relationship between gulls and pigeons through some plover-like ancestor.

On the coast of Maine many adult gulls, apparently non-
breeding birds that spend the day about harbors or hunting
along shore, repair to some small rocky islet at sunset and
may be seen in little groups or singly till nearly dusk, wing-
ing their way out to join the others. In such localities they
are comparatively free from disturbance but are quick to
change their sleeping-place if alarmed. Probably this
method of repairing to a common point of safety for the
night's rest is the usual one. Dr. C. W. Townsend, however, believes that they may at times spend the night resting
upon the water. This is the case certainly with many
water birds, such as the ducks and swans, and there are instances on record of the sleeping birds being frozen in by a
sudden cold snap and unable to extricate themselves from
the ice.

It is interesting here to notice that some at least of the
species of terns, relatives of gulls though they be, are
quite unable to rest for any length of time upon the water.
As a test of this point, in connection with over-sea flights,
J. B. Watson showed by experiment that, although Noddy
Terns *can* rest on the surface of the water over night, they
prefer not to and perch upon floating blocks or other foot-

hold if possible. Sooty Terns, however, quickly become water-logged and after two to four hours are no longer able to rise from the surface. The two species are therefore quite different in their ability to sleep on the water.

Many if not most water birds sleep with the head laid back upon the shoulders, and the end of the bill buried in the scapular feathers. Indeed, this seems to be a very general posture in sleeping birds. In a bird with a moderate neck, this position allows the neck muscles to be relaxed in some degree, for the head is pillowed on the back and so does not need the support of the muscles that usually hold it up. It may be also that by burying the front end of the head sidewise among the scapulars there is just enough tension between the feathers of the two parts (pointing in opposite directions) to keep the head from slipping off.

In Scott's Voyage of the "Discovery," Wilson briefly recounts some experiences with Emperor Penguins, the largest and perhaps the most primitive of this strange group. "He sleeps," says this author, "upright with the tip of his long curved bill tucked in behind his flipper." This position, with neck bent over and relaxed, is probably in most birds the one of least muscular tension. Dr. F. M. Chapman has published photographs of nesting colonies of Brown Pelicans and of Flamingos in which a similar sleeping posture is assumed. This habit of sleeping on the nest in the noon hours is well illustrated in one photograph showing a considerable part of the Flamingo colony enjoying a siesta with their long necks twisted grotesquely backward to allow of the bill being tucked among the scapular feathers.

The same author in an intimate study of a nesting colony of Boobies, a small tropical species of gannet, found that "sitting or brooding birds spend the night upon the nest with their mate standing at their side," though the close resemblance of the two sexes made it impossible to determine which bird undertook the nest duty. After the young Booby is hatched and has grown too large to be brooded, "it passes the night on the ground between the two parents who stand on either side, all three with their heads tucked under their scapulars."

Writing of the Laysan Albatross of the Pacific, Dr. W. K. Fisher speaks of numbers of the young birds sleeping at night, "their eyes tightly closed and bills tucked under their wings. Some of them did not awake till touched and then naturally were much startled. The old birds, on the other hand, seem to be wide awake at night, but about 9 or 10 o'clock in the morning they frequently sleep near their young, with the bill and one eye covered by the wing." Possibly their activity at night may be connected with their feeding on squid, which are more apt to be at the surface then than by day.

Black Ducks, in localities where they feed much by night, frequently may be seen during the day fast asleep in that part of some large pond most distant from shore. This is a common sight on our reservoirs or larger ponds in eastern Massachusetts. With necks laid back on their shoulders and bills tucked among the shoulder feathers they look like black buoys anchored there. It is said that they sometimes paddle automatically with one foot to keep from drifting in a wind, but I have never seen this. When on shore they often sleep, standing balanced on one foot, with the head laid back on the shoulder and the other foot tucked up among the feathers of the abdomen. Swans sleep with their heads laid back in a similar way, allowing the long necks to relax, and I doubt not that this posture is the commonest sleeping position among birds.

Herrick has recorded some interesting notes on the sleep of the Red-eyed Vireo, a nesting pair of which he once had under observation. He found that, while the male apparently roosted nearby, the female invariably slept on the nest during the period when the young were in need of covering. At from fifteen to twenty minutes after sundown she was regularly at her post, and seemed to go at once to sleep, with her head turned back and buried deep in the feathers between the shoulders. If aroused in the night by a movement of the observer's hand, she would peck feebly at a raised finger, but if not further molested, she would close her eyes and slowly settle her head again in its former position. If actually driven off, she would return at once and in a moment be fast asleep.

Birds that go about in flocks often roost in large companies. Many descriptions have been given of Robin roosts. Usually in New England these roosts are used for a part of the season only, for the local Robins which thus come together depart in fall for the south. On their return in spring a common roost is sometimes established by the birds of a locality, but such roosts seem to be much less in number of individuals than those of fall. I recall one which was established on a bushy island in a large pond, and the evening caroling of the males as they arrived made a splendid April chorus before they quieted down with the gathering dusk. When the nesting begins the females apparently remain on their nests at night, but certain males, at least, continue to resort nightly to the roost, deserting the vicinity of the nest till morning. Such at least appears to be fairly well established by the observations of the late Dr. Walter Faxon, William Brewster, and others. Brewster gives some interesting notes on a roost established in a thicket of lilacs in his own garden at Cambridge. This was frequented in March by the newly arrived local birds and throughout the month of May he noted some fifty or more nightly, all old males apparently. By the middle of June these were joined by the first broods of young and a month or so later by the adult females with their second broods. Early in August the numbers reached upwards of seven hundred birds. He discovered that a curious pattering sound made as the birds came in at dusk, and which he at first supposed to be caused by their wings striking the leaves, is really made by the snapping bills of the birds as they threaten each other in the contest for particular perches. It may be that if individuals could be identified they would be found to have each a particular perch to which they nightly went. This is the case with pigeons, and they may be seen resentfully driving away an intruder if he happens to alight too near. Brewster found that after the Robins had once quite settled down for the night he could pass within a yard or two of the branches where they roosted without disturbing them. On several occasions, however, he had known the entire company to leave the roost in the middle of the night with loud excited calling, disturbed perhaps by a Screech Owl. Robins usually select for their roosting places some dense growth of swampy woods, such as a thicket of young red maples with bushy undergrowth, rising from mud or standing pools. Such a roost I watched many evenings at Lexington a few years since. During May the birds came in singly, following certain flight lines. They were probably chiefly if not almost altogether males. More than once I noticed that male birds of pairs breeding nearby would start calling after sunset, then sing a few moments before flying off in the direction of the roost. As summer came on the young birds, easily distinguished by their cracked voices, came in also to the roost, and by late August the numbers greatly increased. The birds streamed in at or shortly after sunset in little flocks, rather silently and in contrast to their conversational gathering earlier in the summer. By mid-September the roost seemed to have been abandoned.

The Bronzed Grackle has rather similar roosting habits, and often will the local Grackles use the same roost with the Robins. This was the case at the Lexington roost, where, on May 15, I counted some forty Grackles of which all but about three were adult males, distinguished by their long tails. They arrived in four or five small groups, soon settling in the chosen thicket. Once they rose in a body only to return a few minutes after. Later on two male birds suddenly flew out in hot pursuit of one of the females but finally returned after a wide sweep. In general they were earlier to bed than the Robins; most of them came before the sun had quite set, gathering first on the higher tree-tops near by, presently scaling in with set wings in slightly undulating course. As with the Robins, the females do not join at the roost till the young are on the wing. Thus it was not till the first of July that I noted the birds at Lexington arriving in parties of adult males with females and grown young. A number of such Grackle roosts have been described. In New Jersey, where the species regularly winters, the roosting place is found to be in use the year through, though the most populous time is of course in fall when birds are arriving from the north. Starlings sometimes join in with them, or may gather by themselves in multitudes.

This habit of roosting in large companies no doubt has certain advantages, such as the social aid of companionship and the lessened chance of being surprised by owls, though on the other hand the whereabouts of such a multitude is likely to be well advertised by the very numbers. I recall the great flocks of weaver-finches that came nightly to roost in the broad grass meadows along the Blue Nile of the Sudan. This was in the winter season when the birds were not breeding. They came in from the day's foraging in the surrounding country at about sunset, settling in the tall reedy grass in dense clouds. By the time they had quieted down the brief tropic dusk had deepened and Nighthawks of several species were already sweeping back and forth above the grass tops for the rising insects. Time and again one of these low-flying birds would pass in its course over the spot occupied by a swarm of the weavers which, as if mistaking the Nighthawk for a bird of prey, would rise in a body to settle again with much chirping as it passed.

The communal roosts of House Sparrows are familiar. These adaptable birds often sleep singly in sheltered crannies of buildings, or pass the night behind a folded blind perched on the cross-bar of the fastening. In summer they resort to thick vines on buildings or even in winter sleep the night out clinging to a twig of a tree. I have often passed under a certain small tree on Boston Common where on a winter's night some dozen or two sparrows sat perched along the bare branches fast asleep, their heads buried in the feathers of their backs, looking in the glare of the street lamps like so many round balls.

Great gatherings of Chimney Swifts have often been described, as they congregate in late summer preparatory to departure. In former times flocks probably roosted inside great hollow trees, but nowadays they often select some large chimney where they assemble at nightfall and, forming a great revolving nimbus about its top, presently pour down inside and settle for the night with much chattering. Presumably they sleep clinging to the rough surface of the bricks and propped by their spiny tails. With other species of swifts, however, it has been recorded that they actually cling one to another like bees when swarming. Thus Sharpe quotes Stuart Baker in regard to the Crested Tree-swift, a large species of India, that they roost in masses, but in treetops, not in hollow trunks. "On arriving at their proposed roosting place," he writes, "they fly round and round, gradually lowering their flight until one bird suddenly makes a sweep and settles on some part of the tree near the top. This is the signal for the rest to perch, and in a few minutes they are all dotted about the higher branches. They then begin to close up with the bird which first alighted on the tree, finally collecting in a feathery ball, one on top of the other. The first attempt, however, is seldom satisfactory, and they scatter abruptly, when the same performance is again gone through. Sometimes this happens again and again before they get settled, but at last the twittering stops and they are asleep for the night. It is wonderful how compactly these birds close up; a flock of eleven appeared not to take up a space more than a foot long by about half that breadth." Baker also remarks the same roosting habit in the Indian Swallow-shrike (*Artamus*). He does not tell us, however, if the head is laid over on the back in sleep, or sunken among the feathers of the breast as in the Nighthawk, the more likely posture perhaps.

The Colies or Mouse-birds of Africa, extraordinary almost parrot-like small birds, are also said by Sharpe to roost together in small parties of six or eight, clinging one to another.

The great autumnal gatherings of swallows for the night's rest have been described by various writers. Miss Abby Bates has written of such a one in Maine, where every autumn immense numbers assembled at evening in a great flock, which after much maneuvering presently settled for the night in the top twigs of a row of large willows by a stream. This roost, though used for only a short while at the close of the summer, was nevertheless habitually resorted to by the birds over a period of years. They were chiefly Barn Swallows.

One must be prepared to find great differences in the sleeping habits of birds, even though they are related species. During a winter in the Sudan, this was observed in case of two species of bee-eaters. One, the Nubian Bee-eater (*Merops nubicus*) a beautiful pink-breasted swallow-tailed species, we found hard to collect, as it spent so much time high in the air. One evening at sunset we marked down a flock of some thirty birds that went to roost in the dense foliage of a green thicket. Thinking to see their awakening the next morning, I stole out while it was yet dark and had nearly reached their resort just at sunrise, when without warning the entire flock arose from the far side of the clump of large bushes and dashed off to a neighboring treetop. On another occasion I disturbed a company of smaller bee-eaters (*Melittophaga*) that were spending the night in what were apparently their own disused nesting tunnels dug in a bank by the river like Bank Swallow holes. Chancing to walk along this bank at sunrise I aroused the entire flock which flew out from directly under me, disturbed, probably, by the vibration of my footsteps. The use of nests of their own or of another species as sleeping places is probably uncommon. An interesting case is reported by Mills of a flock of Gray-crowned Leucostictes that came nightly during at least part of the winter to roost in the abandoned retort-shaped nests of a colony of Cliff Swallows under a high rocky cliff in Wyoming. They seemed to lose none of their watchfulness while in these nests and flew out at once if too closely approached in early evening. They had not the certainty of entering that the Swallows had, but hovered at the door of the nest before making a dive at it, and occasionally missed their hold of the bottle-neck entrance even then. These are ground-feeding birds, but evidently appreciated the shelter and safety of these nests as roosting places, where they would be in no danger of becoming snowed in, in case of a storm.

In our cold northern winters sheltered nooks must be hard to find. Tree Sparrows will resort to some frozen marsh where, among the broken-down clumps of cattails or at the foot of thick clumps of grass, they find protected places in which there is shelter from wind or snow, as well as comparative security from a surprise attack, for the stiff reeds would rustle to the least touch. In such places I have sometimes found them, but the flock scatters out to sleep instead of gathering into one spot.

The Ruffed Grouse's habit of plunging into a snowdrift from the wing, and spending the night under the shelter of the snow is well known. In regions subject to occasional sudden changes of temperature, however, it often proves fatal if a light rain falls and a freeze crusts over the snow so that the birds cannot break forth next morning. The fox also catches some of them. Quail, as is well known, roost together on the ground in a circle, all facing out, so that if danger approaches, the entire flock scatters like a bombshell in every direction in a most disconcerting way.

It is natural that hole-nesting birds should seek shelter at night in cavities. Chickadees do so, and I have on occasion followed the birds in the winter woods of a late afternoon and seen them finally enter some natural cavity, for example at the base of a tree partly surrounded by snow. The Brown Creeper has the interesting habit of clinging, head up, in a depression in a tree trunk. I once discovered a Creeper roosting in a hollow about as big as my cupped hand near the top of a fire-scar at the base of a chestnut tree where the live bark slightly overhung the burned area. The accumulation of droppings indicated that the bird had been in the habit of coming to the spot during the winter.

Several English authors have of late testified to a like curious manner of roosting on the part of the Tree-creeper, a close ally of our own Brown Creeper. In several instances these birds were found to have excavated small hollows in the soft bark of giant Sequoias, grown in parks, and in these the birds passed the night. In one such tree there were ten or eleven holes, apparently dug out of the bark, some two and one half to three inches long by two inches deep, on all sides of the trunk at from three to eight feet from the ground, below the lowermost branches. One bird was watched at dusk in such a roosting cavity, and was seen to rest with its head right in the hole and completely hidden from sight, so that only the tail, part of the back, and wings were visible. Another writer observed the same habit, but notes that the bird clung in its depression in such a position that its back was "on a level with the rugged bark of the tree, its beak pointing straight upward." He adds that of several holes in these trees only those on the lee side were occupied. Since this tree has only been introduced into England for about 75 years, the habit of excavating these roosting cavities in its bark must be a recent one. Perhaps the usual roosting place of the creeper is of a slightly different nature. At all events another English writer tells of an old alder stump some ten feet high in which were a number of small circular holes about one and one half inches in diameter, made and used by these birds for roosting. In a decaying willow nearby were several similar holes cut into the exposed wood. It seems likely that these holes may have been at least begun by woodpeckers, for the creeper's slender bill seems ill adapted for excavating.

The little Bat Parakeet, *Loriculus,* earns its name from its habit of hanging head down by one foot while sleeping, a most remarkable attitude even for a parrot. Other peculiar roosting habits have been reported for certain parrots.

Among the woodpeckers the habit of roosting in a cavity is probably common. An unusual situation was that used by a Cambridge Flicker which came nightly one August to roost inside our kitchen chimney which had a T-shaped funnel of earthenware, with a diameter of perhaps six inches. The bird (a female) arrived about one-half hour before sunset, flew to the entrance and, if uneasy, would stay looking out of the hole for some while, finally backing down into the vertical part of the funnel, and so disappearing for the night. But what seems to me one of the most interesting habits of all is that shared by both Downy and Hairy Woodpeckers, birds apparently rather closely related. These familiar woodpeckers actually chisel out for themselves in the fall of the year a roosting cavity similar to the hole they make in a dead limb for nesting in the spring.   I have reason to believe that the birds we see making new roosting holes in our city elms in October and November are birds that have come in from elsewhere to their accustomed winter quarters and so are not birds that have been on the ground the entire year.   This, however, is a matter that can best be settled through banding such individuals and following their movements.   Apparently both male and female make their own holes, showing that the cavity-making habit is common to both sexes just as among the wrens the males make "cock nests" and, as some have thought, for a similar nocturnal refuge.   The construction of these so-called "cock nests" by the Common Wren (*Troglodytes parvulus*) of Europe is well known; and our own species, the House Wren, does the same thing as well as the Long-billed Marsh Wren.   A number of observers in England attest to the use of these extra nests as roosting places as well as temporary quarters for the young.   Such nests differ from the one in which the eggs are laid, through having no lining.   Bentham relates that he once found a nest with five young, near which was one of these unlined nests.   On the evening following that on which they left the nests, he was surprised to find the entire brood inside the "cock nest," where they remained three days more and were fed by their parents.   After this they came to it only at night to roost and forsook it altogether at the end of two weeks more.   This testimony is corroborated by other English observers.   One states positively that the male is the builder and that the "cock nests" may be as many as five to one of the brood nests.   The birds may continue to sleep in them till winter, for the species is resident in the British

Isles.   Indeed, a Scotch naturalist, Walton, states that they are built at other times than the breeding season, for he has found them in process of construction in autumn. That even with this shelter the little birds sometimes fail to get the protection needed, is shown by the same writer who once found, in a sheltered ravine in the west of Scotland, one of these unlined nests containing the bodies of six mature wrens, the sixth with its tail and part of its body protruding from the nest.   All had apparently been frozen to death.

Here, then, in at least two unrelated groups of birds, the woodpeckers and the wrens, a roosting nest, if such it may be called, is constructed, and this, too, by the male as well as by the female bird.

CHAPTER XIII

BIRD MIGRATION

MANKIND delights in a mystery of whatever sort, that thrill of something unknown to be discovered! For long years the migration of birds has stood as a delightful and mysterious riddle of Nature, but now bids fair to clear away and unfold more wonderful things than we dreamed of. The autumnal disappearance of birds was anciently accounted for in sundry ways. Swallows, it was firmly believed, spent the winter buried in the mud, and I recall an account in a scientific journal of barely one hundred years ago, telling of the digging up of some of these birds in their winter sleep near Cambridge. European Cranes were supposed to carry on their backs some of the smaller land birds of weak flight and so to bear them to warmer climes. Nor was it so very long ago that the ornithologist Gätke, of Helgoland, affirmed that migrating birds ascended to a great height and then on the wings of winds "that blew between the worlds," bore away southward at incredible speed, covering vast distances in a very short time.

But during the last fifty years a very great deal has been found out. The times and general migration routes of most of our North American birds are now fairly well ascertained in a general way and are found to vary with different species. Most of our insect-eating birds retire to the southern States, many going farther, even into South America for the winter. There seem to be several ways by which small land birds pass to the southern continent. A very few cross the Caribbean Sea or follow the West Indian chain of islands. Thus Bobolinks gather in the southern rice fields and go thence by way of Cuba across to western Brazil, and the Black-poll Warbler crosses in the same way. The greater number of species, however, either cross the Gulf of Mexico or follow its western shore and so stream in to Central and South America for the winter season. Some species have a different route in spring from that in fall. Thus the Connecticut and the Orange-crowned Warblers visit our coast in small numbers rather regularly in their southward journey, but proceed far to the west in the spring return. With many species nesting in the middle west of northern United States and Canada, there seems to be a general movement in fall directly to the Atlantic coast, which is then followed to the south. Many ducks do this and some of them, passing on to Virginia and the Carolinas return north in spring by an interior route following waterways. The frequent records of western birds that reach us in fall perhaps indicate that they do the same or follow the transcontinental winds eastward. Some of the water birds have developed extraordinary migration courses, the best known of which is perhaps that of the Golden Plover. This bird leaves its arctic breeding haunts and, reaching eastern Labrador, apparently takes a course overseas direct for Venezuela. Yet it seems incredible that the entire course of 2500 miles can possibly be made, as is generally believed, in a single flight. The same route was used in former days by the Eskimo Curlew, a bird now nearly wiped out. Easterly winds at the time of the fall flight were frequently sufficient to turn these migrating birds in on to our shores, but at other times they seldom were taken. This fact has been developed by A. H. Clark into a theory that in general the birds kept their course oversea by adjusting their flight so that the wind was constantly "abeam." As a matter of fact, we are very ignorant of the whereabouts of these flocks at such times, and I personally believe that they may rest on the water and even obtain food from it, as Phalaropes do. Their wintering ground is eastern Argentina, which they leave in spring and follow north along the Central American coast, Gulf of Mexico, and central United States to Mackenzie, very exceptionally reaching the New England coast in spring. The Pacific Golden Plover makes a similar remarkable journey, breeding in Siberia and Alaska, and migrating in fall to the Hawaiian Islands and even to New Zealand.

According to Cooke, the longest migration route of any bird is that of the Arctic Tern that nests within the arctic circle and returns in winter to the south as far as the antarctic circle, a distance of 11,000 miles, an almost incredible flight, implying an average daily speed of at least 75 miles in order to perform the requisite flying alone in ten months. Yet the Wilson's Petrel certainly does almost as well, for it breeds within the antarctic circle in the southern summer and returns north, reaching our coasts in June, probably following the Gulf Stream.

Another remarkable migrant of former times was the Great Auk, whose breeding places on this side of the Atlantic were one or perhaps two small islands off Newfoundland. In winter the bird was common on the Massachusetts and Maine shores, as attested by a few records and a number of bones from Indian shell-heaps. Since it was unable to fly in the air it evidently reached our shores by sea, either swimming on the surface, or after the manner of auks, flying under water. The penguins of the Antarctic also undertake extensive migrations, partly by swimming and under-water flight, partly by being rafted short distances on floating ice-cakes as the warmer season comes to a close in their southern home.

While the general facts ascertained as to the migration of various birds apply in the main to the *species*, we need now to know more of the course of the *individual*. And facts of this kind are already becoming common knowledge. This is due chiefly to the experimental study of migration by marking birds in such a way that we can identify the individual again. By "banding" birds with a numbered ring, this is now easily accomplished, and already in America many thousand birds have been so marked. Twenty years ago this method of study was undertaken in Europe on a large scale, and with such zeal that by 1911, over 110,000 birds had been banded or "ringed" (as they call it "over there") in Germany, Hungary, and England.

The idea of marking birds so that they might subsequently be identified if captured, is not new. As long ago as 1740, in Europe, Frisch tied red threads about the legs of a number of swallows, thinking to test the belief, then general, that these birds passed the winter buried in the mud and came forth again like frogs in the spring. For he reasoned that if they were under water all winter, the threads would have their color quite washed out by spring, but if the threads would have remained unfaded he would have inferential proof that the birds had gone south with other migrants. In the following years some of these "banded" swallows returned and were caught, with their red threads still bright, so that Frisch believed he had experimental proof against the hibernation theory.

There were other occasional attempts at marking birds in Europe during the 19th century, one especially by Baron van der Heyden of Holland, who placed marked rings about the necks (not feet) of wild geese and ducks in an attempt to learn something as to their age and migration. He found that many of these birds returned yearly to their accustomed breeding places. One Gray-lag Goose was known to have come for 35 years to the Friesian neighborhood.

The results already obtained in Europe furnish a considerable mass of accurate information as to the movements of individual birds and some of the more important cases are worth reviewing here for comparison with results already being obtained through similar work on our own continent. These results have been lately summarized by von Lucanus (1923) and afford a mass of definite facts as to migration that are very illuminating.

Of the Black-headed Gull (*Larus ridibundus*), a common European species resembling our Laughing Gull, a great many young have been banded in the nesting colonies of the British Isles, Denmark, Germany, and Hungary. The numerous recoveries of these banded birds show that in autumn there are three principal routes taken from central Europe to the Atlantic and Mediterranean Sea. Some birds keep westward to the seacoasts of England, France, and Portugal, to northern Africa where many winter; others on reaching the mouth of the Rhine in their westward course turn south here, continuing up the Rhine to the Swiss Lakes and across to the valley of the Rhone, which they follow to the Mediterranean Sea; still others pass directly south from northern Prussia to the Danube and the Italian coasts. Several banded in England were recovered in winter in the Azores.   Most interesting is the report of two of these gulls banded in Prussia, one of which was recovered near Barbados in the West Indies, the other on the coast of Vera Cruz, Gulf of Mexico.   This recalls the case of a Common Tern banded by Dr. J. C. Phillips on our Massachusetts coast, that was recovered in Nigeria, West Africa. Thus among these strong-flying sea birds there is direct evidence that in autumn they leave the northern continents to winter in equatorial seas, and that there may be an interchange of species in those latitudes, whereby some from America reach Africa, while others from Europe reach the American tropics.   If this interchange extends to other seasons, it may be that occasionally European-bred birds will come north in spring to nest on our coast, or American birds may breed in Europe.   Such a fact, if established, would help explain why there has been no noticeable local race developed on either side of the North Atlantic among such birds as the terns.

Other interesting facts with regard to the European Black-headed Gulls were also established.   Thus the wintering of the same bird for at least two successive seasons at Geneva was proved.   Also the probability is indicated that birds from the same nesting colony migrate in groups more or less together, for gunners shot two birds from a large flock that had been banded at the same locality. Again, it appears that as with many species, those bred in the British Isles may pass the entire year in that vicinity, and are joined in winter by a large influx of gulls that had summered in the marshes of central Europe.   There is thus a general westerly trend of migration to the more equable shores of England and northern France where the influence of the warmer ocean-currents is felt.   It was found that young gulls start their wanderings early, for nestlings banded in mid-June in Prussia were taken in southern France in late August. A very interesting conclusion from banded birds is that these gulls do not breed until two years old, and until then they frequently remain in their winter quarters without returning northward, or wander about the seacoasts until ready to pair. Adult birds were found to return to their original nesting colonies in some cases, but in others they turned up at some distance away.

Herring Gulls (*Larus argentatus*) banded in central Europe were shown in some cases to have remained the year round in the same general region. A Lesser Black-backed Gull (*Larus fuscus*) was banded in Prussia in late November and recaptured thirteen days later at a distance of 1000 kilometers, making thus an average rate of about 50 miles daily.

Many cases are already on record of terns (Common, Arctic, Sandwich) banded as breeding birds on the coasts of the North and Baltic Seas and on the English or Dutch coasts, that were taken later in the year on the coasts of Spain or France. One Sandwich Tern banded in England was retaken on the Ivory Coast of tropical Africa, and in several instances terns were recaptured after four, five, or seven years.

Results of banding Mallard, Widgeon, and Teal are interesting as indicating slightly different habits for each species. The Mallard and Widgeon are practically non-migratory in the British Isles. But the Teal goes a long way, for three banded in Lapland and in St. Petersburg were recovered in southern Europe; while Teal from Sweden and Denmark are found to winter in the more equable climate of the British Isles. There may be a general dispersal for the nesting season, for Mallards banded as nestlings in Holland and England, turned up later as breeding birds in Prussia, France, and Sweden, while English-bred Teal were found nesting in Germany. On the other hand, some of the English-bred Mallards have been found two or even three years later in the place of their birth.

Pintail Ducks have been extensively banded in the autumn duck-drives on the west coast of Jutland, and of these over 65 were later reported from their nesting grounds in southern Sweden and northern Russia and Finland, so that it is believed the birds passing down the Danish coasts in fall are drawn from the northern parts of Russia in the main. Moreover, some of these birds were recaptured in Jutland in succeeding years, indicating that they follow a known route to their wintering grounds in southern Europe and the Mediterranean.

With geese of at least certain species, it seems fairly proved that families migrate together, the parents with the young. The larger flocks are composed of numerous families in loose association. This indeed was already assumed but lacked the definite proof. If captive birds are allowed to raise a brood of young, the latter will not migrate south in fall so long as their parents are prevented from going.

By recoveries of banded birds, it is now shown conclusively that although in most of Europe the European Woodcock is a migrant, in the British Isles it either does not migrate at all or moves only a little way. Thus of 27 birds recovered, eight, banded on their breeding grounds in northern England and Scotland, wintered on the west and south coasts of Ireland, two others wintered in the south

A FLOCK OF CANADA GEESE AT CURRITUCK
Courtesy of Albert F. Bigelow, phot.

of England and sixteen banded in England as nestlings remained near their home neighborhood. The birds of the British Isles therefore behave differently from those on the continent, for the latter are forced by the increasing cold of winter to leave their inland marshes, and this they do in the fall, while those of the more clement regions, as in England, are able to remain the year round. In this way no doubt have arisen some of the local British races of birds, through their more sedentary habits.

The migration of the familiar White Stork of central Europe has been studied by means of banded birds, and the more easily on account of its semidomestic nature. In Holland, Germany, Hungary, Denmark, Sweden, and southern Russia a great number of nestlings were thus marked. From those recaptured, it is established that the birds from this area winter regularly in South Africa, some 9000 kilometers distant in a straight line. But the returns show that the birds do not take a direct course southward. Instead there are two distinct routes by which the birds reach their winter home: the first is an eastern route across Hungary and the Balkan States to Asia Minor and Palestine, thence southward along the great valley of the Nile and the African lakes to South Africa; the second route is by way of France and Spain to Gibraltar and thence across the western Sahara to the lake region of central Africa. The region of the River Weser in western Germany is at about the dividing line between the two groups of birds, those to the *east* of this line migrating by the first route, those to the *west* by the second, while those in the Weser region itself go indifferently by one or the other. The return migration in spring is by the same routes, the birds breeding in western Europe coming back by way of

Gibraltar, those of eastern Europe by way of the Nile valley, Syria, and the Balkans. In other words, it seems as if they endeavor to avoid crossing any considerable body of water but follow over a land route either way.

It was discovered further that in 83 cases birds banded in the nest returned to the neighborhood of their origin, possibly following the old birds. They do not breed, however, until their second year, but wander irregularly about, until in the second spring they settle down usually in the neighborhood of their original home. There are also a certain number of old and young that do not breed but stay in small groups in the general region. In four cases birds were killed shortly after departure for the south whose actual time of leaving was known. These birds were found to have averaged 12 ̄ miles a day at first, but the average pace is slower later on for it takes them two and a half to three months to reach South Africa. The return migration in spring is nearly twice as fast, occupying about three or four weeks. I have dwelt upon the stork at length because its case illustrates a few of the many points that can be established through returns from banded birds.

Several species of herons have been banded in Europe, and appear to migrate uniformly in fall to the west and southwest, in part coastwise. An interesting thing is the tendency of immature birds to wander in all directions from their home grounds as soon as they can shift for themselves, a sort of explosion in all directions from the colony. This was found to be the case with the Black-crowned Night Heron (*Nycticorax nycticorax*), the Common Heron (*Ardea cinerea*), and other species, and is quite in accord with results obtained from marking birds in our own country, especially in case of the Night Heron colonies at Wenham and Barnstable. Pheasants and partridges were proved to be very stationary.

In 1911 and 1912 the Biological Society of Gothenburg banded 154 young of the Rough-legged Hawk in Swedish Lapland, of which twenty were subsequently captured in their winter wanderings. Most of them had taken a southerly direction along the Swedish coast to Germany and Hungary. One bird captured on its wintering ground in East Prussia was retaken two winters later at no great distance away in Brandenburg Province, showing the tendency to return to the same general wintering place. In another instance it was proved that the Duck Hawk may breed the spring following its hatching, and while still in the first year's plumage.

In Europe the Common Swift (*Cypselus apus*) is a familiar species breeding under eaves of houses. They return yearly to the same spot to nest, and there are two cases on record where the same pair of mated birds returned for three successive years to the same identical nest-box, showing an exemplary marital faithfulness.

An Hungarian observer banded upwards of 2000 of the common House Martins and Swallows in nesting colonies with most interesting results. He proved that with both species the same individuals return to their homes with remarkable regularity, nesting yearly not only in or on the the same building but frequently using the same nest from season to season. One swallow used the same nest for six successive years. In some cases the same two birds were found to be mated for several years; in other cases, marked birds found new mates in later years or even mated with a different bird for a second brood in the same season, as Mr. S. P. Baldwin found the House Wrens may do in

Ohio.   English-bred swallows have been retaken in winter in South Africa.

The European Nutcracker, a northern bird somewhat like our western species, is one that breaks out at intervals in an invasion into southern Europe.   One of these invasions, occurring in October, 1917, gave opportunity for banding many, of which four were subsequently recovered at localities indicating that the invasion had continued in a general southwesterly direction at a rate of from 7 to 20 miles a day.

The movements of the Starling are interesting to us on account of its growing abundance here, since its introduction in New York City in 1890.   From the many returns of banded birds, it seems that in Holland and England Starlings are practically resident the year round in the case of individual birds.   A little farther from the influence of the sea, as in Finland, Norway, Denmark, and northern Germany, while some birds do not migrate, many others do, passing along the coasts of the North Sea to Holland, northern France, and the British Isles.   This means a great increase of the Starling population in England during the winter.   Many from south-central Europe, as Austria and Hungary, move still farther south and west to Italy, southern France, Spain, and even Algeria, while their places are partly taken in the winter season by others from still farther north.   Young Starlings banded in the nest were found to be of independent nature and start wandering as soon as they are strong on the wing.   They start migrating before the adults, too, for young banded in the Baltic Provinces were taken in North Germany and Holland even in July. In many cases such young birds were found to have returned to their home locality to nest in following years, sometimes for four or five seasons, as proved by their numbered bands.

Many finches are found to be non-migratory as to individual birds, such for example as the House Sparrow, Bulfinch, Goldfinch. Skylarks, though migratory in central Europe where the winters are severe, are not so in the British Isles or on the southwest coasts of Europe where the climate is more equable.

Other interesting results were had with nuthatches and several species of tits (or chickadees). Thus, many nuthatches banded in winter at a feeding station were found nesting in the neighborhood the following spring, returning again in the succeeding winter to the feeding station. The young broods, however, in some cases stayed in the locality of their home the following winter, but in others seemed to disperse entirely to other regions. The case of titmice is somewhat similar. Adult birds that have once settled in a locality were found to keep rather closely to it throughout the year in central Europe, whereas the young birds seem to forsake it completely. At all events of 100 young Great Tits (*Parus major*) banded one summer in Hungary, not one appeared the following year at the feeding station frequented by their parents, and of 170 Coal Tits (*Parus ater*) banded as nestlings, only one turned up the next winter at the feeding station, although many of the parent birds of the region came regularly. Yet in the following spring a few of these young birds *did* return to nest in the land of their birth. These results indicate that many of the migrant tits must be young of the year, and in our own country there is evidence of the same thing. It will be interesting when we are able to assemble sufficient facts, to compare the ways of our own with the European tits.

Some of the European thrushes seem to behave rather similarly, for of over 100 young of the European Blackbird (*Turdus merula*) banded at Frankfurt, Germany, only one was known to have returned to its home region, and of another 100 banded in the Berlin Zoölogical Gardens, only two were known to have returned to that neighborhood in succeeding years, while of 120 nestlings banded at Hamburg, Germany, not one was ever heard from again.

Finally, an interesting case is recorded of a Robin Redbreast that returned for at least two seasons to the same winter quarters in Holland, just as we now know with our Tree Sparrow the same individuals come back to the same region with which they are familiar, to spend the winter.

Many other additional cases could be given of banded birds that throw light on the nature of their individual movements. Already the results obtained in our own country are important. The work of Mr. S. Prentiss Baldwin in Ohio and in Georgia is now familiar. He has shown that in Georgia the resident species are very sedentary, seldom going far from their chosen haunt, and that the migrants arriving in early spring are birds that have passed that way before and are returning over a known route familiar to them. All this goes to show that migration is not a haphazard wandering but a definite and orderly proceeding. We are measurably nearer a solution of its causes and methods. The point to be emphasized from this brief review of some of the European investigations is that there is no general rule. Every species is a law unto itself, and even the same species may behave very differently in different parts of its range. Some remain in the same place if climate and food-supply favor, while others leave for more clement skies if the winter seasons are too rigorous in their nesting area so as to deprive them of their necessary food.   In still other cases, birds that are usually sedentary, rarely going far from special haunts, are at times forced out from great areas for reasons that we do not yet wholly understand.   Familiar instances are the occasional winter invasions of Crossbills, Redpolls, or Pine Grosbeaks, which may then visit us in numbers.   Such eruptions are presumably due to the failure of food in the northern haunts.   Crossbills, for example, come in winters when the crop of spruce cones in the northern forests fails them. Thus in the fall of 1924 there was an unusual influx of Arctic Three-toed Woodpeckers into eastern New England, even reaching New Jersey, possibly as a result of the great spring and summer drought in parts of Canada and a consequent reduction in the supply of bark-beetle larvæ that cannot well sustain great dryness.   This bird is resident the year round in the northern forests and its visits to this State are most exceptional.

Such diversity in the manner of migration in different birds points, I think, to the conclusion that each migratory species has developed this habit of changing its seasonal haunts in accordance with its own separate need and in its own particular way.   Yet we can probably trace the steps in the evolution of migration by taking examples here and there from birds that show this trait in greater or lesser degree.   The fact that the Starlings in England remain all the year surely indicates that here there is no need for migration since the birds can sustain themselves the year round.   The further fact that they are joined by others from no great distance north and east where winter conditions are severe, must prove that in this species migration is partly developed among those individuals that have need to move. They go only so far as is necessary to reach stable conditions where they can remain comfortably. Unlike the Golden Plover they do not undertake a trip to the southern hemisphere.

We have acquired a great deal of information as to the manner of bird migration, its time, its destination in general, the lines of flight. We still must solve these two questions: (1) why do birds migrate, and (2) how do those that make long journeys over land and sea find their way?

One of the primary causes of migration is no doubt the need for seeking a sufficient food-supply. Thus it seems obvious that the insect-eating birds that live among foliage are forced to leave us with the autumnal disappearance of the insects and the fall of the protecting foliage. In case of the simpler types of migration, this supply may be close at hand. Thus a Song Sparrow might easily winter in southern New England if it retired from a brush-grown pasture to a neighboring swamp with a brook that kept always open. The swamp might be nearer or farther off, involving a migration perhaps of only a few rods or miles. Some South American birds are known to make a vertical migration, coming to the sea level in winter and ascending to higher levels among the Andes in summer, as in case of Condors and Flamingos. This tides over the winter season; but what sends birds back from their winter to their summer homes? Various causes have been suggested, such as the need for suitable nest-sites, of which the warmer or tropic haunts might not offer a sufficient quantity, or it may be the need for certain sorts of food, or greater quantities. No doubt many species when nesting require a certain average area of domain and so are much spread out at this time. Agriculturalists have worked out the approximate number of acres of particular kinds of land that are needed to sustain a single cow or a sheep, and similar facts may be learned in a more or less approximate way for birds. Counts of the numbers of each species nesting in relatively large areas of the same kind of country, such as those made by Forbes and Gross (1922) in the level parts of Illinois, show strikingly that the average number of Mourning Doves, for instance, that may populate a certain territory is relatively small and does not increase beyond a certain maximum. There is a spatial element that roughly controls the number of bird inhabitants of a single species, or of several species that can, by reason of some diversity of habits, get along together and find sustenance and living room in a given area. A suggestive article by English (1923) puts forth the idea that birds may migrate from the southern tropical latitudes to the high north for the benefit derived from a longer period of daylight. He postulates the fact that the tropical or subtropical representatives of a species usually lay fewer eggs than those of the more temperate climes. Thus the Mockingbirds of the West Indies lay usually three eggs, but five is usual farther north; the West Indian forms of Yellow and Prairie Warblers seldom lay more than two eggs, but four or five in our latitude. This may mean that the stationary species are unable to raise more than these numbers of young, or that the danger for the migratory form is more. In late May and early June, the height of the nesting season, there are about 12¼ hours of daylight under the equator, 14 to 16 near the tropic, 18 in the latitude of England, and nearly 24 in parts of Scandinavia. The birds' "working day" in our latitude may therefore be nearly half again as long as in the Tropics, giving time to rear more young, or perhaps spreading the additional labor over more time so that the strain is less. It is interesting to see that in night birds the rule may work the other way, too; for in the north the Nighthawk and Whippoorwill lay but two eggs and their "working night" is shorter than those of tropical relatives, as the Frog-mouths, Oil-birds, and other Nighthawks that lay three or four eggs and have a longer night to work in. The suggestion is a good one despite objections that may arise. One might even add that the waning year with days already shorter in August is a cause of *southward* migration to keep pace with a longer day, more hours of activity, and shorter daily periods without food. We shall be in a better position to test this theory when we know how much food migratory birds need daily and how long they can go fasting without discomfort. Such perhaps are some of the more immediate causes of migration.

With an increasing distance of migration comes in the second and most puzzling fact. How does the bird find its way? This, after all, is the great mystery of bird migration. But even this, I think, will eventually be made plain. With some birds we know that in autumn adults precede the young in the first southward movements so that it may be they act as guides for the latter on the journey already familiar to themselves. Thus with some of the warblers or some of the shore-birds (for example the Black-breasted Plover) the adults first appear from the north and later the young with a proportion of older birds. Many birds migrate by day, as swallows or Nighthawks that feed as they go; others travel mainly by night, perhaps from one feeding station or resting-place to another, as in case of the

SNOW GEESE AT CURRITUCK

Courtesy of Albert F. Bigelow, phot.

Ruddy Duck. On almost any autumn night in eastern New England the frequent calls of passing warblers, sparrows, and thrushes come to us from no great distance overhead, and we may suppose that by these notes old and young are enabled to keep in touch as they pass southward. By contrast, in the spring these notes are seldom heard. Are we to conclude that there is less need for comradeship on the return journey? An interesting trait with many common species is that the males arrive in spring before the females. This is true of the Robin, the Bronzed Grackle and the Red-winged Blackbird, as well as sundry others. Apparently in these cases the first arrivals of males include birds that are returning to a familiar breeding ground. Still other birds migrate in fall in families, both parents and young together, as in the case of the Canada Geese; while in others still, the young seem to act more or less independently. Thus the records of banded birds show, unexpectedly, that with the Black-crowned Night Heron, the young on attaining their growth start off in all directions, north, south, east or west from the home colony going often long distances northward in summer, before retreating southward in autumn. Young banded Starlings were found even in July to have traveled from northern Germany to Holland, long before the parents move, and such young appear to return in later years to the place of their birth in certain cases. The movements of these young birds in summer seem more in the nature of erratic wanderings than of real migration, yet it may be that they learn a good deal of country in this way. Later in the year such birds presumably reach their usual winter quarters, but exactly how this is accomplished we do not yet know.

It is supposed that with many migratory species definite routes are learned through following prominent topographical features, such as great north-and-south river valleys or coast-lines. On the other hand some species of birds, as will later be shown, can find their way over long stretches of sea where there are no landmarks to guide them. Birds, then, appear to have a good sense of locality, if such it may be called, nor is this surprising perhaps, when we consider their mobility and the wider sweep of horizon that the altitude of their flight gives them.

That birds may quickly learn a new migration route and thus take advantage of new territory is perhaps indicated by the visits of the Evening Grosbeak to New England in recent years. This fine bird breeds in western Alberta and, in slightly different form from southern British Columbia and northwestern Montana southward at higher altitudes and eastward to the Rocky Mountains of Colorado and New Mexico. In winter it regularly appears east of the Rockies to the Mississippi Valley. Its presence in New England was practically unknown previous to the winter of 1889–90 when a considerable incursion took place into various of the New England States, where they attracted much attention by their handsome livery. For over twenty years no more were seen here, until in 1903 a single bird was reported from Cape Cod, and in the next winter a number came. Since that time hardly a winter has passed without a visit from these birds to our section of the country so that we have come now to regard them almost as much a winter visitor to be expected as the Pine Grosbeaks and Crossbills and Redpolls. Had it been possible to "band" some of these many visitors and discover if they returned in succeeding years, we might believe that these pioneers had repeated their previous journey and with others had learned a new route to the East, which has now by traditional use become familiar to certain groups of these birds. It is possible, as first suggested I think, by the late Dr. Walter Faxon, that the frequent planting of the Box Elder of late years in central Canada and parts of the West, has been a factor in tolling the birds across to the Atlantic coast, for the seeds of this tree are a favorite food and are probably to be had in much greater abundance now than fifty years ago over the intermediate country. The ability to return to a given spot is a matter depending in part upon close observation and in part upon a training in finding the way. The unknown factor now is whether this knowledge can become automatic or as we say "instinctive." We may therefore think of bird migration, even in its most developed form, as a specialized "homing instinct," the precise working of which must still remain for further study.

The desire to return to some particular spot which with ourselves may be called "home," is a very widespread one. It is found not only in mammals and birds, but in fishes that come back to spawn in their natal streams, and a certain "homing instinct" has lately been proved in case of salamanders. It is strong in ourselves as well. What Englishman is there, in whatever remote corner of earth, to whom England is not "home," and in whom there is ever a fond hope of returning to spend his old age?

Traces of an attachment for familiar localities are shown in very humble forms of life. The common limpet of our tide pools may possess it in marked degree. A recent author has given the results of his investigations on limpets of two genera which he marked by filing grooves in their shells for later identification.   In this way he followed the watery wanderings of several of these snail-like creatures for a number of days, keeping a tracing of their track.   At high water they would crawl freely about over a radius of one or two feet, but showed a marked tendency to come back between tides to a particular spot, often for several days at a time, then would move on to another place that seemed worth staying in for a longer period.   Bees have highly developed homing faculties, but apparently learn the location of the hive and its neighborhood before they are able to return by air-line from very far.   Ants show the same thing.

In many birds the results of bird-banding have already shown that not only do birds have summer homes to which they regularly return, but that the same individuals have likewise *winter* localities to which they as regularly resort in the winter season.   In birds, therefore, we may now suppose that the "homing instinct" or desire to seek a certain spot is in migratory species of a two-fold nature: for in spring the bird is driven to seek its special nesting area and in autumn is equally drawn to the wintering home.   The two forces are of equal strength and alternate in their action.   It is a normal response to the pulse of the year.

But how do birds find their way over thousands of miles back to the same dooryard or tree?   There is the real mystery!   And although the solution is not yet reached, the following experiments are suggestive of lines of attack in finding the answer.

It is an interesting thing that this homing faculty can be developed in such a non-migratory bird as our common pigeon, in which one would least suspect its presence.

Those who keep Carrier Pigeons know very well that individual birds vary greatly in their ability to find their way, and that a bird must not only develop this ability but must also in some degree know the country over which it is flown in order to obtain best results. In some experiments conducted by Hodge (1894) a number of years ago, he endeavored to learn something definite concerning this so-called homing instinct. He took five young birds from Massachusetts to Madison, Wisconsin, and placed them in a pigeon-loft the only view from which was directly against the wall of an adjacent building. After six months these birds were released from their loft for the first time, one by one, and their actions watched. In each case the pigeon released flew to a nearby roof and sat for a number of minutes looking this way and that. The first bird, for example, sat fifteen minutes on one side of a chimney, then flitted to the other side of the chimney and stood there five minutes gazing carefully about. It then flew to another house farther off, then to a still more distant one, each time carefully scanning its surroundings as before. Finally it flew off out of sight behind a hill and after half an hour returned to its loft. Each of the pigeons loosed for the first time behaved in practically the same way, as if they were gaining a knowledge of their original surroundings and then a little of the neighboring country. All these were young birds not previously released. One of the *old* birds acted quite differently when released at Madison. After circling a few times, it flew straight away and was not seen for three days, when failing no doubt to find trace of the familiar Massachusetts country, it returned to the loft. After Hodge's

pigeons had been given a few days of freedom in order that
they might learn the exact location of their home, six were
picked out at random and carried in an open wire cage to
the top of a hill about half a mile distant, while at the same
time six others, also taken at random, were carried to the
same spot in a cage closely wrapped in a black shawl. Of
the first six pigeons, five on being released started for home
at once, one, however, after a few preliminary side swings;
while the sixth starting in the wrong direction, finally turned
and alighted on the first house in the home direction. The
comparison with the six birds loosed from the covered cage
is most instructive. Not a single one made a direct course
for home. Two began circling in the wrong direction, one
of them going far astray and searching over the entire city
of Madison. The others, after circling or swinging back
and forth a few times, finally saw familiar ground and
headed for home. There seemed to be, then, no *instinctive*
sense of direction. The birds in the open cage were able
to see how they were going and so to keep in mind the general direction of their home-loft and, when released, easily
started in the right way, while those in the covered cage
had to recover from the break in continuity of their position
and make a general survey of their surroundings until some
familiar part was found to give them their location.

Watson and Lashley (1915) have gathered some interesting notes on long-distance flight in Homing Pigeons.
American fanciers have for years trained and raced these
pigeons, and some very remarkable flights have been made,
even of one thousand miles and over. The method is to
train the more capable birds at first over short distances and
then gradually to increase the distance a hundred miles at a

time, up to one thousand miles. The story of Hobo, a bird
that once held the world's record for this distance, is a most
interesting one. He made a number of flights during three
years of distances gradually increasing up to 400 and 617
miles (Little Rock, Arkansas, to Milwaukee). The fourth
year (1901) the bird was taken, after preliminary distances,
to Houston, Texas, a thousand miles away in an air line,
and there liberated with twenty-five others. All the birds
took the homeward course at once, and Hobo was the first
to arrive at Milwaukee, after an absence of 9 days, 20
hours, 15 minutes. This performance has since been
beaten many times. A world champion, Bullet D-1872,
loosed at Abilene, Texas, reached its loft in Fort Wayne,
Indiana, an air-line distance of 1010 miles in 1 day, 11 hours,
6 seconds, which in contrast to Hobo's record, may indicate a continuous flight. Other birds in similar flights
made the distance in a few hours more. But this remarkable faculty is not found in all the birds. Thus out of 100
Homing Pigeons trained on flights of 500 to 700 miles in
the direction from Baltimore to Key West, not one ever
returned when they were released at Key West. The action of the homing birds may vary, some starting directly
for home, others circling first. A speed of fifty miles an
hour is a good average on the mid-distance flights.

In the South Sea Islands, Frigate Birds are used after
the manner of Homing Pigeons to carry messages between
islands.

Further studies were made by Watson and Lashley on
Noddy and Sooty Terns in the nesting colonies of the
Tortugas, off the Florida coast. These birds arrive there
in late April to breed and leave again in September. With

these species it seemed there would be less chance of their returning from a distance by the aid of landmarks, for the small islet where they nested is surrounded by ocean. In three different years marked Sooty and Noddy Terns were carried varying distances and released. They seemed to have little difficulty in returning and were usually back in a few hours even when carried to Key West, 65 miles away. Going farther, three Noddies and two Sooties were taken by steamer in the direction of New York, and released off Cape Hatteras, approximately 850 miles in a direct line. Nearly six days later both Sooties were back at their respective nests, and several days later one of the Noddy Terns, plainly marked with dabs of oil paint, was also seen back at the nesting colony, but its mate had meanwhile formed new "affiliations" so that it was not permitted to alight on its nest.

Six of each species taken to New York Harbor and there released were never heard of more, though this was no doubt in part due to the poor condition in which they reached that place. Better results attended birds placed in covered cages and released in the Gulf of Mexico, some 460 miles west of their nesting colony. Of the seven birds (four Sooties, three Noddies) all with one exception started back east on being freed, while the seventh, after a short flight west, came about suddenly and departed eastward with the others, all flying within a few feet of the water. Two of the Noddies returned, each in three days, but none of the four Sooties was ever seen again. This is the first successful flight of a homing bird over open water with no shoreline visible.

In a second attempt, twelve of each species were taken by boat to Galveston, Texas, and released as follows:

2 Noddies released at 418 miles from Key West, none returned.
6 Sooties, 4 Noddies released at 585 miles from Key West; 5 Sooties, 3 Noddies returned.
6 Sooties, 4 Noddies released at 855 miles from Key West; 2 Sooties, 1 Noddy returned.

Of the last three (Galveston), the two Sooties returned in 6 and 7 ¼ days, the Noddy in twelve days. These results are the more remarkable, for the birds reached Galveston tired out by confinement, and when freed went at once to fishing.

The conclusion seems warranted that these two species can find their way over nearly 1000 miles of open sea. Exactly how this is accomplished is not yet clear, nor do various suggested explanations seem to bring the solution nearer. The experimenters consider, however, that a distinction may be drawn between what they call "proximate orientation," that is, where the bird gets its bearings through recognition of familiar surroundings near home (as in the case of Hodge's pigeons), and "distant orientation," where the bird takes the right course when far from any such visual aid. It is the latter faculty which birds making long-distance migration seem to possess, and the explanation of which we still seek. We must recall, however, that these birds have probably been migrating for an immensely long period, and a route as long as that now taken, for example, by the Golden Plover, may have only gradually become of such length. The learning of the route may have been an age-long process, or there may be other explanations. At all events, the case of the homing pigeons seems to indicate an ability to keep constantly oriented with regard to a given spot, so that as we say of ourselves, the bird does not lose its bearings. Exactly how this is accomplished remains to be explained. At present speculation is fascinating but until more facts are at hand on which to build, it is rather futile. Nevertheless the experimental study by means of marked birds may confidently be expected to solve the question eventually. After all, it is a blessing to know that there still *is* a mystery to tantalize us.

CHAPTER XIV

NOMENCLATURE AND CLASSIFICATION

To most persons not professional naturalists, the subject of scientific nomenclature is one of vast mystery, and classification is even farther remote from their known world. But this need not be so. Nomenclature is merely the naming of things in a logical way so that in talking of them we may have some word or words that will indicate the same thing universally, as well to an American as to an educated Russian. Nomenclature, or the naming of things, began no doubt with early man as soon as he learned to communicate with his fellows. Yet his wants were probably simple. Among the jolly African natives, we see the early stages of nomenclature. Large or easily distinguished birds, for example, are given simple names, but most of the smaller host are just "little birds." So in Xenophon's account of the Ten Thousand Greeks and their march through Asia Minor, any small bird was called *struthós,* or sparrow, while the Ostrich which they saw for the first time was named *megalós struthós,* or the big sparrow. Nomenclature implies then (1) a distinction between objects as well as (2) a grouping of similar ones under distinctive names. Men early learned to distinguish birds into groups with certain common characteristics, as owls, hawks, ducks, swans, sparrows. Such words indicate the kind, or in Latin the *gens* or *genus.* The Latin word *Anas* or duck is therefore a generic term. But when more intimate knowledge led to distinguishing more than one kind of duck, some descriptive word had to be added. So in the earlier natural histories we find this done. Latin was the universal language of scholars long after the Roman Empire fell and is in some degree to this day. The earlier books on natural history in the 16th and 17th centuries were nearly all in this language, and even in the early part of the 19th century Latin was the language of works on classification. As knowledge grew, and more careful distinctions were made, the number of birds or other animals of a single "kind" or "genus" was found often to be many, so that with the generic name additional descriptive words had to be used. Thus in Aldrovandus's Ornithology, late in the 16th century, the Indian Kite was spoken of as *Falco rubris alis Indicus* (the Indian Falcon with red wings), though for better-known birds he used a single term as *Chrysaëtus* for the Golden Eagle, or *Aquila alba* for the white-tailed species. Obviously to use an entire descriptive phrase each time one wished to speak of a particular sort of bird, is inconvenient, nor would everyone use the same combination, so that naturalists in writing of different animals came to use as short and distinctive phrases as possible. Botanists in particular set the fashion.

In 1707 was born Carolus Linnæus, as his name is Latinized, a Swedish naturalist, who conceived the idea of preparing a brief descriptive catalogue of all the known plants and animals of the world. The first edition of this great work appeared in 1735 and before the century was out had reached no less than thirteen editions, the last of which was edited by this great man's pupil, Gmelin. As this task progressed Linnæus apparently felt that there must be some concise way of naming the thousands of different plants and animals so that they might be referred to conveniently, rather than described by a phrase. His system was therefore to use a Latin noun for each large group or genus of related beings, and a second word, either a descriptive adjective or an appropriate noun, for the species. Unlike his predecessors, therefore, he came to use consistently only two names to signify each distinct sort of plant or animal: first the kind, or generic name, as *Anas* for a duck, followed by the sort or specific name, as *acuta* (sharp), thus *Anas acuta* Linnæus for the Pintail (meaning sharp-tailed duck), or a noun, as *sponsa* (a bride), for the Wood Duck or Bride Duck. This use of two names is called therefore *bionomial* nomenclature, for it implies two terms, the first of which designates *similarity,* and is called the *genus* or generic name; while the second denotes *diversity* and is called the *species* or specific name.

Zoölogists are now in agreement that the 10th edition of Linnæus's great work, the Systema Naturæ, published in 1758, be taken as the starting-point for the nomenclature of vertebrate animals. Since Linnæus's day, and indeed during his lifetime, the discovery and naming of animals and plants progressed apace, nor have we quite yet reached the complete inventory of the kinds of either. It frequently befell that the same species was named and described more than once, either because two persons chanced to be working unknown to each other, on the same subject, or different sexes, plumages, or parts of one and the same thing were thought to represent distinct species, or in other ways it came about that more than one Latin name was given the same animal. In such cases we in later years have tried to find out the *first* name published, and this becomes the recognized name of the species, all the others synonyms, unless indeed the first specific name prove to have already been used in the same genus, when it is ruled out, for the name is thereby "preoccupied" and the first available of the synonyms must then take its place. Or if there are no such, a new name must be coined. It may be imagined that with the many writers and many species to be named, it often happens that a name already in use is given to some such second species. But the rule is purely a logical one: that no two species can have the same combination of names. It is due to these efforts to run down the earliest published names and to identify them certainly that those of many birds, for example, have been changed during the intensive work of recent years. Much as we may regret the inconvenience of such changes in our own day, the ideal of a final stable result for the future is the goal of present efforts. We are unfortunately still passing through this period of revision of names.

The name of the original describer of a species follows the Latin name, and in case a change is subsequently made by transferring the species described to some other genus, the author's name is enclosed in parenthesis. This is often a puzzle to printers and others who mistake the omission of the parenthesis for a clerical error, and add one where none should be. For while the *species* name once properly given cannot be changed, the name of the *genus* may be, if some later investigator finds the species has been erroneously placed, or if on more careful study it seems best to regroup species once thought of as belonging to a single genus. Thus we now call the Wood Duck *Lampronessa sponsa* (Linnæus). Difficulties often arise from not being able to tell certainly from a description alone what species is meant. Names were formerly based in many cases upon published pictures of birds, but the best usage is to designate a particular specimen as the one described and this becomes the *type specimen,* to which reference is made in case of future doubts. Type specimens should be most carefully preserved, preferably in some large museum of general accessibility.

Such, very briefly, are the general methods of naming species. Yet difficulties and most unexpected complications sometimes arise, to be decided often with difficulty. The more exact study of single species has shown, too, that in some cases further refinement in distinction can be made. In a wide-ranging bird, for instance the Horned Lark, that occurs from the arctic regions to the barrens of certain mountains in northern South America, the different climatic conditions in various parts of its range produce a gradual change, so that northern birds may be large and bright-colored, the desert-living ones pale and small, while those of other areas are still different, yet all are Horned Larks. Where these differences correspond with certain geographic areas, each with its particular climatic conditions, a *sub-species* is recognized and a third name, or trinomial, is given it. Often it is difficult to tell where one subspecies leaves off and another begins, so gradual may be the change from one to the other extreme. Sometimes, too, the change is fairly abrupt so that there is doubt whether to call two closely allied birds distinct species or whether they may be considered each a subspecies of a single kind of bird. A convenient test is that if all the specimens can be referred without doubt to one or the other sort, they are species, as in the case of our Downy and Hairy Woodpeckers, which agree essentially in most characters except size and in certain dark marks on the tail. With subspecies, however, there are, at least on the borders of adjoining ranges, individuals that are intermediate in one way or another, so that the extremes are completely bridged. This is called *intergradation*.

Nomenclature, or this system of giving names, offers also a means whereby we may express the relationships of living beings by arranging them in groups according to their kind. Thus the various geographic subspecies constitute a single species. By grouping together closely related species we form a genus, and several nearly similar genera may constitute a family, or a family may include a single genus if no near relatives are known.

In zoölogy the family name is made by adding the ending *-idæ* to the stem of the name of the original or type genus. The larger divisions of birds are orders, and may include one or more families or only a single species in an order, depending partly on the importance of the differences and in part on our estimate of their importance. Such a classification is first of all for convenience, but its usefulness is increased by making it express our knowledge of relationships. Since this knowledge is imperfect, so is our arrangement of groups liable to error and gradual correction.

The earliest classification of animals had usually much to do with their use from a human standpoint. Thus in the 11th chapter of Leviticus, the Mosaic law divides birds into those which were "unclean" or not fit to eat and those which were suitable for food. "And these are they which ye shall have in abomination among the fowls; they shall not be eaten, they are an abomination; the eagle, the ossifrage, and the ospray. And the vulture, and the kite after his kind; every raven after his kind; and the owl, and the night hawk, and the cuckow, and the hawk after his kind, and the little owl, and the cormorant, and the great owl, and the swan, and the pelican, and the geir-eagle, and the stork, the heron after her kind, and the lapwing, and the bat." It will be seen that most of these birds are flesh-eaters, and some carrion-eaters, whence perhaps the "abomination"; yet I have eaten cormorant on occasion and liked it well enough.

In the ancient library of Nineveh, dating from about B. C. 668, there have been found inscribed tablets showing that the Assyrians had some knowledge of natural history and a rough classification of animals. Gregory (1910) has quoted briefly from this account, and states that birds were divided into classes such as those of rapid flight, sea birds, or marsh birds. In the Middle Ages the utilitarian point of view was that with which people were most concerned. Thus an account of the Swallow in 1584 mentions chiefly that its ashes are good for improving the eyesight, whereas the smoke from a burning swallow produces blindness.

But a true classification must be based on genealogy, just as our own family trees are based on relationships. For this reason we find it out of the question to arrange the species of living birds in a continuous series that shall express their degree of kinship, simply because all living species are contemporaries, and rarely do we know much of their ancestry. The best analogy is that of a many-branched tree, whose leaves are all at the flattened top. Every leaf will represent a living species of bird, each cluster of leaves a genus, and each group of twigs whose stems run to a common branch may be a family. That is, the various related groups have diverged in their development but trace their ancestry back to a common stock in the more or less remote past. The living species of to-day are represented in a cross-section of the topmost twigs. Many groups are easily made from adjacent twigs but often there are long branches whose living species are not obviously related to their near contemporaries. These are often isolated primitive species, such as the New Zealand *Apteryx,* that have survived here and there like living fossils, with no near relatives now known.

There have been many attempts to arrange birds in an orderly sequence, beginning with the most primitive and passing to the more specialized. There has been much research, much diversity of opinion, but at the present day a general agreement has been nearly reached and it remains to settle the minor points. The system proposed by Fürbringer in 1888 is the basis of the most modern classification of birds, and this has been amplified by Gadow, Sharpe, Beddard, and others. It will suffice to give the outline of this, without attempting to enumerate the distinctive traits of the different divisions.

The known species of birds are divided into two great groups: (1) Archæornithes or ancient birds, and (2) Neornithes or later birds. The first group includes only the *Archæopteryx* or lizard-tailed bird, that extraordinary fossil from the Jurassic slates of Bavaria. The second group includes the rest of the known birds. They are placed in twenty-one chief groups or orders, and the name of each order is given the uniform ending *"-iformes,"* just as each of its families has the ending *"-idæ"* plus the stem of the type genus.

Beginning with the fossil toothed birds, *Hesperornis* and *Ichthyornis,* each of which is placed in a separate order,

DOUBLE-WATTLED CASSOWARY (*Casuarius galeatus*)
Courtesy of National Zoölogical Park

there come next the true Ostriches, the Rheas or South American ostriches, the cassowaries, the extinct New Zealand moas, the extinct giant-birds of Madagascar, and the kiwis or *Apteryxes* of New Zealand, each of which is considered to have the rank of a separate order. All these are in many important points of structure primitive birds, survivors from very ancient times. They were formerly placed in a separate group called the Ratite birds on account of lacking a keel on the breastbone, but it is now believed that this distinction is of less importance, for the keel was independently added as a support for muscles in the species of strong flight. The partridge-like tinamous of South America are by some placed near these ostrich-like birds. They show likeness to the Ostriches in the structure of the palate, but otherwise have leanings toward the fowls. No doubt they retain certain primitive characters once common to many birds.

The penguins form a special order (Sphenisciformes) and are among the most primitive of living birds in many ways. Their feathers are almost scale-like on the wings, which are highly modified for swimming. The bones of their skulls are less solidly fused than with most birds. They have no special feather tracts, but are uniformly covered, and their tarsal bones are barely fused into a cannon bone, for traces of the three original bones still appear.

The loons and grebes form a single order (Colymbiformes) though the two types, one with webbed, the other with lobed toes, constitute each a separate division or family. The petrels and albatrosses form a group (Procellariiformes) not nearly related to any of the others; all are birds of the open sea and have peculiar tubular nostrils.

Next comes the large assemblage of stork-like birds, which includes a various company, some very unlike the others. Thus the cormorants and gannets, herons, true storks, ibises, and flamingos are grouped in this order, Ciconi-iformes, each, however, constituting a distinct family.

Of this group the cormorants retain a hooked beak which is likewise seen in embryo herons. But the other members have it straight and tapering for fish-catching, a trait probably acquired therefore as a later adaptation. Some are web-footed, and the division comprising tropic-birds, pelicans, cormorants, darters, gannets, and frigate-birds is peculiar in having all four toes included in the web. The herons and storks have adopted tree and land habits to such a degree that the web has disappeared and the legs and toes are lengthened, but the flamingo combines the web on three front toes and the elongated leg. The duck-like birds are perhaps not distantly related but with the South American screamers, which are a sort of land duck, perhaps of a primitive ancestral kind, they constitute a separate order (Anseriformes). The vultures, falcons, eagles, kites, and hawks are probably more nearly akin to cormorants and herons than we are apt to think, though placed in a group by themselves (Falconiformes). Their hooked beaks and strong feet recall those of the cormorants. The order Gal-liformes is a very distinct and rather primitive group including the pheasants and fowls. A remarkable feature of one of the groups of this order, the Curassows, fowl-like birds of tropical America, is that they build a nest in a tree and lay two eggs only. The curious Hoatzin, with claws in the wing-fingers of the young, is included here as an aberrant branch. All the living fowls are land birds, but some have traces of a web between the toes.

EUROPEAN FLAMINGOS (*Phœnicopterus roseus*) AT THE NATIONAL ZOÖLOGICAL PARK
Courtesy of National Zoölogical Park

The crane-like birds (Gruiformes) are poorly represented in North America, but include a few cranes and
rails. One, the Whooping Crane, is now nearly extinct,
though formerly common. An interesting but small point
of difference between herons and cranes is that, although
both are long-legged and long-necked, the herons, in flying,
curl the long neck in an S-shape with the head drawn back
near the shoulders, but the cranes and rails hold it stretched
out in front. In the structure of palate (schizognathous)
and nostrils (slit-like) they differ anatomically from herons.
The young are præcocial.

A most interesting group of water birds is that containing the plover-like species (Charadriiformes). They illustrate very well what Osborn has called "adaptive radia-
tion"; that is, various members of the group have taken
up differing ways of life and become somewhat changed in
consequence. Huxley believed the true plovers (e. g., our
Golden Plover) were the most generalized of the group.
They are closely related to the sandpipers and snipes in
one direction, and to gulls and terns in another, the one
group being thus adapted for marsh and shore life, the
other to a different life along coasts or lakes, while a third
branch includes the auks, guillemots and puffins, with their
peculiar upright posture and diving habits. In another direction still the plover-type seems to lead to the pigeons,
which may therefore be thought of as water birds that have
taken up land habits. Traces of this former state are
seen perhaps in some of their traits, such as the readiness
with which they wade into water to bathe, sometimes even
alighting on the surface of deep water. They also delight
to lie or stand in quiet groups after feeding, just as gulls
do. There is a curious group of Old-World birds, called

sand-grouse, which in many ways indicate the transition from plovers to pigeons. They have somewhat the habits of quail, but are active by night.

There is an interesting point about the birds of all these orders of Neornithes so far mentioned, which is that they are *walkers* or *runners,* moving the legs alternately, and holding them out behind as they fly. Though some of them, (such as pigeons, hawks, and herons) may perch freely in trees, they are nevertheless typically ground birds and in this respect differ widely from the Passeriformes, or great order of perching birds which typically are twig-hoppers that jump from perch to perch, seizing it with both feet, and in flight holding the feet forward against the breast. The feet of these birds have four strong toes for grasping whereas in many of the walking types of birds the hind toe is reduced in size so as to be in some cases nearly function-less, or it has altogether disappeared. I believe this differ-ence is a very ancient one. The oldest known bird, *Arch-æopteryx,* has a typical perching foot, and I have not the slightest doubt that there existed at the same time other birds with a walking type of foot. The two types un-doubtedly go back an immense distance in time. Where passerine birds have taken again to ground habits, they have learned to walk or run, but this is probably a second-ary adaptation. The larks are walkers, some of the spar-rows run well, while others both hop or run, as the Robin that runs on comfortable flat surfaces, but hops if there is grass. This order, Passeriformes, includes most of the sparrow-, wren-, warbler-, and thrush-like birds, and con-tains over a third of the living species, approximately seven thousand in number. It is divided for convenience into about 65 families, but the general agreement in important characters is relatively close. As Gadow says, the chief structural difference between a Chickadee and a Crow is in size. This group of birds is usually considered the most specialized. They are chiefly of small or medium size, and the primaries are reduced to either ten or nine, while their syrinx has a more complex muscle system than in most other orders of birds. They include therefore the best singing birds, though in many the song is relatively simple or, as in the Crow, hardly developed. Yet even the Crow has many different modulations of his characteristic *caw*.

There are two other large and varied groups of land birds which are in many respects more primitive though perhaps not distantly related to the sparrow-like birds, namely the cuckoo-like birds (Cuculiformes) and the roller-like birds (Coraciiformes). The cuckoo tribe have a yoke-toed foot (two toes in front, two behind) and with them are now included the parrots, which evidently were separated long ago, for no living links are known. Their remains are found fossil in Miocene deposits in France. The rollers are Old-World birds, but they are related to the kingfishers, swifts, hummingbirds, woodpeckers, and goatsuckers. Most of us are not in the habit of thinking of owls as related to nighthawks and whippoorwills, but their place is really here rather than near the hawks with which they were formerly associated. A superficial point of resemblance is the fact that nearly all these birds lay white eggs, and most owls are, like the goatsuckers, night birds. The beautiful little bee-eaters surprise one by nesting in holes in a bank, like kingfishers.

While birds of both the cuckoo and the roller tribes are quite at home in trees, they are not active twig-hoppers. Parrots climb about in the branches by means of feet and bill, woodpeckers hitch themselves jerkily up the trunks or even hop rather clumsily on the ground, but most of these birds flit from spot to spot rather than walk, hop, or run. Their feet are often small and weak as in swifts and hummingbirds. It would be interesting to know how the feet are held in all these birds while flying. I am certain that in some cuckoos they are stretched behind, and this is the case also in owls. The legs are so short in others of these two groups that it is a point difficult to be certain of. Probably the primitive method of holding them out behind largely obtains however.

By way of convenient summary, the orders of birds are given again below, arranged in general beginning with the least specialized and ending with those that seem farthest from the original stock. This is the arrangement adopted by Knowlton and Ridgway (1909).

CLASS AVES.

Subclass I—ARCHÆORNITHES .....Archæopteryx

Subclass II—NEORNITHES ....

Order 1.—Hesperornithiformes .. Hesperornis

Order 2.—Ichthyornithiformes .. Ichthyornis

Order 3.—Struthioniformes .... True ostriches (Africa, India, fossil)

Order 4.—Rheiformes .... South American rheas

Order 5.—Casuariiformes ......Cassowaries and emus

Order 6.—Crypturiformes ......tinamous (South American)

Order 7.—Dinornithiformes ....moas (New Zealand; extinct)

Order 8.—Æpyornithiformes....giant-birds (Madagascar; extinct)

Order 9.—Apterygiformes .....kiwi (New Zealand)

Order 10.—Sphenisciformes ..... penguins (southern oceans)

Order 11.—Colymbiformes ...... loons and grebes (mainly northern hemisphere)

Order 12.—Procellariiformes .... petrels, albatrosses (pelagic)

Order 13.—Ciconiiformes .... cormorants, pelicans, herons, storks, flamingos

Order 14.—Anseriformes .... screamers (South America); swans, geese, ducks

Order 15.—Falconiformes .... vultures, hawks, eagles

Order 16.—Galliformes .... fowls, hoatzin, hemipodes

Order 17.—Gruiformes .... cranes, rails, bustards

Order 18.—Charadriiformes ..... plovers, shore birds, jaçanas, sand-grouse, pigeons

Order 19.—Cuculiformes .... cuckoos and parrots

Order 20.—Coraciiformes ...... rollers, kingfishers, owls, goatsuckers, hummingbirds, swifts, woodpeckers

Order 21.—Passeriformes .... flycatchers, larks, thrushes, wrens, swallows, crows, warblers, finches.

In closing these brief outlines of certain general matters relating to birds, I wish to call attention again to the evolutionary viewpoint from which they have been treated. There is much discussion at the present day concerning "evolution" by persons having the most superficial knowledge of what it implies. To many it means merely that "men came from monkeys," an indignity that seems too great to be borne; so that certain of our eminent country-men have been led into making open warfare against what they call "evolution," believing that such doctrine is false and agnostic.   Few laymen, however, have the slightest knowledge of the vast and illuminating discoveries made by skilled and devoted men within the last fifty years.   It is now as firmly established as any of our knowledge that throughout the period during which life has existed on this globe, there have been growth and development, progress from stage to stage through the generations of living be-ings that have gone before.   For progress comes with ef-fort, stagnation with ease, and atrophy from disuse.   Evo-lution, far from being the fallacy that some would have us believe, is really the most hopeful thing I can think of in our existence.

THE END

REFERENCES AND INDEX

REFERENCES

Adams, Charles C.
  1909. The ecological succession of birds. *In* An Ecological Survey of Isle Royale, Lake Superior. 8vo, Lansing, Michigan, p. 121-154.

Ashby, Edwin
  1922. Notes on the mound-building birds of Australia, with particulars of features peculiar to the Mallee-fowl, *Leipoa ocellata* Gould, and a suggestion as to their origin. Ibis, ser. 11, vol. 4, p. 702-709.

Averill, C. K.
  1923. Form of egg and extent of migration. Condor, vol. 25, p. 163-165.

Barrell, Joseph
  1917. Rhythms and the measurements of geologic time. Bull. Geol. Soc. Amer., vol. 28, p. 745-904, pl. 43-46.

Beddard, F. E.
  1898. The structure and classification of birds. 8vo, London, New York and Bombay, xx + 548 pp., illustr.

Beebe, C. W.
  1915. A tetrapteryx stage in the ancestry of birds. Zoologica, N. Y. Zool. Soc., vol. 2, p. 39-52, 3 pls.

Bornstein, Frieda
  1912. Ueber Regeneration der Federn und Beziehungen zwischen Federn und Schuppen. Arch. f. Naturgesch., 1911, vol. 1, suppl. 4, p. 1-11, pl. 1-2.

Broom, R.
  1913. On the South-African Pseudosuchian *Euparkeria* and allied genera. Proc. Zool. Soc. London, 1913, p. 619-633, pl. 75-79.

Chapman, F. M.
  1896. The ornithology of Columbus' first voyage, Papers presented to the World's Congress on Ornithology, edited by Mrs. E. I. Rood and Dr. Elliot Coues. 8vo, Chicago, p. 181-185.

Church, Sir A. H.
  1913. Notes on turacin and turacin-bearers. Proc. Zool. Soc. London, 1913, p. 639-643.

Clark, H. L.
  1918. Tail-feathers and their major upper coverts. Auk, vol. 35, p. 113-123.

Coburn, C. A.
  1914. The behavior of the Crow, *Corvus americanus,* Aud. Journ. Animal Behavior, vol. 4, p. 185-201.

Cole, L. J., and Kirkpatrick, W. F.
  1915. Sex ratios in pigeons, together with observations on the laying, incubation and hatching of the eggs. Bull. Agric. Exp. Sta. R. I. State College, no. 162, p. 463-512.

Craig, Wallace
  1908. The voices of pigeons regarded as a means of social control. Amer. Journ. Sociology, vol. 14, p. 86-100.

Dall, W. H.
  1915. Spencer Fullerton Baird, a biography including selections from his correspondence with Audubon, Agassiz, Dana, and others. 8vo, Philadelphia & London. xvi + 462 pp., 19 pls.

Dwight, Jonathan, Jr.
1900. The sequence of plumages and moults of the passerine birds of New York. Annals N. Y. Acad. Sci., vol. 13, p. 73-360, pl. 1-7.

English, T. M. S.
1923. On the greater length of the day in high latitudes as a reason for spring migration. Ibis, ser. 11, vol. 5, p. 418-423.

Faxon, Walter
1915. Relics of Peale's Museum. Bull. Mus. Comp. Zoöl., vol. 59, p. 117-148.

Finn, Frank
1919. Bird behaviour, psychical and physiological. 8vo, London, x + 363 pp., illustr.

Forbes, S. A., and Gross, A. O.
1922. The numbers and local distribution in summer of Illinois land birds of the open country. Bull. Illinois Dept. of Registration and Education, Nat. Hist. Surv. Div., vol. 14, p. 185-218, pl. 35-70.

Fuerbringer, Max
1888. Untersuchungen zur Morphologie und Systematik der Vögel, zugleich ein Beitrag zur Anatomie der Stütz- und Bewegungsorgane. Koninkl. Zoöl. Genootsch. Natura Artis Magistra, Amsterdam, Bijdrag tot de Dierkunde, vol. 15, 2 pts., folio, 4 + 1 + 1751 pp., 30 pls.

Gregory, W. K.
1910. The orders of mammals. Bull. Amer. Mus. Nat. Hist., vol. 27, p. 1-524, text-fig. 1-32.

Gregory, W. K.
1916. Theories of the origin of birds. Annals N. Y. Acad. Sci., vol. 27, p. 31-38.

Grinnell, Joseph
1920. The existence of sea birds a relatively safe one. Condor, vol. 22, p. 101-110.

Grinnell, Joseph
1921. The principle of rapid peering in birds. Univ. of California Chronicle, Berkeley, Calif., 1921, p. 392-396.

Grinell, Joseph, Bryant, H. C., and Storer, T. I.
1918. The game birds of California. 8vo, Semicentennial Publ. Univ. of California, Berkeley, x + 642 pp., 15 pls., 94 text-figs.

Görnitz, Karl
1923. Versuch einer Klassifikation der häufigsten Federfärbungen. Journ. f. Ornith., vol. 71, p. 127-131.

Görnitz, Karl, and Rensch, B.
1924. Ueber die violette Färbung der Vogelfedern. Journ. f. Ornith., vol. 72, p. 113-118.

Gunn, T. E.
1912. On the presence of two ovaries in certain British birds. Proc. Zool. Soc. London, 1912, p. 63-79, pl. 2-5.

Gurney, J. H.
1922. On the sense of smell possessed by birds. Ibis, ser. 11, vol. 4, p. 225-253, pl. 1.

Hankin, E. H.
1914. Animal flight, a record of observation. 8vo, London, p. i-viii, 9-405, index, illustr.

Herrick, F. H.
1905. The home life of wild birds. A new method of the study and photography of birds. 8vo, New York and London, xxv + 255 pp., illustr.

Herrick, F. H.
1911. Nests and nest-building in birds. Journ. Animal Behavior, vol. 1, p. 159-192, 244-277, 336-373.

Herrick, F. H.
1917. Audubon the naturalist. A history of his life and time. 8vo, New York, 2 vols., illustr.

Hodge, C. F.
1894. The method of homing pigeons. Popular Sci. Monthly, vol. 44, p. 758-775, text-fig. 1-12.

Howard, H. E.
1920. Territory in bird life. 8vo

London, xiii + 308 pp., illustr.

Hussey, R. F.
1917. A study of the reactions of certain birds to sound stimuli. Journ. Animal Behavior, vol. 7, p. 207-219.

Knowlton, F. H.
1909. Birds of the world, a popular account, with a chapter on the anatomy of birds by Frederic A. Lucas . . . the whole edited by Robert Ridgway. 8vo, New York, xiii + 873 pp., illustr.

Lönnberg, Einar
1904. On the homologies of the different pieces of the compound rhamphotheca of birds. Arkiv f. Zool., vol. 1, p. 473-512, 13 text-figs.

Lucanus, Friedrich von
1923. Die Rätsel des Vogelzuges. Ihre Lösung auf experimentellem Wege durch Luftfahrt und Vogelberingung. 8vo, Langenfalza, ed. 2, xi + 243 pp.

Lucas, F. A.
1895. The weapons and wings of birds. Rept. U. S. Nat. Mus. for 1893, p. 653-663, pl. 1, text-fig. 1-8.

Lucas, F. A.
1897. The tongues of birds. Rept. U. S. Nat. Mus. for 1895, p. 1001-1020a, pl. 1-2.

Matthew, W. D.
1915. Climate and evolution. Annals N. Y. Acad. Sci., vol. 24, p. 171-318, 33 text-figs.

Meinertzhagen, Richard
1920. Some preliminary remarks on the altitude of the migratory flight of birds, with special reference to the Palæarctic region. Ibis, ser. 11, vol. 2, p. 920-936.

Meinertzhagen, Richard
1921. Some preliminary remarks on the velocity of migratory flight among birds, with special reference to the Palæarctic region. Ibis, ser. 11, vol. 3, p. 228-238.

Mitchell, P. C.

1911. On longevity and relative viability in mammals and birds; with a note on the theory of longevity. Proc. Zool. Soc. London, 1911, p. 425-548.

Mousley, H.
1919. "The singing tree," or how near to the nest do the male birds sing? Auk, vol. 36, p. 339-348.

Müller, Bruno
1908. The air-sacs of the pigeon. Smithsonian Misc. Coll., vol. 50, p. 365-414, pl. 45-49.

Parker, G. H.
1906. Double hens' eggs. Amer. Naturalist, vol. 40, p. 13-25.

Steiner, Hans
1916. Das Problem der Diastataxie des Vogelflügels. Vierteljahrsschr. d. Naturf. Ges. Zürich, vol. 61, p. 488-502.

Stephens, T. C.
1917. The feeding of nestling birds. Journ. Animal Behavior, vol. 7, p. 191-206.

Stone, Witmer
1896. The molting of birds with special reference to the plumages of the smaller land birds of eastern North America. Proc. Acad. Nat. Sci. Philadelphia, 1896, p. 108-167, pl. 4-5.

Stone, Witmer
1899. Some Philadelphia ornithological collections and collectors, 1784-1850. Auk, vol. 16, p. 166-177.

Strong, R. M.
1902. The development of color in the definitive feather. Bull. Mus. Comp. Zoöl., vol. 40, p. 145-185, pl. 1-9.

Strong, R. M.
1911. On the olfactory organs and the sense of smell in birds. Journ. Morphol., vol. 22, p. 619-660, 2 pls.

Thayer, G. H.
1909. Concealing-coloration in the animal kingdom. An exposition of the laws of disguise through

color and pattern: being a summary of Abbott H. Thayer's discoveries. With an introductory essay by A. H. Thayer. 8vo, New York, xix + 260 pp., illustr.

Turner, William
1903. Turner on birds: a short and succinct history of the principal birds noticed by Pliny and Aristotle, first published by Doctor William Turner, 1544. Edited by A. H. Evans. 8vo, Cambridge, xviii + 223 pp.

Watson, J. B.
1915. Studies on the spectral sensitivity of birds. Papers from Dept. Marine Biol. Carnegie Inst. Washington, vol. 7, p. 85-104.

Watson, J. B., and Lashley, K. S.

1915. Homing and related activities of birds. Papers from Dept. Marine Biol. Carnegie Inst. Washington, vol. 7, p. 1-60, pl. 1-6.

Wells, M. M.
1917. The behavior of limpets with particular reference to the homing instinct. Journ. Animal Behavior, vol. 7, p. 387-395.

Wetmore, Alexander
1920. The function of powder downs in herons. Condor, vol. 22, p. 168-170, 2 text-figs.

Wetmore, Alexander
1921. A study of the body temperature of birds. Smithsonian Misc. Coll., Vol. 72, no. 12, 52 pp.

INDEX

Catalog
of
DOVER BOOKS

BOOKS EXPLAINING SCIENCE

(Note: The books listed under this category are general introductions, surveys, reviews, and non-technical expositions of science for the interested layman or scientist who wishes to brush up. Dover also publishes the largest list of inexpensive reprints of books on intermediate and higher mathematics, mathematical physics, engineering, chemistry, astronomy, etc., for the professional mathematician or scientist. For our complete Science Catalog, write Dept. catrr., Dover Publications, Inc., 180 Varick Street, New York 14, N. Y.)

CONCERNING THE NATURE OF THINGS, Sir William- Bragg. Royal Institute Christmas Lectures by Nobel Laureate. Excellent plain-language introduction to gases, molecules, crystal structure, etc. explains "building blocks" of universe, basic properties of matter, with simplest, clearest examples, demonstrations. 32pp. of photos; 57 figures. 244pp. 5⅜ x 8.
T31 Paperbound **$1.35**

MATTER AND LIGHT, THE NEW PHYSICS, Louis de Broglie. Non-technical explanations by a Nobel Laureate of electro-magnetic theory, relativity, wave mechanics, quantum physics, philosophies of science, etc. Simple, yet accurate introduction to work of Planck, Bohr, Einstein, other modern physicists. Only 2 of 12 chapters require mathematics. 300pp. 5⅜ x 8.
T35 Paperbound **$1.60**

THE COMMON .SENSE OF THE EXACT SCIENCES, W. K. Clifford. For 70 years, Clifford's work has been acclaimed as one of the clearest, yet most precise introductions to mathematical symbolism, measurement, surface boundaries, position, space, motion, mass and force, etc. Prefaces by Bertrand Russell and Karl Pearson. Introduction by James Newman. 130 figures. 249pp. 5⅜ x 8.
T61 Paperbound **$1.60**

THE NATURE OF LIGHT AND COLOUR IN THE OPEN AIR, M. Minnaert. What causes mirages? haloes? "multiple" suns and moons? Professor Minnaert explains these and hundreds of other fascinating natural optical phenomena in simple terms, tells how to observe them, suggests hundreds of experiments. 200 illus; 42 photos. xvi + 362pp.
T196 Paperbound **$1.95**

SPINNING TOPS AND GYROSCOPIC MOTION, John Perry. Classic elementary text on dynamics of rotation treats gyroscopes, tops, how quasi-rigidity is induced in paper disks, smoke rings, chains, etc, by rapid motion, precession, earth's motion, etc. Contains many easy-to-perform experiments. Appendix on practical uses of gyroscopes. 62 figures. 128pp.
T416 Paperbound **$1.00**

A CONCISE HISTORY OF MATHEMATICS, D. Struik. This lucid, easily followed history of mathematics from the Ancient Near East to modern times requires no mathematical background itself, yet introduces both mathematicians and laymen to basic concepts and discoveries and the men who made them. Contains a collection of 31 portraits of eminent mathematicians. Bibliography. xix + 299pp. 5⅜ x 8.
T255 Paperbound **$1.75**

THE RESTLESS UNIVERSE, Max Born. A remarkably clear, thorough exposition of gases, electrons, ions, waves and particles, electronic structure of the atom, nuclear physics, written for the layman by a Nobel Laureate. "Much ·more thorough and deep than most attempts . . . easy and delightful," CHEMICAL AND ENGINEERING NEWS. Includes 7 animated sequences showing motion of molecules, alpha particles, etc. 11 full-page plates of photographs. Total of nearly 600 illus. 315pp. 6⅛ x 9¼.
T412 Paperbound **$2.00**

WHAT IS SCIENCE?, N. Campbell. The role of experiment, the function of mathematics, the nature of scientific laws, the limitations of science, and many other provocative topics are explored without technicalities by an eminent scientist. "Still an excellent introduction to scientific philosophy," H. Margenau in PHYSICS TODAY. 192pp. 5⅜ x 8.
S43 Paperbound **$1.25**

FADS AND FALLACIES IN THE NAME OF SCIENCE, Martin Gardner. The standard account of the various cults, quack systems and delusions which have recently masqueraded as science: hollow earth theory, Atlantis, dianetics, Reich's orgone theory, flying saucers, Bridey Murphy, psionics, irridiagnosis, many other fascinating fallacies that deluded tens of thousands. "Should be read by everyone, scientist and non-scientist alike," R. T. Birge, Prof. Emeritus, Univ. of California; Former President, American Physical Society. Formerly titled, "In the Name of Science." Revised and enlarged edition. x + 365pp. 5⅜ x 8.
T394 Paperbound **$1.50**

THE STUDY OF THE HISTORY OF MATHEMATICS, THE STUDY OF THE HISTORY OF SCIENCE, G. Sarton. Two books bound as one. Both volumes are standard introductions to their fields by an eminent science historian. They discuss problems of historical research, teaching, pitfalls, other matters of interest to the historically oriented writer, teacher, or student. Both have extensive bibliographies. 10 illustrations. 188pp. 5⅜ x 8.   T240 Paperbound **$1.25**

THE PRINCIPLES OF SCIENCE, W. S. Jevons. Unabridged reprinting of a milestone in the development of symbolic logic and other subjects concerning scientific methodology, probability, inferential validity, etc. Also describes Jevons' "logic machine," an early precursor of modern electronic calculators. Preface by E. Nagel. 839pp. 5⅜ x 8.   S446 Paperbound **$2.98**

SCIENCE THEORY AND MAN, Erwin Schroedinger. Complete, unabridged reprinting of "Science and the Human Temperament" plus an additional essay "What is an Elementary Particle?" Nobel Laureate Schroedinger discusses many aspects of modern physics from novel points of view which provide unusual insights for both laymen and physicists. 192 pp. 5⅜ x 8.
T428 Paperbound **$1.35**

BRIDGES AND THEIR BUILDERS, D. B. Steinman & S. R. Watson. Information about ancient, medieval, modern bridges; how they were built; who built them; the structural principles employed; the materials they are built of; etc. Written by one of the world's leading authorities on bridge design and construction. New, revised, expanded edition. 23 photos; 26 line drawings, xvii + 401pp. 5⅜ x 8.   T431 Paperbound **$1.95**

HISTORY OF MATHEMATICS, D. E. Smith. Most comprehensive non-technical history of math in English. In two volumes. Vol. I: A chronological examination of the growth of mathematics from primitive concepts up to 1900. Vol. II: The development of ideas in specific fields and areas, up through elementary calculus. The lives and works of over a thousand mathematicians are covered; thousands of specific historical problems and their solutions are clearly explained. Total of 510 illustrations, 1355pp. 5⅜ x 8. Set boxed in attractive container.   T429, T430 Paperbound, the set **$5.00**

PHILOSOPHY AND THE PHYSICISTS, L. S. Stebbing. A philosopher examines the philosophical implications of modern science by posing a lively critical attack on the popular science expositions of Sir James Jeans and Arthur Eddington. xvi + 295pp. 5⅜ x 8.
T480 Paperbound **$1.65**

ON MATHEMATICS AND MATHEMATICIANS, R. E. Moritz. The first collection of quotations by and about mathematicians in English. 1140 anecdotes, aphorisms, definitions, speculations, etc. give both mathematicians and layman stimulating new insights into what mathematics is, and into the personalities of the great mathematicians from Archimedes to Euler, Gauss, Klein, Weierstrass. Invaluable to teachers, writers. Extensive cross index. 410pp. 5⅜ x 8.
T489 Paperbound **$1.95**

NATURAL SCIENCE, BIOLOGY, GEOLOGY, TRAVEL

A SHORT HISTORY OF ANATOMY AND PHYSIOLOGY FROM THE GREEKS TO HARVEY, C. Singer. A great medical historian's fascinating intermediate account of the slow advance of anatomical and physiological knowledge from pre-scientific times to Vesalius, Harvey. 139 unusually interesting illustrations. 221pp. 5⅜ x 8.   T389 Paperbound **$1.75**

THE BEHAVIOUR AND SOCIAL LIFE OF HONEYBEES, Ronald Ribbands. The most comprehensive, lucid and authoritative book on bee habits, communication, duties, cell life, motivations, etc. "A MUST for every scientist, experimenter, and educator, and a happy and valuable selection for all interested in the honeybee," AMERICAN BEE JOURNAL. 690-item bibliography. 127 illus.; 11 photographic plates. 352pp. 5⅜ x 8⅜.   S410 Clothbound **$4.50**

TRAVELS OF WILLIAM BARTRAM, edited by **Mark Van Doren.** One of the 18th century's most delightful books, and one of the few first-hand sources of information about American geography, natural history, and anthropology of American Indian tribes of the time. "The mind of a scientist with the soul of a poet," John Livingston Lowes. 13 original illustrations, maps. Introduction by Mark Van Doren. 448pp. 5⅜ x 8.   T326 Paperbound **$2.00**

STUDIES ON THE STRUCTURE AND DEVELOPMENT OF VERTEBRATES, Edwin Goodrich. The definitive study of the skeleton, fins and limbs, head region, divisions of the body cavity, vascular, respiratory, excretory systems, etc., of vertebrates from fish to higher mammals, by the greatest comparative anatomist of recent times. "The standard textbook," JOURNAL OF ANATOMY. 754 illus. 69-page biographical study. 1186-item bibliography. 2 vols. Total of 906pp. 5⅜ x 8.
Vol. I: S449 Paperbound **$2.50**
Vol. II: S450 Paperbound **$2.50**

DOVER BOOKS

THE BIRTH AND DEVELOPMENT OF THE GEOLOGICAL SCIENCES, F. D. Adams. The most complete and thorough history of the earth sciences in print. Covers over 300 geological thinkers and systems; treats fossils, theories of stone growth, paleontology, earthquakes, vulcanists vs. neptunists, odd theories, etc. 91 illustrations, including medieval, Renaissance wood cuts, etc. 632 footnotes and bibliographic notes. 511pp. 308pp. 5⅜ x 8.   T5 Paperbound **$2.00**

FROM MAGIC TO SCIENCE, Charles Singer. A close study of aspects of medical science from the Roman Empire through the Renaissance. The sections on early herbals, and "The Visions of Hildegarde of Bingen," are probably the best studies of these subjects available. 158 unusual classic and medieval illustrations. xxvii + 365pp. 5⅜ x 8.   T390 Paperbound **$2.00**

SAILING ALONE AROUND THE WORLD, Captain Joshua Slocum. Captain Slocum's personal account of his single-handed voyage around the world in a 34-foot boat he rebuilt himself. A classic of both seamanship and descriptive writing. "A nautical equivalent of Thoreau's account," Van Wyck Brooks. 67 illus. 308pp. 5⅜ x 8.   T326 Paperbound **$1.00**

TREES OF THE EASTERN AND CENTRAL UNITED STATES AND CANADA, W. M. Harlow. Standard middle-level guide designed to help you know the characteristics of Eastern trees and identify them at sight by means of an 8-page synoptic key. More than 600 drawings and photographs of twigs, leaves, fruit, other features. xiii + 288pp. 4⅝ x 6½.   T395 Paperbound **$1.35**

FRUIT KEY AND TWIG KEY ("Fruit Key to Northeastern Trees," "Twig Key to Deciduous Woody Plants of Eastern North America"), **W. M. Harlow.** Identify trees in fall, winter, spring. Easy-to-use, synoptic keys, with photographs of every twig and fruit identified. Covers 120 different fruits, 160 different twigs. Over 350 photos. Bibliographies. Glossaries. Total of 143pp. 5⅝ x 8⅜.   T511 Paperbound **$1.25**

INTRODUCTION TO THE STUDY OF EXPERIMENTAL MEDICINE, Claude Bernard. This classic records Bernard's far-reaching efforts to transform physiology into an exact science. It covers problems of vivisection, the limits of physiological experiment, hypotheses in medical experimentation, hundreds of others. Many of his own famous experiments on the liver, the pancreas, etc., are used as examples. Foreword by I. B. Cohen. xxv + 266pp. 5⅜ x 8.   T400 Paperbound **$1.50**

THE ORIGIN OF LIFE, A. I. Oparin. The first modern statement that life evolved from complex nitro-carbon compounds, carefully presented according to modern biochemical knowledge of primary colloids, organic molecules, etc. Begins with historical introduction to the problem of the origin of life. Bibliography. xxv + 270pp. 5⅜ x 8.   S213 Paperbound **$1.75**

A HISTORY OF ASTRONOMY FROM THALES TO KEPLER, J. L. E. Dreyer. The only work in English which provides a detailed picture of man's cosmological views from Egypt, Babylonia, Greece, and Alexandria to Copernicus, Tycho Brahe and Kepler. "Standard reference on Greek astronomy and the Copernican revolution," SKY AND TELESCOPE. Formerly called "A History of Planetary Systems From Thales to Kepler." Bibliography. 21 diagrams. xvii + 430pp. 5⅜ x 8.   S79 Paperbound **$1.98**

URANIUM PROSPECTING, H. L. Barnes. A professional geologist tells you what you need to know. Hundreds of facts about minerals, tests, detectors, sampling, assays, claiming, developing, government regulations, etc. Glossary of technical terms. Annotated bibliography. x + 117pp. 5⅜ x 8.   T309 Paperbound **$1.00**

DE RE METALLICA, Georgius Agricola. All 12 books of this 400 year old classic on metals and metal production, fully annotated, and containing all 289 of the 16th century woodcuts which made the original an artistic masterpiece. A superb gift for geologists, engineers, libraries, artists, historians. Translated by Herbert Hoover & L. H. Hoover. Bibliography, survey of ancient authors. 289 illustrations of the excavating, assaying, smelting, refining, and countless other metal production operations described in the text. 672pp. 6¾ x 10¾. Deluxe library edition.   S6 Clothbound **$10.00**

DE MAGNETE, William Gilbert. A landmark of science by the man who first used the word "electricity," distinguished between static electricity and magnetism, and founded a new science. P. F. Mottelay translation. 90 figures. lix + 368pp. 5⅜ x 8.   S470 Paperbound **$2.00**

THE AUTOBIOGRAPHY OF CHARLES DARWIN AND SELECTED LETTERS, Francis Darwin, ed. Fascinating documents on Darwin's early life, the voyage of the "Beagle," the discovery of evolution, Darwin's thought on mimicry, plant development, vivisection, evolution, many other subjects Letters to Henslow, Lyell, Hooker, Wallace, Kingsley, etc. Appendix. 365pp. 5⅜ x 8.   T479 Paperbound **$1.65**

A WAY OF LIFE AND OTHER SELECTED WRITINGS OF SIR WILLIAM OSLER. 16 of the great physician, teacher and humanist's most inspiring writings on a practical philosophy of life, science and the humanities, and the history of medicine. 5 photographs. Introduction by G. L. Keynes, M.D., F.R.C.S. xx + 278pp. 5⅜ x 8.   T488 Paperbound **$1.50**

CATALOG OF

LITERATURE

WORLD DRAMA, B. H. Clark. 46 plays from Ancient Greece, Rome, to India, China, Japan. Plays by Aeschylus, Sophocles, Euripides, Aristophanes, Plautus, Marlowe, Jonson, Farquhar, Goldsmith, Cervantes, Molière, Dumas, Goethe, Schiller, Ibsen, many others. One of the most comprehensive collections of important plays from all literature available in English. Over ⅓ of this material is unavailable in any other current edition. Reading lists. 2 volumes. Total of 1364pp. 5⅜ x 8.
Vol. I, T57 Paperbound **$2.00**
Vol. II, T59 Paperbound **$2.00**

MASTERS OF THE DRAMA, John Gassner. The most comprehensive history of the drama in print. Covers more than 800 dramatists and over 2000 plays from the Greeks to modern Western, Near Eastern, Oriental drama. Plot summaries, theatre history, etc. "Best of its kind in English," NEW REPUBLIC. 35 pages of bibliography. 77 photos and drawings. Deluxe edition. xxii + 890pp. 5⅜ x 8. T100 Clothbound **$5.95**

THE DRAMA OF LUIGI PIRANDELLO, D. Vittorini. All 38 of Pirandello's plays (to 1935) summarized and analyzed in terms of symbolic techniques, plot structure, etc. The only authorized work. Foreword by Pirandello. Biography. Bibliography. xiii + 350pp. 5⅜ x 8.
T435 Paperbound **$1.98**

ARISTOTLE'S THEORY OF POETRY AND THE FINE ARTS, S. H. Butcher, ed. The celebrated "Butcher translation" faced page by page with the Greek text; Butcher's 300-page introduction to Greek poetic, dramatic thought. Modern Aristotelian criticism discussed by John Gassner. lxxvi + 421pp. 5⅜ x 8.
T42 Paperbound **$2.00**

EUGENE O'NEILL: THE MAN AND HIS PLAYS, B. H. Clark. The first published source-book on O'Neill's life and work. Analyzes each play from the early THE WEB up to THE ICEMAN COMETH. Supplies much information about environmental and dramatic influences. ix + 182pp. 5⅜ x 8. T379 Paperbound **$1.25**

INTRODUCTION TO ENGLISH LITERATURE, B. Dobrée, ed. Most compendious literary aid in its price range. Extensive, categorized bibliography (with entries up to 1949) of more than 5,000 poets, dramatists, novelists, as well as historians, philosophers, economists, religious writers, travellers, and scientists of literary stature. Information about manuscripts, important biographical data. Critical, historical, background works not simply listed, but evaluated. Each volume also contains a long introduction to the period it covers.

Vol. I: **THE BEGINNINGS OF ENGLISH LITERATURE TO SKELTON, 1509, W. L. Renwick. H. Orton.** 450pp. 5⅛ x 7⅛. T75 Clothbound **$3.50**

Vol. II: **THE ENGLISH RENAISSANCE, 1510-1688, V. de Sola Pinto.** 381pp. 5⅛ x 7⅛.
T76 Clothbound **$3.50**

Vol. III: **THE AUGUSTANS AND ROMANTICS, 1689-1830, H. Dyson, J. Butt.** 320pp. 5⅛ x 7⅛.
T77 Clothbound **$3.50**

Vol. IV: **THE VICTORIANS AND AFTER, 1830-1914, E. Batho, B. Dobrée.** 360pp. 5⅛ x 7⅛.
T78 Clothbound **$3.50**

EPIC AND ROMANCE, W. P. Ker. The standard survey of Medieval epic and romance by a foremost authority on Medieval literature. Covers historical background, plot, literary analysis, significance of Teutonic epics, Icelandic sagas, Beowulf, French chansons de geste, the Niebelungenlied, Arthurian romances, much more. 422pp. 5⅜ x 8. T355 Paperbound **$1.95**

THE HEART OF EMERSON'S JOURNALS, Bliss Perry, ed. Emerson's most intimate thoughts, impressions, records of conversations with Channing, Hawthorne, Thoreau, etc., carefully chosen from the 10 volumes of The Journals. "The essays do not reveal the power of Emerson's mind . . .as do these hasty and informal writings," N. Y. TIMES. Preface by B. Perry. 370pp. 5⅜ x 8. T447 Paperbound **$1.85**

A SOURCE BOOK IN THEATRICAL HISTORY, A. M. Nagler. (Formerly, "Sources of Theatrical History.") Over 300 selected passages by contemporary observers tell about styles of acting, direction, make-up, scene designing, etc., in the theatre's great periods from ancient Greece to the Théâtre Libre. "Indispensable complement to the study of drama," EDUCATIONAL THEATRE JOURNAL. Prof. Nagler, Yale Univ. School of Drama, also supplies notes, references. 85 illustrations. 611pp. 5⅜ x 8. T515 Paperbound **$2.75**

THE ART OF THE STORY-TELLER, M. L. Shedlock. Regarded as the finest, most helpful book on telling stories to children, by a great story-teller. How to catch, hold, recapture attention; how to choose material; many other aspects. Also includes: a 99-page selection of Miss Shedlock's most successful stories; extensive bibliography of other stories. xxi + 320pp. 5⅜ x 8. T245 Clothbound **$3.50**

THE DEVIL'S DICTIONARY, Ambrose Bierce. Over 1000 short, ironic definitions in alphabetical order, by America's greatest satirist in the classical tradition. "Some of the most gorgeous witticisms in the English language," H. L. Mencken. 144pp. 5⅜ x 8. T487 Paperbound **$1.00**

MUSIC

A DICTIONARY OF HYMNOLOGY, John Julian. More than 30,000 entries on individual hymns, their authorship, textual variations, location of texts, dates and circumstances of composition, denominational and ritual usages, the biographies of more than 9,000 hymn writers, essays on important topics such as children's hymns and Christmas carols, and hundreds of thousands of other important facts about hymns which are virtually impossible to find anywhere else. Convenient alphabetical listing, and a 200-page double-columned index of first lines enable you to track down virtually any hymn ever written. Total of 1786pp. 6¼ x 9¼. 2 volumes.   **T133. The Set, Clothbound $15.00**

STRUCTURAL HEARING, TONAL COHERENCE IN MUSIC, Felix Salzer. Extends the well-known Schenker approach to include modern music, music of the middle ages, and Renaissance music. Explores the phenomenon of tonal organization by discussing more than 500 compositions, and offers unusual new insights into the theory of composition and musical relationships. "The foundation on which all teaching in music theory has been based at this college," Leopold Mannes, President, The Mannes College of Music. Total of 658pp. 6½ x 9¼. 2 volumes.   **S418 The set, Clothbound $8.00**

A GENERAL HISTORY OF MUSIC, Charles Burney. The complete history of music from the Greeks up to 1789 by the 18th century musical historian who personally knew the great Baroque composers. Covers sacred and secular, vocal and instrumental, operatic and symphonic music; treats theory, notation, forms, instruments; discusses composers, performers, important works. Invaluable as a source of information on the period for students, historians, musicians. "Surprisingly few of Burney's statements have been invalidated by modern research . . . still of great value," NEW YORK TIMES. Edited and corrected by Frank Mercer. 35 figures. 1915pp. 5½ x 8½. 2 volumes.   **T36 The set, Clothbound $12.50**

JOHANN SEBASTIAN BACH, Phillip Spitta. Recognized as one of the greatest accomplishments of musical scholarship and far and away the definitive coverage of Bach's works. Hundreds of individual pieces are analyzed. Major works, such as the B Minor Mass and the St. Matthew Passion are examined in minute detail. Spitta also deals with the works of Buxtehude, Pachelbel, and others of the period. Can be read with profit even by those without a knowledge of the technicalities of musical composition. "Unchallenged as the last word on one of the supreme geniuses of music," John Barkham, SATURDAY REVIEW SYNDICATE. Total of 1819pp. 5⅜ x 8. 2 volumes.   **T252 The set, Clothbound $10.00**

HISTORY

THE IDEA OF PROGRESS, J. B. Bury. Prof. Bury traces the evolution of a central concept of Western civilization in Greek, Roman, Medieval, and Renaissance thought to its flowering in the 17th and 18th centuries. Introduction by Charles Beard. xl + 357pp. 5⅜ x 8.
T39 Clothbound $3.95
T40 Paperbound $1.95

THE ANCIENT GREEK HISTORIANS, J. B. Bury. Greek historians such as Herodotus, Thucydides, Xenophon; Roman historians such as Tacitus, Caesar, Livy; scores of others fully analyzed in terms of sources, concepts, influences, etc., by a great scholar and historian. 291pp. 5⅜ x 8.   **T397 Paperbound $1.50**

HISTORY OF THE LATER ROMAN EMPIRE, J. B. Bury. The standard work on the Byzantine Empire from 395 A.D. to the death of Justinian in 565 A.D., by the leading Byzantine scholar of our time. Covers political, social, cultural, theological, military history. Quotes contemporary documents extensively. "Most unlikely that it will ever be superseded," Glanville Downey, Dumbarton Oaks Research Library. Genealogical tables. 5 maps. Bibliography. 2 vols. Total of 965pp. 5⅜ x 8.   **T398, T399 Paperbound, the set $4.00**

GARDNER'S PHOTOGRAPHIC SKETCH BOOK OF THE CIVIL WAR, Alexander Gardner. One of the rarest and most valuable Civil War photographic collections exactly reproduced for the first time since 1866. Scenes of Manassas, Bull Run, Harper's Ferry, Appomattox, Mechanicsville, Fredericksburg, Gettysburg, etc.; battle ruins, prisons, arsenals, a slave pen, fortifications; Lincoln on the field, officers, men, corpses. By one of the most famous pioneers in documentary photography. Original copies of the "Sketch Book" sold for $425 in 1952. Introduction by E. Bleiler. 100 full-page 7 x 10 photographs (original size). 244pp. 10¾ x 8½
T476 Clothbound $6.00

THE WORLD'S GREAT SPEECHES, L. Copeland and L. Lamm, eds. 255 speeches from Pericles to Churchill, Dylan Thomas. Invaluable as a guide to speakers; fascinating as history past and present; a source of much difficult-to-find material. Includes an extensive section of informal and humorous speeches. 3 indices: Topic, Author, Nation. xx + 745pp. 5⅜ x 8.
T468 Paperbound $2.49

FOUNDERS OF THE MIDDLE AGES, E. K. Rand. The best non-technical discussion of the transformation of Latin paganism into medieval civilization. Tertullian, Gregory, Jerome, Boethius, Augustine, the Neoplatonists, other crucial figures, philosophies examined. Excellent for the intelligent non-specialist. "Extraordinarily accurate," Richard McKeon, THE NATION. ix + 365pp. 5⅜ x 8.   **T369 Paperbound $1.85**

THE POLITICAL THOUGHT OF PLATO AND ARISTOTLE, Ernest Barker. The standard, comprehensive exposition of Greek political thought. Covers every aspect of the "Republic" and the "Politics" as well as minor writings, other philosophers, theorists of the period, and the later history of Greek political thought. Unabridged edition. 584pp. 5⅜ x 8.
T521 Paperbound **$1.85**

PHILOSOPHY

THE GIFT OF LANGUAGE, M. Schlauch. (Formerly, "The Gift of Tongues.") A sound, middle-level treatment of linguistic families, word histories, grammatical processes, semantics, language taboos, word-coining of Joyce, Cummings, Stein, etc. 232 bibliographical notes. 350pp. 5⅜ x 8.
T243 Paperbound **$1.85**

THE PHILOSOPHY OF HEGEL, W. T. Stace. The first work in English to give a complete and connected view of Hegel's entire system. Especially valuable to those who do not have time to study the highly complicated original texts, yet want an accurate presentation by a most reputable scholar of one of the most influential 19th century thinkers. Includes a 14 x 20 fold-out chart of Hegelian system. 536pp. 5⅜ x 8.
T254 Paperbound **$2.00**

ARISTOTLE, A. E. Taylor. A lucid, non-technical account of Aristotle written by a foremost Platonist. Covers life and works; thought on matter, form, causes, logic, God, physics, metaphysics, etc. Bibliography. New index compiled for this edition. 128pp. 5⅜ x 8.
T280 Paperbound **$1.00**

GUIDE TO PHILOSOPHY, C. E. M. Joad. This basic work describes the major philosophic problems and evaluates the answers propounded by great philosophers from the Greeks to Whitehead, Russell. "The finest introduction," BOSTON TRANSCRIPT. Bibliography, 592pp. 5⅜ x 8.
T297 Paperbound **$2.00**

LANGUAGE AND MYTH, E. Cassirer. Cassirer's brilliant demonstration that beneath both language and myth lies an unconscious "grammar" of experience whose categories and canons are not those of logical thought. Introduction and translation by Susanne Langer. Index. x + 103pp. 5⅜ x 8.
T51 Paperbound **$1.25**

SUBSTANCE AND FUNCTION, EINSTEIN'S THEORY OF RELATIVITY, E. Cassirer. This double volume contains the German philosopher's profound philosophical formulation of the differences between traditional logic and the new logic of science. Number, space, energy, relativity, many other topics are treated in detail. Authorized translation by W. C. and M. C. Swabey. xii + 465pp. 5⅜ x 8.
T50 Paperbound **$2.00**

THE PHILOSOPHICAL WORKS OF DESCARTES. The definitive English edition, in two volumes, of all major philosophical works and letters of René Descartes, father of modern philosophy of knowledge and science. Translated by E. S. Haldane and G. Ross. Introductory notes. Total of 842pp. 5⅜ x 8.
T71 Vol. 1, Paperbound **$2.00**
T72 Vol. 2, Paperbound **$2.00**

ESSAYS IN EXPERIMENTAL LOGIC, J. Dewey. Based upon Dewey's theory that knowledge implies a judgment which in turn implies an inquiry, these papers consider such topics as the thought of Bertrand Russell, pragmatism, the logic of values, antecedents of thought, data and meanings. 452pp. 5⅜ x 8.
T73 Paperbound **$1.95**

THE PHILOSOPHY OF HISTORY, G. W. F. Hegel. This classic of Western thought is Hegel's detailed formulation of the thesis that history is not chance but a rational process, the realization of the Spirit of Freedom. Translated and introduced by J. Sibree. Introduction by C. Hegel. Special introduction for this edition by Prof. Carl Friedrich, Harvard University. xxxix + 447pp. 5⅜ x 8.
T112 Paperbound **$1.85**

THE WILL TO BELIEVE and HUMAN IMMORTALITY, W. James. Two of James's most profound investigations of human belief in God and immortality, bound as one volume. Both are powerful expressions of James's views on chance vs. determinism, pluralism vs. monism, will and intellect, arguments for survival after death, etc. Two prefaces. 429pp. 5⅜ x 8.
T294 Clothbound **$3.75**
T291 Paperbound **$1.65**

INTRODUCTION TO SYMBOLIC LOGIC, S. Langer. A lucid, general introduction to modern logic, covering forms, classes, the use of symbols, the calculus of propositions, the Boole-Schroeder and the Russell-Whitehead systems, etc. "One of the clearest and simplest introductions," MATHEMATICS GAZETTE. Second, enlarged, revised edition. 368pp. 5⅜ x 8.
S164 Paperbound **$1.75**

MIND AND THE WORLD-ORDER, C. I. Lewis. Building upon the work of Peirce, James, and Dewey, Professor Lewis outlines a theory of knowledge in terms of "conceptual pragmatism," and demonstrates why the traditional understanding of the a priori must be abandoned. Appendices. xiv + 446pp. 5⅜ x 8.
T359 Paperbound **$1.95**

THE GUIDE FOR THE PERPLEXED, M. Maimonides One of the great philosophical works of all time, Maimonides' formulation of the meeting-ground between Old Testament and Aristotelian thought is essential to anyone interested in Jewish, Christian, and Moslem thought in the Middle Ages. 2nd revised edition of the Friedlander translation. Extensive introduction. lix + 414pp. 5⅜ x 8.
T351 Paperbound **$1.85**

DOVER BOOKS

THE PHILOSOPHICAL WRITINGS OF PEIRCE, J. Buchler, ed. (Formerly, "The Philosophy of Peirce.") This carefully integrated selection of Peirce's papers is considered the best coverage of the complete thought of one of the greatest philosophers of modern times. Covers Peirce's work on the theory of signs, pragmatism, epistemology, symbolic logic, the scientific method, chance, etc. xvi + 386pp. 5 3/8 x 8.
T216 Clothbound **$5.00**
T217 Paperbound **$1.95**

HISTORY OF ANCIENT PHILOSOPHY, W. Windelband. Considered the clearest survey of Greek and Roman philosophy. Examines Thales, Anaximander, Anaximenes, Heraclitus, the Eleatics, Empedocles, the Pythagoreans, the Sophists, Socrates, Democritus, Stoics, Epicureans, Sceptics, Neo-platonists, etc. 50 pages on Plato; 70 on Aristotle. 2nd German edition tr. by H. E. Cushman. xv + 393pp. 5⅜ x 8.
T357 Paperbound **$1.75**

INTRODUCTION TO SYMBOLIC LOGIC AND ITS APPLICATIONS, R. Carnap. A comprehensive, rigorous introduction to modern logic by perhaps its greatest living master. Includes demonstrations of applications in mathematics, physics, biology. "Of the rank of a masterpiece," Z. für Mathematik und ihre Grenzgebiete. Over 300 exercises. xvi + 241pp. 5⅜ x 8.
Clothbound **$4.00**
S453 Paperbound **$1.85**

SCEPTICISM AND ANIMAL FAITH, G. Santayana. Santayana's unusually lucid exposition of the difference between the independent existence of objects and the essence our mind attributes to them, and of the necessity of scepticism as a form of belief and animal faith as a necessary condition of knowledge. Discusses belief, memory, intuition, symbols, etc. xii + 314pp. 5⅜ x 8.
T235 Clothbound **$3.50**
T236 Paperbound **$1.50**

THE ANALYSIS OF MATTER, B. Russell. With his usual brilliance, Russell analyzes physics, causality, scientific inference, Weyl's theory, tensors, invariants, periodicity, etc. in order to discover the basic concepts of scientific thought about matter. "Most thorough treatment of the subject," THE NATION. Introduction. 8 figures. viii + 408pp. 5⅜ x 8.
T231 Paperbound **$1.95**

THE SENSE OF BEAUTY, G. Santayana. This important philosophical study of why, when, and how beauty appears, and what conditions must be fulfilled, is in itself a revelation of the beauty of language. "It is doubtful if a better treatment of the subject has since appeared," PEABODY JOURNAL. ix + 275pp. 5⅜ x 8.
T238 Paperbound **$1.00**

THE CHIEF WORKS OF SPINOZA. In two volumes. Vol. I: The Theologico-Political Treatise and the Political Treatise. Vol. II: On the Improvement of Understanding, The Ethics, and Selected Letters. The permanent and enduring ideas in these works on God, the universe, religion, society, etc., have had tremendous impact on later philosophical works. Introduction. Total of 862pp. 5⅜ x 8.
T249 Vol. I, Paperbound **$1.50**
T250 Vol. II, Paperbound **$1.50**

TRAGIC SENSE OF LIFE, M. de Unamuno. The acknowledged masterpiece of one of Spain's most influential thinkers. Between the despair at the inevitable death of man and all his works, and the desire for immortality, Unamuno finds a "saving incertitude." Called "a masterpiece," by the ENCYCLOPAEDIA BRITANNICA. xxx + 332pp. 5⅜ x 8.
T257 Paperbound **$1.95**

EXPERIENCE AND NATURE, John Dewey. The enlarged, revised edition of the Paul Carus lectures (1925). One of Dewey's clearest presentations of the philosophy of empirical naturalism which reestablishes the continuity between "inner" experience and "outer" nature. These lectures are among the most significant ever delivered by an American philosopher. 457pp. 5⅜ x 8.
T471 Paperbound **$1.85**

PHILOSOPHY AND CIVILIZATION IN THE MIDDLE AGES, M. de Wulf. A semi-popular survey of medieval intellectual life, religion, philosophy, science, the arts, etc. that covers feudalism vs. Catholicism, rise of the universities, mendicant orders, and similar topics. Bibliography. viii + 320pp. 5⅜ x 8.
T284 Paperbound **$1.75**

AN INTRODUCTION TO SCHOLASTIC PHILOSOPHY, M. de Wulf. (Formerly, "Scholasticism Old and New.") Prof. de Wulf covers the central scholastic tradition from St. Anselm, Albertus Magnus, Thomas Aquinas, up to Suarez in the 17th century; and then treats the modern revival of scholasticism, the Louvain position, relations with Kantianism and positivism, etc. xvi + 271pp. 5⅜ x 8.
T296 Clothbound **$3.50**
T283 Paperbound **$1.75**

A HISTORY OF MODERN PHILOSOPHY, H. Höffding. An exceptionally clear and detailed coverage of Western philosophy from the Renaissance to the end of the 19th century. Both major and minor figures are examined in terms of theory of knowledge, logic, cosmology, psychology. Covers Pomponazzi, Bodin, Boehme, Telesius, Bruno, Copernicus, Descartes, Spinoza, Hobbes, Locke, Hume, Kant, Fichte, Schopenhauer, Mill, Spencer, Langer, scores of others. A standard reference work. 2 volumes. Total of 1159pp. 5⅜ x 8.
T117 Vol. 1, Paperbound **$2.00**
T118 Vol. 2, Paperbound **$2.00**

LANGUAGE, TRUTH AND LOGIC, A. J. Ayer. The first full-length development of Logical Positivism in English. Building on the work of Schlick, Russell, Carnap, and the Vienna school, Ayer presents the tenets of one of the most important systems of modern philosophical thought. 160pp. 5⅜ x 8.
T10 Paperbound **$1.25**

ORIENTALIA AND RELIGION

THE MYSTERIES OF MITHRA, F. Cumont. The great Belgian scholar's definitive study of the Persian mystery religion that almost vanquished Christianity in the ideological struggle for the Roman Empire. A masterpiece of scholarly detection that reconstructs secret doctrines, organization, rites. Mithraic art is discussed and analyzed. 70 illus. 239pp. 5⅜ x 8.
T323 Paperbound **$1.85**

CHRISTIAN AND ORIENTAL PHILOSOPHY OF ART. A. K. Coomaraswamy. The late art historian and orientalist discusses artistic symbolism, the role of traditional culture in enriching art, medieval art, folklore, philosophy of art, other similar topics. Bibliography. 148pp. 5⅜ x 8.
T378 Paperbound **$1.25**

TRANSFORMATION OF NATURE IN ART, A. K. Coomaraswamy. A basic work on Asiatic religious art. Includes discussions of religious art in Asia and Medieval Europe (exemplified by Meister Eckhart), the origin and use of images in Indian art, Indian Medieval aesthetic manuals, and other fascinating, little known topics. Glossaries of Sanskrit and Chinese terms. Bibliography. 41pp. of notes. 245pp. 5⅜ x 8.
T368 Paperbound **$1.75**

ORIENTAL RELIGIONS IN ROMAN PAGANISM, F. Cumont. This well-known study treats the ecstatic cults of Syria and Phrygia (Cybele, Attis, Adonis, their orgies and mutilatory rites); the mysteries of Egypt (Serapis, Isis, Osiris); Persian dualism; Mithraic cults; Hermes Trismegistus, Ishtar, Astarte, etc. and their influence on the religious thought of the Roman Empire. Introduction. 55pp. of notes; extensive bibliography. xxiv + 298pp. 5⅜ x 8.
T321 Paperbound **$1.75**

ANTHROPOLOGY, SOCIOLOGY, AND PSYCHOLOGY

PRIMITIVE MAN AS PHILOSOPHER, P. Radin. A standard anthropological work based on Radin's investigations of the Winnebago, Maori, Batak, Zuni, other primitive tribes. Describes primitive thought on the purpose of life, marital relations, death, personality, gods, etc. Extensive selections of ōriginal primitive documents. Bibliography. xviii + 420pp. 5⅜ x 8.
T392 Paperbound **$2.00**

PRIMITIVE RELIGION, P. Radin. Radin's thoroughgoing treatment of supernatural beliefs, shamanism, initiations, religious expression, etc. in primitive societies. Arunta, Ashanti, Aztec, Bushman, Crow, Fijian, many other tribes examined. "Excellent," NATURE. New preface by the author. Bibliographic notes. x + 322pp. 5⅜ x 8.   T393 Paperbound **$1.85**

SEX IN PSYCHO-ANALYSIS, S. Ferenczi. (Formerly, "Contributions to Psycho-analysis.") 14 selected papers on impotence, transference, analysis and children, dreams, obscene words, homosexuality, paranoia, etc. by an associate of Freud. Also included: THE DEVELOPMENT OF PSYCHO-ANALYSIS, by Ferenczi and Otto Rank. Two books bound as one. Total of 406pp. 5⅜ x 8.   T324 Paperbound **$1.85**

THE PRINCIPLES OF PSYCHOLOGY, William James. The complete text of the famous "long course," one of the great books of Western thought. An almost incredible amount of information about psychological processes, the stream of consciousness, habit, time perception, memory, emotions, reason, consciousness of self, abnormal phenomena, and similar topics. Based on James's own discoveries integrated with the work of Descartes, Locke, Hume, Royce, Wundt, Berkeley, Lotse, Herbart, scores of others. "A classic of interpretation," PSYCHIATRIC QUARTERLY. 94 illus. 1408pp. 2 volumes. 5⅜ x 8.
T381 Vol. 1, Paperbound **$2.50**
T382 Vol. 2, Paperbound **$2.50**

THE POLISH PEASANT IN EUROPE AND AMERICA, W. I. Thomas, F. Znaniecki. Monumental sociological study of peasant primary groups (family and community) and the disruptions produced by·a new industrial system and emigration to America, by two of the foremost sociologists of recent times. One of the most important works in sociological thought. Includes hundreds of pages of primary documentation; point by point analysis of causes of social decay, breakdown of morality, crime, drunkenness, prostitution, etc. 2nd revised edition. 2 volumes. Total of 2250pp. 6 x 9.   T478 2 volume set, Clothbound **$12.50**

FOLKWAYS, W. G. Sumner. The great Yale sociologist's detailed exposition of thousands of social, sexual, and religious customs in hundreds of cultures from ancient Greece to Modern Western societies. Preface by A. G. Keller. Introduction by William Lyon Phelps. 705pp. 5⅜ x 8.   S508 Paperbound **$2.49**

BEYOND PSYCHOLOGY, Otto Rank. The author, an early associate of Freud, uses psychoanalytic techniques of myth-analysis to explore ultimates of human existence. Treats love, immortality, the soul, sexual identity, kingship, sources of state power, many other topics which illuminate the irrational basis of human existence. 291pp. 5⅜ x 8.   T485 Paperbound **$1.75**

ILLUSIONS AND DELUSIONS OF THE SUPERNATURAL AND THE OCCULT, D. H. Rawcliffe. A rational, scientific examination of crystal gazing, automatic writing, table turning, stigmata, the Indian rope trick, dowsing, telepathy, clairvoyance, ghosts, ESP, PK, thousands of other supposedly occult phenomena. Originally titled "The Psychology of the Occult." 14 illustrations. 551pp. 5⅜ x 8.   T503 Paperbound **$2.00**

YOGA: A SCIENTIFIC EVALUATION, Kovoor T. Behanan. A scientific study of the physiological and psychological effects of Yoga discipline, written under the auspices of the Yale University Institute of Human Relations. Foreword by W. A. Miles, Yale Univ. 17 photographs. 290pp. 5⅜ x 8. T505 Paperbound **$1.65**

HOAXES, C. D. MacDougall. Delightful, entertaining, yet scholarly exposition of how hoaxes start, why they succeed, documented with stories of hundreds of the most famous hoaxes. "A stupendous collection . . . and shrewd analysis, "NEW YORKER. New, revised edition. 54 photographs. 320pp. 5⅜ x 8. T465 Paperbound **$1.75**

CREATIVE POWER: THE EDUCATION OF YOUTH IN THE CREATIVE ARTS, Hughes Mearns. Named by the National Education Association as one of the 20 foremost books on education in recent times. Tells how to help children express themselves in drama, poetry, music, art, develop latent creative power. Should be read by every parent, teacher. New, enlarged, revised edition. Introduction. 272pp. 5⅜ x 8. T490 Paperbound **$1.50**

LANGUAGES

NEW RUSSIAN-ENGLISH, ENGLISH-RUSSIAN DICTIONARY, M. A. O'Brien. Over 70,000 entries in new orthography! Idiomatic usages, colloquialisms. One of the few dictionaries that indicate accent changes in conjugation and declension. "One of the best," Prof. E. J. Simmons, Cornell. First names, geographical terms, bibliography, many other features. 738pp. 4½ x 6¼. T208 Paperbound **$2.00**

MONEY CONVERTER AND TIPPING GUIDE FOR EUROPEAN TRAVEL, C. Vomacka. Invaluable, handy source of currency regulations, conversion tables, tipping rules, postal rates, much other travel information for every European country plus Israel, Egypt and Turkey. 128pp. 3½ x 5¼. T260 Paperbound **60¢**

MONEY CONVERTER AND TIPPING GUIDE FOR TRAVEL IN THE AMERICAS (including the United States and Canada), **C. Vomacka.** The information you need for informed and confident travel in the Americas: money conversion tables, tipping guide, postal, telephone rates, etc. 128pp. 3½ x 5¼. T261 Paperbound **65¢**

DUTCH-ENGLISH, ENGLISH-DUTCH DICTIONARY, F. G. Renier. The most convenient, practical Dutch-English dictionary on the market. New orthography. More than 60,000 entries: idioms, compounds, technical terms, etc. Gender of nouns indicated. xviii + 571pp. 5½ x 6¼. T224 Clothbound **$2.50**

LEARN DUTCH!, F. G. Renier. The most satisfactory and easily-used grammar of modern Dutch. Used and recommended by the Fulbright Committee in the Netherlands. Over 1200 simple exercises lead to mastery of spoken and written Dutch. Dutch-English, English-Dutch vocabularies. 181pp. 4¼ x 7¼. T441 Clothbound **$1.75**

PHRASE AND SENTENCE DICTIONARY OF SPOKEN RUSSIAN, English-Russian, Russian-English. Based on phrases and complete sentences, rather than isolated words; recognized as one of the best methods of learning the idiomatic speech of a country. Over 11,500 entries, indexed by single words, with more than 32,000 English and Russian sentences and phrases, in immediately usable form. Probably the largest list ever published. Shows accent changes in conjugation and declension; irregular forms listed in both alphabetical place and under main form of word. 15,000 word introduction covering Russian sounds, writing, grammar, syntax. 15-page appendix of geographical names, money, important signs, given names, foods, special Soviet terms, etc. Travellers, businessmen, students, government employees have found this their best source for Russian expressions. Originally published as U.S. Government Technical Manual TM 30-944. iv + 573pp. 5⅝ x 8⅜. T496 Paperbound **$2.75**

PHRASE AND SENTENCE DICTIONARY OF SPOKEN SPANISH, Spanish-English, English-Spanish. Compiled from spoken Spanish, emphasizing idiom and colloquial usage in both Castilian and Latin-American. More than 16,000 entries containing over 25,000 idioms—the largest list of idiomatic constructions ever published. Complete sentences given, indexed under single words —language in immediately usable form, for travellers, businessmen, students, etc. 25-page introduction provides rapid survey of sounds, grammar, syntax, with full consideration of irregular verbs. Especially apt in modern treatment of phrases and structure. 17-page glossary gives translations of geographical names, money values, numbers, national holidays, important street signs, useful expressions of high frequency, plus unique 7-page glossary of Spanish and Spanish-American foods and dishes. Originally published as U.S. Government Technical Manual TM 30-900. iv + 513pp. 5⅝ x 8⅜. T495 Paperbound **$1.75**

SAY IT language phrase books

"SAY IT" in the foreign language of your choice! We have sold over ½ million copies of these popular, useful language books. They will not make you an expert linguist overnight, but they do cover most practical matters of everyday life abroad.

Over 1000 useful phrases, expressions, with additional variants, substitutions.

Modern! Useful! Hundreds of phrases not available in other texts: "Nylon," "air-conditioned," etc.

The ONLY inexpensive phrase book **completely indexed.** Everything is available at a flip of your finger, ready for use.

Prepared by native linguists, travel experts.

Based on years of travel experience abroad.

This handy phrase book may be used by itself, or it may supplement any other text or course; it provides a living element. Used by many colleges and institutions: Hunter College; Barnard College; Army Ordnance School, Aberdeen; and many others.

Available, 1 book per language:

Danish (T818) 75¢	**Italian** (T806) 60¢
Dutch T(817) 75¢	**Japanese** (T807) 60¢
English (for German-speaking people) (T801) 60¢	**Norwegian** (T814) 75¢
English (for Italian-speaking people) (T816) 60¢	**Russian** (T810) 75¢
English (for Spanish-speaking people) (T802) 60¢	**Spanish** (T811) 60¢
Esperanto (T820) 75¢	**Turkish** (T821) 75¢
French (T803) 60¢	**Yiddish** (T815) 75¢
German (T804) 60¢	**Swedish** (T812) 75¢
Modern Greek (T813) 75¢	**Polish** (T808) 75¢
Hebrew (T805) 60¢	**Portuguese** (T809) 75¢

LISTEN & LEARN language record sets

LISTEN & LEARN is the only language record course designed especially to meet your travel needs, or help you learn essential foreign language quickly by yourself, or in conjunction with any school course, by means of the automatic association method. Each set contains three 33⅓ rpm long- playing records — 1½ hours of recorded speech by eminent native speakers who are professors at Columbia, N.Y.U., Queens College and other leading universities. The sets are priced far below other sets of similar quality, yet they contain many special features not found in other record sets:

* Over 800 selected phrases and sentences, a basic vocabulary of over 3200 words.
* Both English and foreign language recorded; with a pause for your repetition.
* Designed for persons with limited time; no time wasted on material you cannot use immediately.
* Living, modern expressions that answer modern needs: drugstore items, "air-conditioned," etc.
* 128-196 page manuals contain everything on the records, plus simple pronunciation guides.
* Manual is fully indexed; find the phrase you want instantly.
* High fidelity recording—equal to any records costing up to $6 each.

The phrases on these records cover 41 different categories useful to the traveller or student interested in learning the living, spoken language: greetings, introductions, making yourself understood, passing customs, planes, trains, boats, buses, taxis, nightclubs, restaurants, menu items, sports, concerts, cameras, automobile travel, repairs, drugstores, doctors, dentists, medicines, barber shops, beauty parlors, laundries, many, many more.

"Excellent . . . among the very best on the market," Prof. Mario Pei, Dept. of Romance Languages, Columbia University. "Inexpensive and well-done . . . an ideal present," CHICAGO SUNDAY TRIBUNE. "More genuinely helpful than anything of its kind which I have previously encountered," Sidney Clark, well-known author of "ALL THE BEST" travel books. Each set contains 3 33⅓ rpm pure vinyl records, 128- 196 page with full record text, and album. One language per set. LISTEN & LEARN record sets are now available in—

FRENCH	the set $4.95		**GERMAN**	the set $4.95
ITALIAN	the set $4.95		**SPANISH**	the set $4.95
RUSSIAN	the set $5.95		**JAPANESE** *	the set $5.95

* Available Sept. 1, 1959

UNCONDITIONAL GUARANTEE: Dover Publications stands behind every Listen and Learn record set. If you are dissatisfied with these sets for any reason whatever, return them within 10 days and your money will be refunded in full.

ART HISTORY

STICKS AND STONES, Lewis Mumford. An examination of forces influencing American architecture: the medieval tradition in early New England, the classical influence in Jefferson's time, the Brown Decades, the imperial facade, the machine age, etc. "A truly remarkable book," SAT. REV. OF LITERATURE. 2nd revised edition. 21 illus. xvii + 228pp. 5⅜ x 8.
T202 Paperbound **$1.60**

THE AUTOBIOGRAPHY OF AN IDEA, Louis Sullivan. The architect whom Frank Lloyd Wright called "the master," records the development of the theories that revolutionized America's skyline. 34 full-page plates of Sullivan's finest work. New introduction by R. M. Line. xiv + 335pp. 5⅜ x 8.
T281 Paperbound **$1.85**

THE MATERIALS AND TECHNIQUES OF MEDIEVAL PAINTING, D. V. Thompson. An invaluable study of carriers and grounds, binding media, pigments, metals used in painting, al fresco and al secco techniques, burnishing, etc. used by the medieval masters. Preface by Bernard Berenson. 239pp. 5⅜ x 8.
T327 Paperbound **$1.85**

PRINCIPLES OF ART HISTORY, H. Wölfflin. This remarkably instructive work demonstrates the tremendous change in artistic conception from the 14th to the 18th centuries, by analyzing 164 works by Botticelli, Dürer, Hobbema, Holbein, Hals, Titian, Rembrandt, Vermeer, etc., and pointing out exactly what is meant by "baroque," "classic," "primitive," "picturesque," and other basic terms of art history and criticism. "A remarkable lesson in the art of seeing," SAT. REV. OF LITERATURE. Translated from the 7th German edition. 150 illus. 254pp. 6⅛ x 9¼.
T276 Paperbound **$2.00**

FOUNDATIONS OF MODERN ART, A. Ozenfant. Stimulating discussion of human creativity from paleolithic cave painting to modern painting, architecture, decorative arts. Fully illustrated with works of Gris, Lipchitz, Léger, Picasso, primitive, modern artifacts, architecture, industrial art, much more. 226 illustrations. 368pp. 6⅛ x 9¼.
T215 Paperbound **$1.95**

HANDICRAFTS, APPLIED ART, ART SOURCES, ETC.

WILD FOWL DECOYS, J. Barber. The standard work on this fascinating branch of folk art, ranging from Indian mud and grass devices to realistic wooden decoys. Discusses styles, types, periods; gives full information on how to make decoys. 140 illustrations (including 14 new plates) show decoys and provide full sets of plans for handicrafters, artists, hunters, and students of folk art. 281pp. 7⅞ x 10¾. Deluxe edition.
T11 Clothbound **$8.50**

METALWORK AND ENAMELLING, H. Maryon. Probably the best book ever written on the subject. Tells everything necessary for the home manufacture of jewelry, rings, ear pendants, bowls, etc. Covers materials, tools, soldering, filigree, setting stones, raising patterns, repoussé work, damascening, niello, cloisonné, polishing, assaying, casting, and dozens of other techniques. The best substitute for apprenticeship to a master metalworker. 363 photos and figures. 374pp. 5½ x 8½.
T183 Clothbound **$7.50**

SHAKER FURNITURE, E. D. and F. Andrews. The most illuminating study of Shaker furniture ever written. Covers chronology, craftsmanship, houses, shops, etc. Includes over 200 photographs of chairs, tables, clocks, beds, benches, etc. "Mr. & Mrs. Andrews know all there is to know about Shaker furniture," Mark Van Doren, NATION. 48 full-page plates. 192pp. Deluxe cloth binding. 7⅞ x 10¾.
T7 Clothbound **$6.00**

PRIMITIVE ART, Franz Boas. A great American anthropologist covers theory, technical virtuosity, styles, symbolism, patterns, etc. of primitive art. The more than 900 illustrations will interest artists, designers, craftworkers. Over 900 illustrations. 376pp. 5⅜ x 8.
T25 Paperbound **$1.95**

ON THE LAWS OF JAPANESE PAINTING, H. Bowie. The best possible substitute for lessons from an oriental master. Treats both spirit and technique; exercises for control of the brush; inks, brushes, colors; use of dots, lines to express whole moods, etc. 220 illus. 132pp. 6⅛ x 9¼.
T30 Paperbound **$1.95**

HANDBOOK OF ORNAMENT, F. S. Meyer. One of the largest collections of copyright-free traditional art: over 3300 line cuts of Greek, Roman, Medieval, Renaissance, Baroque, 18th and 19th century art motifs (tracery, geometric elements, flower and animal motifs, etc.) and decorated objects (chairs, thrones, weapons, vases, jewelry, armor, etc.). Full text. 3300 illustrations. 562pp. 5⅜ x 8.
T302 Paperbound **$2.00**

THREE CLASSICS OF ITALIAN CALLIGRAPHY. Oscar Ogg, ed. Exact reproductions of three famous Renaissance calligraphic works: Arrighi's OPERINA and IL MODO, Tagliente's LO PRESENTE LIBRO, and Palatino's LIBRO NUOVO. More than 200 complete alphabets, thousands of lettered specimens, in Papal Chancery and other beautiful, ornate handwriting. Introduction. 245 plates. 282pp. 6⅛ x 9¼.
T212 Paperbound **$1.95**

THE HISTORY AND TECHNIQUES OF LETTERING, A. Nesbitt. A thorough history of lettering from the ancient Egyptians to the present, and a 65-page course in lettering for artists. Every major development in lettering history is illustrated by a complete alphabet. Fully analyzes such masters as Caslon, Koch, Garamont, Jenson, and many more. 89 alphabets, 165 other specimens. 317pp. 5⅜ x 8.
T427 Paperbound **$2.00**

LETTERING AND ALPHABETS, J. A. Cavanagh. An unabridged reissue of "Lettering," containing the full discussion, analysis, illustration of 89 basic hand lettering tyles based on Caslon, Bodoni, Gothic, many other types. Hundreds of technical hints on construction, strokes, pens, brushes, etc. 89 alphabets, 72 lettered specimens, which may be reproduced permission-free. 121pp. 9¾ x 8.   T53 Paperbound **$1.25**

THE HUMAN FIGURÉ IN MOTION, Eadweard Muybridge. The largest collection in print of Muybridge's famous high-speed action photos. 4789 photographs in more than 500 action-strip-sequences (at shutter speeds up to 1/6000th of a second) illustrate men, women, children—mostly undraped—performing such actions as walking, running, getting up, lying down, carrying objects, throwing, etc. "An unparalleled dictionary of action for all artists," AMERICAN ARTIST. 390 full-page plates, with 4789 photographs. Heavy glossy stock, reinforced binding with headbands. 7⅞ x 10¾.   T204 Clothbound **$10.00**

ANIMALS IN MOTION, Eadweard Muybridge. The largest collection of animal action photos in print. 34 different animals (horses, mules, oxen, goats, camels, pigs, cats, lions, gnus, deer, monkeys, eagles—and 22 others) in 132 characteristic actions. All 3919 photographs are taken in series at speeds up to 1/1600th of a second, offering artists, biologists, cartoonists a remarkable opportunity to see exactly how an ostrich's head bobs when running, how a lion puts his foot down, how an elephant's knee bends, how a bird flaps his wings, thousands of other hard-to-catch details. "A really marvelous series of plates," NATURE. 380 full-pages of plates. Heavy glossy stock, reinforced binding with headbands. 7⅞ x 10¾.   T203 Clothbound **$10.00**

THE BOOK OF SIGNS, R. Koch. 493 symbols—crosses, monograms, astrological, biological symbols, runes, etc.—from ancient manuscripts, cathedrals, coins, catacombs, pottery. May be reproduced permission-free. 493 illustrations by Fritz Kredel. 104pp. 6⅛ x 9¼.   T162 Paperbound **$1.00**

A HANDBOOK OF EARLY ADVERTISING ART, C. P. Hornung. The largest collection of copyright-free early advertising art ever compiled. Vol. I: 2,000 illustrations of animals, old automobiles, buildings, allegorical figures, fire engines, Indians, ships, trains, more than 33 other categories! Vol II: Over 4,000 typographical specimens; 600 Roman, Gothic, Barnum, Old English faces; 630 ornamental type faces; hundreds of scrolls, initials, flourishes, etc. "A remarkable collection," PRINTERS' INK.

Vol. I: Pictorial Volume. Over 2000 illustrations. 256pp. 9 x 12.   T122 Clothbound **$10.00**
Vol. II: Typographical Volume. Over 4000 speciments. 319pp. 9 x 12.   T123 Clothbound **$10.00**
Two volume set, Clothbound, only **$18.50**

DESIGN FOR ARTISTS AND CRAFTSMEN, L. Wolchonok. The most thorough course on the creation of art motifs and designs. Shows you step-by-step, with hundreds of examples and 113 detailed exercises, how to create original designs from geometric patterns, plants, birds, animals, humans, and man-made objects. "A great contribution to the field of design and crafts," N. Y. SOCIETY OF CRAFTSMEN. More than 1300 entirely new illustrations. xv + 207pp. 7⅞ x 10¾.   T274 Clothbound **$4.95**

HANDBOOK OF DESIGNS AND DEVICES, C. P. Hornung. A remarkable working collection of 1836 basic designs and variations, all copyright-free. Variations of circle, line, cross, diamond, swastika, star, scroll, shield, many more. Notes on symbolism. "A necessity to every 'designer who would be original without having to labor heavily," ARTIST and ADVERTISER. 204 plates. 240pp. 5⅜ x 8.
T125 Paperbound **$1.90**

THE UNIVERSAL PENMAN, George Bickham. Exact reproduction of beautiful 18th century book of handwriting. 22 complete alphabets in finest English roundhand, other scripts, over 2000 elaborate flourishes, 122 calligraphic illustrations, etc. Material is copyright-free. "An essential part of any art library, and a book of permanent value," AMERICAN ARTIST. 212 plates. 224pp. 9 x 13¾.   T20 Clothbound **$10.00**

AN ATLAS OF ANATOMY FOR ARTISTS, F. Schider. This standard work contains 189 full-page plates, more than 647 illustrations of all aspects of the human skeleton, musculature, cutaway portions of the body, each part of the anatomy, hand forms, eyelids, breasts, location of muscles under the flesh, etc. 59 plates illustrate how Michelangelo, da Vinci, Goya, 15 others, drew human anatomy. New 3rd edition enlarged by 52 new illustrations by Cloquet, Barcsay. "The standard reference tool," AMERICAN LIBRARY ASSOCIATION. "Excellent," AMERICAN ARTIST. 189 plates, 647 illustrations. xxvi + 192pp. 7⅞ x 10⅝.   T241 Clothbound **$6.00**

AN ATLAS OF ANIMAL ANATOMY FOR ARTISTS, W. Ellenberger, H. Baum, H. Dittrich. The largest, richest animal anatomy for artists in English. Form, musculature, tendons, bone structure, expression, detailed cross sections of head, other features, of the horse, lion, dog, cat, deer, seal, kangaroo, cow, bull, goat, monkey, hare, many other animals. "Highly recommended," DESIGN. Second, revised, enlarged edition with new plates from Cuvier, Stubbs, etc. 288 illustrations. 153pp. 11⅜ x 9.   T82 Clothbound **$6.00**

ANIMAL DRAWING: ANATOMY AND ACTION FOR ARTISTS, C. R. Knight. 158 studies, with full accompanying text, of such animals as the gorilla, bear, bison, dromedary, camel, vulture, pelican, iguana, shark, etc., by one of the greatest modern masters of animal drawing. Innumerable tips on how to get life expression into your work. "An excellent reference work," SAN FRANCISCO CHRONICLE. 158 illustrations. 156pp. 10½ x 8½.
T426 Paperbound **$2.00**

DOVER BOOKS

THE CRAFTSMAN'S HANDBOOK, Cennino Cennini. The finest English translation of IL LIBRO DELL' ARTE, the 15th century introduction to art technique that is both a mirror of Quatrocento life and a source of many useful but nearly forgotten facets of the painter's art. 4 illustrations. xxvii + 142pp. D. V. Thompson, translator. 6⅛ x 9¼.   T54 Paperbound **$1.50**

THE BROWN DECADES, Lewis Mumford. A picture of the "buried renaissance" of the post-Civil War period, and the founding of modern architecture (Sullivan, Richardson, Root, Roebling), landscape development (Marsh, Olmstead, Eliot), and the graphic arts (Homer, Eakins, Ryder). 2nd revised, enlarged edition. Bibliography. 12 illustrations. xiv + 266 pp. 5⅜ x 8.   T200 Paperbound **$1.65**

STIEGEL GLASS, F. W. Hunter. The story of the most highly esteemed early American glassware, fully illustrated. How a German adventurer, "Baron" Stiegel, founded a glass empire; detailed accounts of individual glasswork. "This pioneer work is reprinted in an edition even more beautiful than the original," ANTIQUES DEALER. New introduction by Helen McKearin. 171 illustrations, 12 in full color. xxii + 338pp. 7⅞ x 10¾.   T128 Clothbound **$10.00**

THE HUMAN FIGURE, J. H. Vanderpoel. Not just a picture book, but a complete course by a famous figure artist. Extensive text, illustrated by 430 pencil and charcoal drawings of both male and female anatomy. 2nd enlarged edition. Foreword. 430 illus. 143pp. 6⅛ x 9¼.   T432 Paperbound **$1.45**

PINE FURNITURE OF EARLY NEW ENGLAND, R. H. Kettell. Over 400 illustrations, over 50 working drawings of early New England chairs, benches, beds cupboards, mirrors, shelves, tables, other furniture esteemed for simple beauty and character. "Rich store of illustrations . . . emphasizes the individuality and varied design," ANTIQUES. 413 illustrations, 55 working drawings. 475pp. 8 x 10¾.   T145 Clothbound **$10.00**

BASIC BOOKBINDING, A. W. Lewis. Enables both beginners and experts to rebind old books or bind paperbacks in hard covers. Treats materials, tools; gives step-by-step instruction in how to collate a book, sew it, back it, make boards, etc. 261 illus. Appendices. 155pp. 5⅜ x 8.   T169 Paperbound **$1.35**

DESIGN MOTIFS OF ANCIENT MEXICO, J. Enciso. Nearly 90% of these 766 superb designs from Aztec, Olmec, Totonac, Maya, and Toltec origins are unobtainable elsewhere! Contains plumed serpents, wind gods, animals, demons, dancers, monsters, etc. Excellent applied design source. Originally $17.50. 766 illustrations, thousands of motifs. 192pp. 6⅛ x 9¼.   T84 Paperbound **$1.85**

AFRICAN SCULPTURE, Ladislas Segy. 163 full-page plates illustrating masks, fertility figures, ceremonial objects, etc., of 50 West and Central African tribes—95% never before illustrated. 34-page introduction to African sculpture. "Mr. Segy is one of its top authorities," NEW YORKER. 164 full-page photographic plates. Introduction. Bibliography. 244pp. 6⅛ x 9¼.   T396 Paperbound **$2.00**

THE PROCESSES OF GRAPHIC REPRODUCTION IN PRINTING, H. Curwen. A thorough and practical survey of wood, linoleum, and rubber engraving; copper engraving; drypoint, mezzotint, etching, aquatint, steel engraving, die sinking, stencilling, lithography (extensively); photographic reproduction utilizing line, continuous tone, photoengravure, collotype; every other process in general use. Note on color reproduction. Section on bookbinding. Over 200 illustrations, 25 in color. 143pp. 5½ x 8½.   T512 Clothbound **$4.00**

CALLIGRAPHY, J. G. Schwandner. First reprinting in 200 years of this legendary book of beautiful handwriting. Over 300 ornamental initials, 12 complete calligraphic alphabets, over 150 ornate frames and panels, 75 calligraphic pictures of cherubs, stags, lions, etc., thousands of flourishes, scrolls, etc., by the greatest 18th century masters. All material can be copied or adapted without permission. Historical introduction. 158 full-page plates. 368pp. 9 x 13.   T475 Clothbound **$10.00**

* * *

A DIDEROT PICTORIAL ENCYCLOPEDIA OF TRADES AND INDUSTRY, Manufacturing and the Technical Arts in Plates Selected from "L'Encyclopédie ou Dictionnaire Raisonné des Sciences, des Arts, et des Métiers," of Denis Diderot, edited with text by C. Gillispie. Over 2000 illustrations on 485 full-page plates. Magnificent 18th century engravings of men, women, and children working at such trades as milling flour, cheesemaking, charcoal burning, mining, silverplating, shoeing horses, making fine glass, printing, hundreds more, showing details of machinery, different steps in sequence, etc. A remarkable art work, but also the largest collection of working figures in print, copyright-free, for art directors, designers, etc. Two vols. 920pp. 9 x 12. Heavy library cloth.   T421 Two volume set **$18.50**

* * *

SILK SCREEN TECHNIQUES, J. Biegeleisen, M. Cohn. A practical step-by-step home course in one of the most versatile, least expensive graphic arts processes. How to build an inexpensive silk screen, prepare stencils, print, achieve special textures, use color, etc. Every step explained, diagrammed. 149 illustrations, 8 in color. 201pp. 6⅛ x 9¼.   T433 Paperbound **$1.45**

MATHEMATICS, MAGIC AND MYSTERY, Martin Gardner. Astonishing feats of mind reading, mystifying "magic" tricks, are often based on mathematical principles anyone can learn. This book shows you how to perform scores of tricks with cards, dice, coins, knots, numbers, etc., by using simple principles from set theory, theory of numbers, topology, other areas of mathematics, fascinating in themselves. No special knowledge required. 135 illus. 186pp. 5⅜ x 8. T335 Paperbound **$1.00**

MATHEMATICAL PUZZLES FOR BEGINNERS AND ENTHUSIASTS, G. Mott-Smith. Test your problem-solving techniques and powers of inference on 188 challenging, amusing puzzles based on algebra, dissection of plane figures, permutations, probabilities, etc. Appendix of primes, square roots, etc. 135 illus. 2nd revised edition. 248pp. 5⅜ x 8. T198 Paperbound **$1.00**

LEARN CHESS FROM THE MASTERS, F. Reinfeld. Play 10 games against Marshall, Bronstein, Najdorf, other masters, and grade yourself on each move. Detailed annotations reveal principles of play, strategy, etc. as you proceed. An excellent way to get a real insight into the game. Formerly titled, "Chess by Yourself." 91 diagrams. vii + 144pp. 5⅜ x 8. T362 Paperbound **$1.00**

REINFELD ON THE END GAME IN CHESS, F. Reinfeld. 62 end games of Alekhine, Tarrasch, Morphy, other masters, are carefully analyzed with emphasis on transition from middle game to end play. Tempo moves, queen endings, weak squares, other basic principles clearly illustrated. Excellent for understanding why some moves are weak or incorrect, how to avoid errors. Formerly titled, "Practical End-game Play." 62 diagrams. vi + 177pp. 5⅜ x 8. T417 Paperbound **$1.25**

101 PUZZLES IN THOUGHT AND LOGIC, C. R. Wylie, Jr. Brand new puzzles you need no special knowledge to solve! Each one is a gem of ingenuity that will really challenge your problem-solving technique. Introduction with simplified explanation of scientic puzzle solving. 128pp. 5⅜ x 8. T167 Paperbound **$1.00**

THE COMPLETE NONSENSE OF EDWARD LEAR. The only complete edition of this master of gentle madness at a popular price. The Dong with the Luminous Nose, The Jumblies, The Owl and the Pussycat, hundreds of other bits of wonderful nonsense. 214 limericks, 3 sets of Nonsense Botany, 5 Nonsense Alphabets, 546 fantastic drawings, much more. 320pp. 5⅜ x 8. T167 Paperbound **$1.00**

28 SCIENCE FICTION STORIES OF H. G. WELLS. Two complete novels, "Men Like Gods" and "Star Begotten," plus 26 short stories by the master science-fiction writer of all time. Stories of space, time, future adventure that are among the all-time classics of science fiction. 928pp. 5⅜ x 8. T265 Clothbound **$3.95**

SEVEN SCIENCE FICTION NOVELS, H. G. Wells. Unabridged texts of "The Time Machine," "The Island of Dr. Moreau," "First Men in the Moon," "The Invisible Man," "The War of the Worlds," "The Food of the Gods," "In the Days of the Comet." "One will have to go far to match this for entertainment, excitement, and sheer pleasure," N. Y. TIMES. 1015pp. 5⅜ x 8. T264 Clothbound **$3.95**

MATHEMAGIC, MAGIC PUZZLES, AND GAMES WITH NUMBERS, R. V. Heath. More than 60 new puzzles and stunts based on number properties: multiplying large numbers mentally, finding the date of any day in the year, etc. Edited by J. S. Meyer. 76 illus. 129pp. 5⅜ x 8. T110 Paperbound **$1.00**

FIVE ADVENTURE NOVELS OF H. RIDER HAGGARD. The master story-teller's five best tales of mystery and adventure set against authentic African backgrounds: "She," "King Solomon's Mines," "Allan Quatermain," "Allan's Wife," "Maiwa's Revenge." 821pp. 5⅜ x 8. T108 Clothbound **$3.95**

WIN AT CHECKERS, M. Hopper. (Formerly "Checkers.") The former World's Unrestricted Checker Champion gives you valuable lessons in openings, traps, end games, ways to draw when you are behind, etc. More than 100 questions and answers anticipate your problems. Appendix. 75 problems diagrammed, solved. 79 figures. xi + 107pp. 5⅜ x 8. T363 Paperbound **$1.00**

CRYPTOGRAPHY, L. D. Smith. Excellent introductory work on ciphers and their solution, history of secret writing, techniques, etc. Appendices on Japanese methods, the Baconian cipher, frequency tables. Bibliography. Over 150 problems, solutions. 160pp. 5⅜ x 8. T247 Paperbound **$1.00**

CRYPTANALYSIS, H. F. Gaines. (Formerly, "Elementary Cryptanalysis.") The best book available on cryptograms and how to solve them. Contains all major techniques: substitution, transposition, mixed alphabets, multafid, Kasiski and Vignere methods, etc. Word frequency appendix. 167 problems, solutions. 173 figures. 236pp. 5⅜ x 8. T97 Paperbound **$1.95**

FLATLAND, E. A. Abbot. The science-fiction classic of life in a 2-dimensional world that is considered a first-rate introduction to relativity and hyperspace, as well as a scathing satire on society, politics and religion. 7th edition. 16 illus. 128pp. 5⅜ x 8. T1 Paperbound **$1.00**

DOVER BOOKS

HOW TO FORCE CHECKMATE, F. Reinfeld. (Formerly "Challenge to Chessplayers.") No board needed to sharpen your checkmate skill on 300 checkmate situations. Learn to plan up to 3 moves ahead and play a superior end game. 300 situations diagrammed; notes and full solutions. 111pp. 5⅜ x 8.   T439 Paperbound **$1.25**

MORPHY'S GAMES OF CHESS, P. W. Sergeant, ed. Play forcefully by following the techniques used by one of the greatest chess champions. 300 of Morphy's games carefully annotated to reveal principles. Bibliography. New introduction by F. Reinfeld. 235 diagrams. x + 352pp. 5⅜ x 8.   T386 Paperbound **$1.75**

MATHEMATICAL RECREATIONS, M. Kraitchik. Hundreds of unusual mathematical puzzlers and odd bypaths of math, elementary and advanced. Greek, Medieval, Arabic, Hindu problems; figurate numbers, Fermat numbers, primes; magic, Euler, Latin squares; fairy chess, latruncles, reversi, jinx, ruma, tetrachrome other positional and permutational games. Rigorous solutions. Revised second edition. 181 illus. 330pp. 5⅜ x 8.   T163 Paperbound **$1.75**

MATHEMATICAL EXCURSIONS, H. A. Merrill. Revealing stimulating insights into elementary math, not usually taught in school. 90 problems demonstrate Russian peasant multiplication, memory systems for pi, magic squares, dyadic systems, division by inspection, many more. Solutions to difficult problems. 50 illus. 5⅜ x 8.   T350 Paperbound **$1.00**

MAGIC TRICKS & CARD TRICKS, W. Jonson. Best introduction to tricks with coins, bills, eggs, ribbons, slates, cards, easily performed without elaborate equipment. Professional routines, tips on presentation, misdirection, etc. Two books bound as one: 52 tricks with cards, 37 tricks with common objects. 106 figures. 224pp. 5⅜ x 8.   T909 Paperbound **$1.00**

MATHEMATICAL PUZZLES OF SAM LOYD, selected and edited by M. Gardner. 177 most ingenious mathematical puzzles of America's greatest puzzle originator, based on arithmetic, algebra, game theory, dissection, route tracing, operations research, probability, etc. 120 drawings, diagrams. Solutions. 187pp. 5⅜ x 8.   T498 Paperbound **$1.00**

THE ART OF CHESS, J. Mason. The most famous general study of chess ever written. More than 90 openings, middle game, end game, how to attack, sacrifice, defend, exchange, form general strategy. Supplement on "How Do You Play Chess?" by F. Reinfeld. 448 diagrams. 356pp. 5⅜ x 8.   T463 Paperbound **$1.85**

HYPERMODERN CHESS as Developed in the Games of its Greatest Exponent, ARON NIMZOVICH, F. Reinfeld, ed. Learn how the game's greatest innovator defeated Alekhine, Lasker, and many others; and use these methods in your own game. 180 diagrams. 228pp. 5⅜ x 8.
                                                                                T448 Paperbound **$1.35**

A TREASURY OF CHESS LORE, F. Reinfeld, ed. Hundreds of fascinating stories by and about the masters, accounts of tournaments and famous games, aphorisms, word portraits, little known incidents, photographs, etc., that will delight the chess enthusiast, captivate the beginner. 49 photographs (14 full-page plates), 12 diagrams. 315pp. 5⅜ x 8.
                                                                                T458 Paperbound **$1.75**

A NONSENSE ANTHOLOGY, collected by **Carolyn Wells.** 245 of the best nonsense verses ever written: nonsense puns, absurd arguments, mock epics, nonsense ballads, "sick" verses, dog-Latin verses, French nonsense verses, limericks. Lear, Carroll, Belloc, Burgess, nearly 100 other writers. Introduction by Carolyn Wells. 3 indices: Title, Author, First Lines. xxxiii + 279pp. 5⅜ x 8.   T499 Paperbound **$1.25**

SYMBOLIC LOGIC and THE GAME OF LOGIC, Lewis Carroll. Two delightful puzzle books by the author of "Alice," bound as one. Both works concern the symbolic representation of traditional logic and together contain more than 500 ingenious, amusing and instructive syllogistic puzzlers. Total of 326pp. 5⅜ x 8.   T492 Paperbound **$1.50**

PILLOW PROBLEMS and A TANGLED TALE, Lewis Carroll. Two of Carroll's rare puzzle works bound as one. "Pillow Problems" contain 72 original math puzzles. The puzzles in "A Tangled Tale" are given in delightful story form. Total of 291pp. 5⅜ x 8.   T493 Paperbound **$1.50**

PECK'S BAD BOY AND HIS PA, G. W. Peck. Both volumes of one of the most widely read of all American humor books. A classic of American folk humor, also invaluable as a portrait of an age. 100 original illustrations. Introduction by E. Bleiler. 347pp. 5⅜ x 8.
                                                                                T497 Paperbound **$1.35**

Dover publishes books on art, music, philosophy, literature, languages, history, social sciences, psychology, handcrafts, orientalia, puzzles and entertainments, chess, pets and gardens, books explaining science, intermediate and higher mathematics mathematical physics, engineering, biological sciences, earth sciences, classics of science, etc. Write to:

Dept. catrr.
Dover Publications, Inc.
180 Varick Street, N. Y. 14, N. Y.